Mid Size Power Boats

A Guide for Discriminating Buyers

by

David H. Pascoe

D.H. Pascoe & Co., Inc.

Mid Size Power Boats

Copyright © 2003 David H. Pascoe
All Rights Reserved

Published by D. H. Pascoe & Company, Inc.
www.yachtsurvey.com

First Printing 2003
Second Printing 2003
Third Printing 2005
Fourth Printing 2007

Printed in the United States of America by Rose Printing, Tallahassee, Florida

ISBN-10: 0-96564-963-6
ISBN-13: 978-0-96564-963-6

LCCN #: 2006-278771

To order copies, visit our web site
www.yachtsurvey.com

Text, photographs, illustration, layout and editing: David H. Pascoe
Layout and editing: Junko A. Pascoe

Introdction   v

Contents   ix

Chapter 1   Basic Considerations 1

Chapter 2   Boat Types: Which is Right for You?   31

Chapter 3   Old Boats, New Boats and Quality   73

Chapter 4   Basic Hull Construction   95

Chapter 5   Evaluating Boat Hulls 135

Chapter 6   Performance and Sea Keeping   169

Chapter 7   Decks & Superstructure   195

Chapter 8   Stress Cracks, Finishes and Surface Defects 223

Chapter 9   Power Options   243

Chapter 10   The Engine Room   279

Chapter 11   Electrical & Plumbing Systems   315

Chapter 12   Design Details   353

Chapter 13   Steering, Controls, Systems 371

Chapter 14   The Art of the Deal 393

Chapter 15   Boat Shopping   407

Chapter 16   The Survey & Post Survey   417

Chapter 17   Boat Builders by Company   433

Glossary   455

Index   465

Introduction

Having spent over three decades giving advice to buyers of both new and used boats, this book contains my answers to the most commonly asked questions. Were this a simple subject, this would have been a short book, but it is not. Boats are probably the largest, most complex and costly consumer products that anyone can buy.

Because boats are so very expensive, it pays to perform considerable research before you buy. Unfortunately, as most experienced boat buyers will attest, there are all too few good sources to turn to in order to get reliable information. There are, of course, innumerable sources offering boat reviews, most of which nearly everyone recognizes as being little more than advertising puff pieces offered by writers associated with publications that derive their income from advertising. As with stock brokers, these are hardly objective sources of advice.

Mid Size Power Boats covers powerboats from around 30 to 55 feet or so. Unlike most other books so styled, this book contains serious criticism of today's boats and the boat building industry in general. In it we take an unabridged and detailed look at the good, the bad and the ugly. My objective is not to offer gratuitous criticism, but to identify those factors that make for good and reliable boats, as well as those that don't. We can only put what's right into perspective by knowing what's wrong, and why it's wrong.

Gaining a knowledge about the industry, its strengths and weaknesses will help you make better choices. It is for that reason that I've gone to considerable length to explain why things are the way they are.

The truth of the matter is that the boat building industry is today, and has always been, a grossly undercapitalized and marginal industry. Its products have never been, and never will be, as high quality and reliable as we'd like them to. Boat building thrives in boom times but usually collapses and goes bankrupt during the lean years. The industry is, to say the least, unstable. This is not anyone's fault; this is inherent in the fact that boat builders produce our most expensive discretionary spending product, and are always the first to feel the effects of economic downturns, but are the last to recover after the economy does.

Many buyers, particularly first time buyers, figure that if they're spending a quarter million dollars or more for a product, that they have a right to expect it to be reliable and of good quality. This entire book is a testament to just how wrong that assumption can be. My objective is to help the reader navigate his way through this swamp of industry economic difficulties that ultimately end up being reflected in the product itself.

In contemplating the purchase of a boat, the buyer has a lot of serious choices to make. While almost all boats look good, particularly new ones, the reality is that there are huge differences to be considered on issues of style and performance.

During the last decade, boat building has undergone huge changes in everything from the style of the boats it produces, the nature of its corporate ownership, quality and materials used in construction. Many of these changes have not been for the better as the industry has largely consolidated into the hands of two big corporations — Brunswick and Genmar — which has resulted in increasing homogeneity, less in the way of product differentiation, more and more cookie-cutter boats that all seem to look alike, and fewer and fewer choices.

Not only have boat builders consolidated, but so, too, has the number of distinct styles of boats. We've witnessed the express style boat come to completely dominate the market, while other styles, such as the motor yacht, almost completely disappear, a casualty of sophisticated marketing that induces all the lemmings to run in the same direction. Corporate boat building has become affected by the same malaise as the auto industry — mind-numbing sameness.

Every year as many existing boaters give up boating as new people enter boating. Studies reveal that over the last two decades the total number of registered boats has actually declined from a high of 22 million in 1987 to the current level of 19 million. The most common reason expressed by those who sell their boats without buying another is a combination of boating being too expensive and too much work. Therefore, one of the central themes of this book is how to identify boats that are more durable and less costly to own.

While one might think that boats have become progressively less maintenance intensive and less costly, the opposite has been true. In large part this has been the result of the increasing demands for luxury and complexity of boats. People want all the bells and whistles. The average boat today is substantially more complex than it was twenty years ago, and more costly, too.

The cost of ownership is directly linked to quality and sophistication. The fancier the boat, the more equipment and systems it has, the more it's going to cost to keep all those things in good working order. And quite naturally, when we demand low initial costs, it goes without saying that the quality of all those bells and whistles will also be lower, meaning that they aren't as durable and ultimately cost more to own because it costs more to keep it all in good condition.

This book details a large number of mistakes that builders are prone to make. At first, the reader may feel overwhelmed by the number of possibilities. In planning this book, I had to make a decision whether to risk overwhelming the reader and possibly discouraging him, or leaving a lot of important detail out. In the end, I decided to err on the side of excess.

On reading to the end, the reader will, no doubt, come to see how it's difficult for even a competent surveyor to check out all possibilities. Hopefully this will convince you of the need to hire a top notch surveyor before you buy.

David H. Pascoe
Destin, Florida
January, 2003

Contents

Introduction v
Contents ix

1. Basic Considerations 1

The Benefits 1
Are You a Candidate for a Being Happy Boat Owner? 2
How Much Time is Involved? 3
Resale Value 5
Boat Size vs Cost 6
The Importance of Proximity 6
Cost/Time Benefits 7
Getting Upside Down 8
Winter Lay Up 9
Why Boat Repairs Are So Costly 9
The Risks 10
    Seaworthiness and Respect for the Sea 10
    Risk From Without and Within 11
    Aye, Aye, Captain! 12
    Inherent Unseaworthiness 13
    Tragedies at Sea 13
Portrait of a Happy Boat Owner 19
Insurance 19
The Cost of Boating 20
Partnerships 21
Charter Arrangements 22
The Nature of the Industry 22
Dealerships 25
Quality Issues 25
Warranties 28
New -vs- Used Boats 29
What to Expect From a New Boat Purchase 30

2. Boat Types: Which is Right for You? 31

Mrs. Boat Buyer 34
Boating Life Styles & Layouts 35
Dual Controls 35
Head Room 36

Sleeping Accommodations 36
Social Spaces 38
The Galley 39
Eating 41
Heads 41
Cockpit Areas 42
Flybridge Sedan 42
Express Cruiser 43
Trawler Style 45
Sport Fisherman 48
Sport Fishing From Other Types 50
Multi Purpose Styles 51
Motor Yacht 53
Bloat Boats & Clumsy Design 53
High Sided Expresses 55
Double Cabin 56
Down Easter 57

Other Basic Design Considerations 58
The Death of Practicality 58
Interior Ventilation 59
Deck Areas 61
Area Sizes 61
Flying Bridges 62
Tops and Enclosures 63
State Rooms 65

Dizzy Desgin and Loony Luxury 67
Unconventional Boat Design 68
Anatomy of Frivolous Design 69

3. Old Boats, New Boats and Quality 73
Service Life of Pleasure Craft 74
The Economics of Older Boats 75
Estimating Costs 76
Approximate Service Life of Boat Components 79
Selecting the Right Boat for Projects 80

New -vs- Used Boats 82
Depreciation of New and Used Boats 83
Quality and the Mid Size Market 85
Old or New, Which Is Better? 87
What Does Quality in Boats Mean? 88
Foreign -vs- Domestic Builders 90

4. Basic Hull Construction 95
Overview of Current Hull Issues 96
Basic Materials 98
Lamination, the Essence of Modern Boat Building 99
Understanding Laminate Strength 99
High Technology and Boat Building 102
Plastics 103
Plywood 104
Composites and Cores 105
Ultra High Density Foams 109
Delamination 110
Putty Cores 111
Foam Cores 114
Surveying Cored Hulls 116
Plywood as a Core 116
The Essentials of Hull Structure 117
Keel 117
Bulkheads 118
Stringers 118
Frames 122
Structural Grids and Grid Liners 122
Tabbing and Taping, a Weak Point 124
Broken Tabbing 125
Decks & Superstructure 126
Deck Join Methods 127
Deck Issues 129
Proper Fillets 130
Rub Rail Materials 131
Windows and Deck Joints 132
Stress Points 133

5. Evaluating Boat Hulls 135
How to Determine the Presence of Cores 136
Examining the Bottom 138
Examining the Hull Sides 139
Deck Join Defects 141
Through Hull Fittings 142
Interior Hull 143
Stringers 146
Limber Holes 148
Bulkheads 149
Checking For Cabin Leaks 150

Fuel Tanks **152**
    Aluminum Fuel Tanks 152
    Black Iron Tanks 156
    Stainless Steel Tanks 157
    Aluminum Water Tanks 157
Mr. Blister **158**
    The Real Cause of Blisters 160
    Barrier Coating 163
    Pre 1996 Boats 164
    Repaired Blisters 164
    Blisters on Used Boats 165
    Repairing Blisters 166
Summary **167**

6. Performance and Sea Keeping **169**
    The Meaning of Sea Keeping 171
    Juggling a Host of Factors 173
    About Speed 176
    Hull Types and Efficiency 178
    Pitching 181
    Vertical Center of Gravity 182
    Passenger Height Above the Water 184
    The Effects of Trim 185
    Shaft Angle, Propeller Pockets and Vee Drives ... 187
    The Effects of Beam 188
    The Effects of Weight 189
    Stability 191
    Dynamic Instability - Chine Riding 192
    Extreme Cases 192
    Summary 193

7. Decks & Superstructure **195**
    Deck Cores 195
    Deck Designs 197
    Gimmicks and Weird Stuff 200
    Making Inspections 201
    Hardware Attachments 202
    Windlasses 204
    Where Does the Water Go? 204
    Rope or Chain Locker 204
    Guttering 206
    Deck Hatches 207
    Deck Problems With Express Cruisers 208

Bow Pulpits 210
Windows & Frames 211
Port Holes 212
Sagging Decks 214
Interior Headliners 215
Flying Bridges 216
Helm Stations Generally 217

8. Stress Cracks, Finishes and Surface Defects 223

Boat Finishes 223
Claims to UV Resistance 224
Stress Cracks 225
Repaired Areas 229
Stress Cracks on Hull Bottoms 231
Gel Coat Voids 233
A Common Question 234
Should Stress Cracks be Repaired? 234
Damage Repair 235
Gel Coat Crazing 235
Dark Colored Boats 236
Blotchy, Discolored Finishes 237
Longevity of Finish 238
Repairing Chips and Dings 238
Cleaning 239
Should Old Boats be Painted? 240
Maintaining the Finish 240

9. Power Options 243

Diesel Myths 244
Gas Versus Diesel 247
The Safety Issue 249
Gas Engine Longevity 249
Diesel Maintenance Issues 250
Diesel Operating Issues 252
Who Really Needs Diesels? 253
Boat Size and Weight 253
Minimum Planing Speed Test 255
Diesel Engines 255
Diesel Power Ratings 255
Brake -vs- Shaft Horsepower 255
Continuous -vs- Intermittent Power 256
Continuous -vs- Intermittent Duty 256

Revolutions Per Minute 257
Diesel Engine Reliability Experience by Manufacturer 258
Detroit Diesel 258
Caterpillar Engines 260
Cummins Diesels 262
Volvo Diesels 263
Yanmar Diesels 264
German Diesels 264
Gas Engines 265
GM Block Engines 265
An Important Rule for Internal Combustion Engines 266
Marinizing Companies 269
Mercruiser 269
Volvo Gas Engines 271
Transmissions 271
Reverse-Reduction Gears 271
Z-F Transmissions 272
Vee Drives 273
Stern Drives - The Bete Noir of Power Boating 273
Alternative Drive Systems 275
Engine Surveys 275
Diesel Engines 275
Gas Engines 277

10. The Engine Room 279
Engine Room Access & Serviceability 283
All About Engine Hour Meters 285
Gas Engine Longevity 287
Diesel Engines 289
Propellering 289
Ventilation 289
Things needed frequent servicing 290
Sizing Up Condition of Used Boat Engines 292
Water and Oil Trails 294
Engine Rust 294
Sources of excessive engine room corrosion 295
The Drive System 297
Engine Mounts 297
Vibration Problems 299
Exhaust Systems 302
Diesel Engine Risers 304
Mufflers 304
Gas Engine Risers 305
Other Quick Checks 306

The Cooling System 307
Look Under the Engines 308
Shaft Seals 308
Installation of Other Components 309
Fuel Filters 309
Fuel Lines 310
Fuel Tank Vents 311
Batteries 311
Water Heaters 312
Battery Chargers 312
Insulation 313

11. Electrical & Plumbing Systems 315

Flexibility is in the Switching 317
AC Power - How Much is Enough? 318
Shore Power Cables 321
Shore Power Connectors 323
Electric Service Panels 324
Circuit Breakers 325
Service Outlets 325
Older Boats 326

Generators 326
Gas or Diesel? 329
Water Where It Shouldn't 331
Inverters: AC Power From Batteries 331
DC Systems 333
Battery Chargers 334
Older Boats 334
Plumbing Systems 335
Sea Cocks 337
Plastic Valves 338
Sea Strainers 338
Plastic Components 339
Plastic Nipples 340
Vacuum Head Systems 341
Boating in a Sewer 341
Standard Electric Pump Systems 342
Waste Plumbing Systems 342
Bilge Pumps 343
Where Does the Water Go? 346
Fresh Water Systems 346
Dockside Water Systems 348
Air Conditioning Systems 348

Assessing the Overall Systems 350
Convenience for Servicing 350

12. Design Details 353

Hey Man, It's Cool 354
Important Changes in Boat Building 354
Computers, CCR & CAD-CAM 354
Eliminating Wood: Enter New Materials 355
High Maintenance, Low Maintenance
  and too Much Clutter 356
Ergonomics 358
Integral Platforms 359
Exhaust Ports 360
Side Exhausts 361
Platform as Patio 362
Boarding Problems 363
Cockpit & Under Deck Storage 364
Fish Boxes 365
Exterior Upholstery 366
Fold-Down Cockpit Seats 367
Hardtops 367
Transom Doors 367
Cockpit Scuppers 367
Windshields and Wipers 368

13. Steering, Controls, Systems
& Equipment 371

Ergonomics at the Helm 371
Engine Control Systems 374
Steering Systems 376
Helm Panel Layouts 376
Tops & Covers 377
Cockpit Appliances 379
Hardware 379

Navigation Instruments **380**
Radars 381
GPS/Plotters 381
Depth Meters 381
Autopilots 382

Other Systems **382**
Air Conditioning 382
Water Makers 384
Water Fixtures 385

Navigation Lights 386
Ground Tackle 386
Anchor Windlasses 387
Bow Thrusters 388
Hydraulic Transom Platforms 388
Safety Gear 389

14. The Art of the Deal 393
Hull Identification Numbers (HIN) 393
Federal Documentation 394
Getting Into the Right Frame of Mind 395
Boat Shows 395
New Boats 396
How About Demos? 396
Seasonal Leftovers 397
Buying a Trade-In 397
Dealerships 398
Optional Equipment 398
Dealer Markup 398
Selecting a Dealer 399
Used Boats 400
Beginning the Search 400
Locating Boats 400
Brokerage Boats 401
Transacting the Sale - Used Boats 402
For Sale, OBO 403
Sellers's Expense, Buyer's Expense 403
OBO Contracts 404
Co-ownership 405
Boat Fraud 405

15. Boat Shopping 407
New Boats 407
Test Runs 408
Used Boats 408
The Florida Market 409
Fresh Water Boats 410
Other Regional Considerations 410
Making Your Own Appraisal 411
Appraisal Books 413
Regional Variations 413
Fickleness of Pricing 414
Repossessions & Salvage 415

16. The Survey & Post Survey 417

Used Boat Surveys 419
What Surveyors Do.. 419
Survey Logistics 420
Engine Surveys 421
Oil Analysis 422
Borescoping 423
Electronic Diesels 423
Gas Engines 424

After the Survey 425

Dealing With Issues 425
Negotiating Deficiencies 428
Who Makes Repairs? 429
Estimating Repair Costs 430
A Few Other Tips... 430

17. Boat Builders by Company 433

Companies 434

Albemarle 434
Albin 434
Azimut 434
Bertram Yacht 435
Bayliner 436
Blackfin 437
Boston Whaler 437
Buddy Davis 438
Cabo 438
Californian 438
Carver 438
Cheoy Lee 439
Chris-Craft 439
Crownline 440
Cruisers, Inc. 440
DeFever 441
East Bay 441
Egg Harbor 441
Formula 441
Fairline 442
Feretti 442
Grand Banks 442
Gulfstar 443
Hatteras 443
Intrepid 444

Island Gypsy 444

Jefferson 444

Kady-Krogen 445

Luhrs 445

Magnum Marine 445

Mainship 445

Maxum 445

Navigator 446

Ocean Yachts 446

Pacemaker 446

Phoenix 447

Post Marine 447

ProLine 447

Pursuit 447

Riviera 448

Sea Ray 448

Tiara 449

Tolly Craft 449

Trojan 449

Viking 450

Wellcraft 450

Companies by Quality Category **451**

Entry Level Builders 451

Mid Level Builders 451

High Quality Production Builders 452

List of Taiwan Boats **453**

Glossary **455**

INDEX **465**

Chapter 1

Basic Considerations

"If I had known then what I know now,"
the seasoned skipper told me,
"I would have skipped the first three boats I owned
And just bought the one I own now.
Would've saved me twenty years of trouble
And several hundred thou."

Most people would agree that it doesn't make much sense to spend tens, even hundreds of thousands of dollars to buy a boat only to find out the hard way that boat ownership and boating is not for you. Unfortunately, thousands of people every year do just that, only to find that owing a boat was a lot more than they bargained for; that boating was not all fun-in-the-sun and chasing mermaids along palm studded beaches. Therefore, in this opening chapter we start out by taking a hard look at what boat ownership is all about by examining the benefits, the risks and the liabilities of being a boat owner.

The Benefits

The benefits of boat ownership are pretty obvious, namely that it's yours and you can use it and go whenever and wherever you wish. It affords not only a recreation for singles and families, but can also serve as an excellent social venue for mixing business and pleasure, or simply pleasure alone. It meets the needs of the socialite and the loner with equal ease.

Another advantage for people who are seriously into boating is the weekend and vacation retreat that can be mobile or stationary, the proverbial floating condo. But for many, boating becomes an avocation and a way of life, much as others take to golf, tennis or skiing. More than merely a means of waterborne transportation, it's a seagoing abode that is vastly more versatile than a motor home, which is severely limited as to where it can go and park. With a boat you can go just about anywhere the water is deep and protected enough to throw out an anchor and create your own "RV park" without paying fees and being crammed together with everyone else's undisciplined, screaming kids!

The foregoing barely scratches the possibilities. However, the would-be boat owner should be made aware that with all that freedom comes a rather hefty price. The remainder of this chapter is devoted to discussing those unpublished price tags.

Are You a Candidate for a Being Happy Boat Owner?

This is a subject you are not likely to find in any other book, mainly because, unlike most other writers, I'm not trying to sell you a boat. It concerns me not a bit whether you buy one or not, so if I save you from making a mistake, this book will have fulfilled its purpose. My job here is to provide you with accurate, honest information, and in that vein I'm going to talk about some of the more serious and unpleasant risks and responsibilities involved in boat ownership. Buying a large boat is something you want to do with your eyes wide open. Like buying stock for your 401k, if you take advice from people who sell the stuff, you're likely to run into trouble.

There are three main and several secondary reasons why people get into trouble with boats: Ownership usually proves more costly than they expected, it involved more work than anticipated, or it turned out that they didn't have as much time as they thought they'd have to use the boat, or any combination of the three. Other more marginal, though no less relevant reasons are that some people buy into something they should know that they can't afford, or that other members of the family don't care for (mainly the wife) but the buyer tries to push on them. A final, and fairly common mistake comes to the person who is determined to buy cheap in a world dictated by the rule that there are no free lunches except from the government. Mercifully, the government doesn't build boats.

It is very easy to get in over one's head financially through not taking the time to add up all the costs, and including a cushion for unanticipated expenses. Many people make the mistake of buying a new boat with the idea that the warranty and insurance are going to eliminate all maintenance and repair costs. Rest assured, these won't. I explain why further on in this chapter.

Maintaining a boat properly is a lot of work. Always has been, always will be; that's just the nature of boats, and unless you're willing to do the work yourself, or can afford to pay someone else (few can), then be prepared to see the resale value of your boat decline very rapidly. If the best you can do is just tolerate the effort of taking care of it, if you don't really enjoy this sort of thing, perhaps you should reconsider.

Remember, as a boat owner, everybody loves you when you take them out for a day of fun, but the usual scenario is that when the fun is over and it's time to do the clean up, repairs and maintenance, those folks tend to disappear or have something better to do. When it comes time to paint the bottom, compound and wax the boat, clean the bilges, change the oil or lay it up for winter and whatnot, chances are you'll be doing it all alone. Those members of the family who so enthusiastically cheered your decision to buy a boat are nowhere to be found when work time rolls around.

It's like the perennial story of the child who wants a puppy. He begs, pleads and swears that he'll take care of it. A week later it's the parents who are cleaning up the endless little "accidents" and feeding it. Ah, the wonderful world of good intentions.

The amount of pleasure that you derive from a boat will be a function of whether you enjoy doing some maintenance, and how often you get to use it. If you get to use it seldom, chances are it will become a burden. I'll discuss the issues of maintenance in greater detail a bit further on.

Boating was, is and always will be, a very costly hobby, sport, recreation or whatever you want to call it. The boating industry has done a lot in recent decades to try to make boating affordable to as many people as possible by making boats as low cost as possible. The only problem with this results from the fact that boats are vessels that float in water, often salt water, which means that boats tend to deteriorate very rapidly unless they are made with consummate skill and the highest quality materials. If not, what we may perceive as a reasonably priced boat can end up being far more expensive than we had ever imagined. The rule of thumb we should always apply to boating is that the need for quality reigns supreme unless we're willing to see our "investment" in a boat deteriorate very rapidly in a less than high quality product.

When we are finished with a boat, unlike many other products, particularly vehicles, we expect it have substantial residual value. Boats are just too big and costly to make them disposable. A final responsibility, one that is to ourselves, is to do our best to ensure that that residual value remains as high as possible. That is the other half of the maintenance equation.

The marketing media, of course, presents only the positive side of boating. Unfortunately, for every hour of fun in the sun, another hour needs to be spent managing and maintaining a boat. One of the primary reasons why first time boat buyers become last time boat buyers is that the boat demanded more time from them than they could afford.

How Much Time is Involved?

Second to the cost issue is the amount of time boat ownership involves for both management and maintenance. It may surprise you when I say that boats require time to be managed. Management time means time involved with issues such as arranging for insurance, dockage and repairs, as well as whatever effect ownership may have on managing your finances and taxes. If you do not perform much in the way of maintenance and repairs yourself, then rest assured that you will spend plenty of time making arrangements for other people to do these things.

Most would-be boat owners will want to know how much time should be devoted to routine maintenance. It's hard to get a handle on the answer to this question simply because some owners will perform all their own maintenance while others will do none. The later, however, are rare because paying others to do everything is normally far too costly for the budgets of the vast majority of midsize boat owners. My own experience and that of many others is that it takes about an hour of work for every hour of pleasure with normal usage. That also assumes, of course, that a boat is maintained to a certain standard, and a consistent rate of usage. This answer is not very satisfactory, so let's see if we can't be more specific. I'll use the example of an owner with a 28 foot express cruiser who performs all his own maintenance – keeping in mind that maintenance does not include things like engine overhauls and other major repairs – and who also maintains his boat to a fairly high standard.

The amount of time spent on maintenance will vary widely depending on the length of the boating season and the owner's proximity to the location where he keeps his boat. Obviously, travel times to and from the boat can be substantial and should be included in our estimate. It's also a demonstrable fact that boats that are kept far from the owner's home are usually among the most poorly maintained. It goes without saying that people who have to travel far just to get to the boat won't much feel like working on it once they get there.

Routine maintenance includes jobs such as cleaning the interior and exterior. Exterior maintenance is not unlike auto maintenance. Boats get dirty mainly from air pollution, which tends to leave black streaks of water runoff that is not easy to remove. And, if you want that shine to last beyond the first year, there is compounding and waxing to do once or twice a year, depending on the climate you're in.

Interior maintenance involves most of the same tasks as housekeeping: the bigger the boat, the more there is to it. There is dusting to do, carpets to be vacuumed and even toilets to be cleaned. And of course, the bigger the galley, the more kitchen tasks there are to do, like cleaning all those spills inside the refrigerator.

Mechanical maintenance is a class all by itself, one in which there is always something to do, even on new boats. Most of the mechanical work usually involves minor repairs and adjustments, as well as making additions and improvements that, although minor, do add up to considerable amounts of time. Time need be taken not only to perform these tasks, but to make the frequent inspections to the various systems to ensure that all is well. Unlike automobiles, with boats we do not just drive them until something goes wrong. Not unless we're stricken with terminal stupidity.

Taken altogether, performing all the various tasks will average two to three hours per week on an annual basis, exclusive of management tasks. Obviously, there will be periods in which the owner will do much more, and much less, but boat maintenance tasks can be expected to entail at least 100 hours per year.

Management tasks include not only paper and telephone work, but also the time it takes to bring a boat in for warranty service or general repairs to a marina or boat yard. On an annual basis, I would estimate an average of another twenty to thirty hours. Therefore, reasonable boat ownership responsibilities can be expected to demand at minimum of at least 120 hours per year. Thus, if you do not enjoy at least some of the tasks of routine maintenance, you're not likely to be a happy boat owner. People who get the most satisfaction from their boats tend to be those who enjoy puttering around on a boat.

The alternative is to ignore maintenance and end up taking a huge resale loss on a poorly maintained boat. Even boats that haven't been maintained that are only a couple years old, can be expected to take big depreciation hits.

Resale Value

And speaking of depreciation, now is as good a time as any to talk about this very important consideration. Having mentioned the effect of maintenance on values, we also need to consider resale costs. The cost of a boat is only partially recoverable. To this extent, the particular boat you choose can easily be more important than how much you pay for it. As a general rule, you lose a lot more on a new boat purchase than a used one.

As with cars, the moment you pay for a new boat, you've probably just lost 20% right off the bat. With a used boat purchase, it is entirely possible to realize a 90% recovery, even after a couple of years. This is highly dependent on both the quality and popularity of a particular model and is unlikely to occur within the class we refer to as entry-level boats which lose value more like cars due to general low quality.

Resale costs also include brokerage fees that generally run 7-10%. Note that selling a boat yourself, while not involving the complex closing issues of real property, can be quite an aggravating experience, so most choose to go with brokerage to avoid these hassles. Also be aware that when boats aren't well maintained and wisely chosen, unpopular types can be a real drag on the market and hard to sell. Resale times of up to a year are not uncommon, during which time the cost of ownership continues.

Many, many people, when they are forced to sell for financial reasons, stop performing the necessary maintenance. This is the most common cause of all failed surveys and lost sales: the boat has problems the owner didn't even know about because he quit maintaining it at the worst possible time, as soon as he hung out the For Sale sign. Consider all of these things as potential costs of ownership.

Boat Size vs Cost

The answer to this may seem glaringly obvious, but the full import of boat size is usually lost on novices from the standpoint that the larger the boat, the more maintenance demanding systems it will contain. Many mid size boats have two heads, which is twice as many to keep operating and keep cleaned. Ditto, shower sumps, water fixtures, lights and so on. Thus, it's not so much a matter of mere size that increases maintenance and ownership costs, but one of magnitude – how much more the boat contains in way of systems and equipment.

You know from your own experiences of home ownership, how demanding it is to keep up with maintenance and repairs. Now imagine how much more difficult it is for a boat that floats in saltwater!

When we move from a 28 footer to a 35 footer, the amount of time required will come close to doubling, jumping from a hundred hours up to nearly two hundred. If you wonder how such a dramatic increase could be possible with only a 25% increase in length, you might also consider why the cost difference between these two boats is also likely to be double. It's because the boat contains so much more. Not only is it longer, but also wider and deeper. And all that additional space contains things that need to be maintained.

Then, too, when you move from the smaller to the larger boat size, we find that the size of the vessel's electrical system increases dramatically to handle the expanded array of electrical equipment. Instead of having only a small refrigerator, now we've got goodies like ice makers, freezers, air conditioning and other systems further adding to all the things that need to be serviced and maintained.

I often find it amusing that the average new 35 footer today comes with as many as two 3" ring binders jam packed with owner's manuals. I also haven't failed to notice that on the vast majority of boats I survey that are only a few years old, most of these manuals have never been so much as opened. No one but a retired person would have time to wade through hundreds of pages of technical stuff; after all, we buy boats for pleasure, not as make-work projects. But just the size of the owner's manuals can give you some inkling of what you are in for when you buy a boat.

The Importance of Proximity

Where you keep your boat – both in season and out – will have a major effect on your boating experience and its cost. Let's use two examples here, the first of which is an owner who lives on waterfront property and keeps his boat at a dock in his back yard. The second is an owner who keeps his boat at a marina thirty miles from his home. The point is obvious, is it not? The second fellow will either spend a huge amount of his boating time driving back and forth – or, more likely will end up not using his boat nearly as much as he anticipated, as well as skimping on maintenance due to a lack of time. Whereas the first owner not only will likely find plenty of time to get things done (he'll do tasks in the evening that the other guy wouldn't be able to do), but he'll also have far more time and opportunity to actually enjoy his boat.

Is it possible to be a distant owner and still enjoy the benefits of the first owner? Yes, and the people who do are the sort that routinely spend weekends aboard their boats. Many boat owners live long distances from where they keep their boats, but solve that problem – at least partially so – by spending weekends on their boats. They take off on Friday night and return Sunday evening. Sometimes they work this arrangement simply because they do not live near a suitable boating area, in other instances they keep their boats a long way from home because they wish to keep their boat in a more desirable location for boating.

Whatever your situation and plans are, be sure to consider the issue of proximity and whether or not you'll really have the time at hand to do the things you want to do, as well as the things you should do. In the end a lot more money may be involved than expected.

Cost/Time Benefits

How much is your free time worth? What are you willing to pay for pleasure? I'd venture to say that not many people ever ask themselves this question before buying a boat. To find the answer simply divide the price of the boat plus the cost of ownership by the number of years you own it times the annual hours of use and you'll have the cost per hour of use.

A typical boat owner in a short season climate (3-4 month summer) will put about 100 hours on the engines. Of course, the time the engines are running is not the only time he's using the boat, so let's double that and say the owner gets 200 hours of use annually. This includes the time spent slurping cocktails on the aft deck. The cost of the boat, estimating very roughly, is $100,000 with another $12,000 for interest on loan, dockage, insurance, fuel and other expenses. Therefore, on an annual basis, his cost per hour of enjoyment comes to about $560.00 per hour.

As you can see, this is an astonishingly high cost. There are 8760 hours in a year, yet the average boat owner gets only 200 hours of use. The remaining 8,560 hours the boat is just sitting unused. We can put this into a better perspective by saying that there are only 10 useable hours per day, which reduces the useable time to 3650 hours, and therefore the boat spends only 3450 hours a year just sitting, but this is little consolation.

The average boater in climates with longer seasons or even all season climates typically gets double the usage from his boat. But averages mean little because some years we use boats more than others. The only reasonable conclusion we can come to is that buying a large boat is not very cost effective investment in terms of getting the most recreational hours for your money. The exception is for the owner for whom boating is his one and only avocation.

Then why do so many people buy boats, and who get so little use of them? The answer is that there is a very high turnover in boat ownership, in part because they discover this the hard way.

For the most part, the high cost of boating is justified by those for whom boating is or becomes an avocation. Meaning that they'll get far more than the average amount of time using the boat. For the owner who takes frequent boating trips and spends many nights on board, that cost of ownership can drop to nearly $100/hour, a rate which is considerably less than outrageous.

Getting Upside Down

Yet another reason people buy boats, don't use them, but still hold onto them, is what we call getting up-side-down financially. That means that the owner owes more on the boat than its market value. He doesn't sell because he'd have to write a large check to his lender just to get rid of it. So, he holds on and holds on, meanwhile the boat deteriorates and deteriorates and becomes worth progressively less and less. In other words, the owner has set a trap for himself from which he can't escape short of having to pay to get rid of his boat.

The way this trap is most often laid is by taking very long term loans with minimal down payments. The marine lending market in recent years has become very competitive offering loans as long as 15-20 years. A 20 year loan doesn't make much sense when the average period of ownership is less than four years, so you can see how easy it is to get upside down. But it was not so long ago that the longest loan period was 5-7 years.

These very long term loans are not healthy for either the lender or the borrower, since the loan term often exceeds the life of the boat. Even worse, a boat is not real estate; it will *never* appreciate in value. Thus, the long term loan with minimal down payment almost guarantees that the borrower will always be upside down, owing more on the boat than its worth.

Since the average period of ownership for all boats is less than four years, you can see that boat loans exceeding more than 7 years are pure folly. The exception, of course, is that you have sufficient wealth that you are not at risk by getting up-side-down on a loan. If this were the case, you'd be smart enough to avoid paying a financier all that interest for 15 years when you could just write a check and save yourself all that money.

Winter Lay Up

If you live in a place where the water turns solid part of the year, there are also winter lay up costs to consider. If the boat has to be hauled out, there is the cost of hauling, shoring and storage during winter months. There is also the cost of covering the boat.

Even if the boat can remain afloat, if frequent subfreezing temperatures occur, the engines and plumbing systems have to be winterized. These are time-consuming tasks that, if done yourself, will take a full weekend, otherwise you pay someone else to do these things at rates exceeding $50/hr. A summary of these expenses for a 35' boat often looks like this:

Winterize vessel, 16 hours@$55/hr.	$880.00
Shrink wrap vessel	400.00
Winter storage, 6 mos@$300/mo	1800.00
Haul, launch & shoring	200.00
Total	$3280.00

These, of course, are expenses that occur every year. Prices will vary widely from one area to another, most often depending on availability of facilities. A call to the service manager of your local boat yard or marina can likely land you a reasonable estimate of what it will cost in your area.

Why Boat Repairs Are So Costly

While I've been listening to boat owners complain about the high prices charged by boat yards and marinas, I can't say that I have a lot of sympathy for them. Boat yards and marinas have to have large amounts of waterfront property which is both costly to purchase and maintain, as well as being subject to higher tax rates and extreme pressures from developers that drive prices and taxes ever higher.

Secondly, throughout most of the country, theirs is a seasonal business that makes it difficult to hire and keep highly qualified personnel. Added to this are the difficulties imposed by the huge range of products wherein standardization is almost non existent. Therefore, it is unreasonable to expect repair and maintenance work on a boat to be priced similarly to that of cars or most other products.

Conversely, if they do manage to find what they consider reasonable prices, boat owners often end up complaining about the quality of work and service. Therefore, no one should contemplate getting into boating without also realizing that this is an expensive recreation. Although it is promoted as a mass market recreation, the truth is closer to it being the pastime of the more affluent.

Typically we do not find "fast, friendly service," to be the norm at boat service facilities. While many may try hard, it's a tough business that has to live with short seasons, terrible working conditions, and a clientele that is almost never satisfied with the cost. Boat yards simply cannot survive doing small, ordinary jobs at low cost, which is why so many mobile services have sprung up around major boating centers to deal with one-shot, smaller jobs. However, these tend not to be very cheap either, since the customer has to pay for things like travel time and all the delays associated with not having everything at their fingertips as the boat yard does. Thus, prices charged by mobile services frequently rival those of boat yards.

The bottom line is that boats are very expensive and the costs of maintaining and repairing them are equally so, no matter how good a deal you got on the original purchase price.

The Risks

Seaworthiness and Respect for the Sea

At the time I originally conceived the manuscript, I had no intention of including the following section. However, the increasing numbers of serious boating casualties that are related to unseaworthy vessels prompted me to reconsider. Seaworthiness is a concept that is difficult to correctly understand, though nearly everyone thinks he understands its meaning.

The term is actually a legal term, and if you know anything about the law, you'll understand that it is unavoidably complicated. Here is the basic *legal* definition:

The fitness of a vessel for a particular voyage with reference the condition of its hull and machinery, the extent of its fuel and provisions, the quality of crew and officers and adaptability to the type of voyage proposed.

While this definition is clear and precise, less obvious is the huge array of judgmental factors it encompasses with words such as "quality," "condition" and "adaptability. Without knowledge and experience, none of these judgments can soundly be made. Note here that this does not merely pertain to ships on the high seas, but equally to a canoe crossing a lake or a river boat.

If a man successfully crossed the Pacific in a bathtub, does that make the bathtub sea worthy? No, it makes the man very lucky: he didn't run into any storms to ruin his day. Another man tries to cross in a well-equipped cruising sailboat. He encounters a storm and the boat is destroyed but the man rescued. That boat was not sea worthy either, for in the judgment of experts, it was not built strongly enough to encounter the conditions that should have been expected. Seaworthiness is not a matter of luck; it's a matter of being prepared for conditions that one would reasonably expect to encounter.

Storms, of course, are a common occurrence, and it is not always possible to escape from them by seeking shelter.

Risk From Without and Within

The ocean, lake or large bay is a dangerous place, despite its usual appearance of placidity. The attitudes of many first-time boat buyers today is radically different than it was in the past, probably due to advertising. Respectful attitudes have also changed due to cell phones, prowling towing services and televised dramatic helicopter rescues (most aren't aware that the rescuers send out bills for their services billed at some $3,500/hr.) Many people now have only have a vague notion that the water can be dangerous, and have almost no comprehension of how fast that placidity can turn into a boiling cauldron of violent water, mainly because the media has portrayed it otherwise.

Few would argue that we live in a risk-adverse society, though many try to eliminate all risk, while others simply pretend everything they do is safe. Recent events reveal how untrue that is as the two tallest buildings in the world came tumbling down with their occupants safely at work behind their desks. One of the things that has always attracted people to boating is the desire for adventure. Adventure is usually achieved by challenging the unknown and therefore entails the element of risk. Boating entails considerable risks that most boaters willingly accept and even enjoy. Yet there are always the risk averse types who fool themselves into believing otherwise. I came to this understanding while dealing with boat owners who were stunned that their boats could sink, overnight, at the dock. Totally flabbergasted, it never occurred to them that their boat could sink.

So how is it they overlooked the painfully obvious? It then occurred to me that these folks really didn't comprehend the fact that their boats remaining afloat was dependent upon them! No, they thought that it would just go on floating forever all by itself. To them the boat was no different than their car. The truth is that all boats are self-sinking without the efforts of owners to keep them afloat. Sooner or later, without help, they will go down.

The element of risk not only comes from without, but from within. Ranking very high among the most common causes of boating accidents is the failure to maintain a boat in seaworthy condition, so let's be sure we understand how the term seaworthy relates to condition. A vessel is properly maintained when the owner takes all reasonable and prudent steps to ensure that no mechanical breakdown will occur by making periodic inspections of all such things that are known to cause problems, not just with the machinery, but as regard to the seaworthiness of the hulls, which includes its plumbing systems. Thus maintenance is not just a matter of fixing things when they break or go bad, but of anticipating the breakdown and taking corrective measures before the fault occurs. Unless this philosophy is adhered to, the vessel will become unseaworthy by virtue of the reality that all things degrade over time.

The dangers of operating a boat are often not obvious. Unlike driving a car, a boat floats on a fluid, water, which can be shallow or deep, clear or murky, moving or not moving. Dangers include, running aground, getting caught in storms, becoming lost, and becoming stranded due to engine failure or running out of fuel. There is also the risk of sinking resulting from striking a submerged or floating object, as well as the failure of some internal plumbing component, as well as the risk of failure to maintain numerous other aspects. Wrapping a large, floating rope around a propeller can rip a shaft out of a boat, leaving a big hole. Almost no boats are equipped to deal with such emergencies. No, they hope that helicopter gets there in time.

With a car, RV or whatnot, you can park it in a driveway or garage and more or less forget about it for an extended period of time. Not so with a boat, for a boat left unattended for long periods of time while afloat may sink, or at the least will deteriorate at a rate that is alarming, for boats require a substantial amount of care. Owning a boat is not unlike owning a horse, for you just can't turn your back on it for very long.

The newcomer to boating should be aware that despite all our high technology and the fairly good safety record of boat builders, to go boating safely one still needs certain knowledge and skills. The need to learn something about seamanship has not disappeared. Seamanship is not just a term that applies to ships on the high seas; it also refers to the skill needed to operate vessels safely on rivers, lakes and bays where storms, wind and waves may not be the only danger.

Aye, Aye, Captain!

As owner of the boat, you are captain of your vessel and in no small measure, master of your fate, if not your soul. Another important factor goes beyond yourself. As boat owner and operator, you are responsible for the safety of your passengers. That means that if you don't know what you're doing, you can be held liable for your mistakes that end up in injury to others. There is a very good reason why, in days of old, the captain of a ship possessed the powers of a sovereign: Ultimately he is responsible for the ship and its passengers since, while in the midst of the ocean he cannot call upon a wide range of government services. In the immediacy of a crisis, all decisions are his to make, including the taking of all actions to ensure safety. Thus, the responsibilities of boat ownership are greater than for any other type of vehicle you could own except for an aircraft.

Many boat owners attempt to forgo the effort it takes to learn how to read and use charts, and navigation aids which are the mariners "road maps". This lack of knowledge is most often the cause of running boats aground, which can damage the hull and engines. In addition to nautical charts, the intelligent boater also learns to read the weather. He knows by experience the very serious dangers of getting caught in a severe weather.

Inherent Unseaworthiness

It is possible that a vessel is inherently unseaworthy, either for a particular use, or for any use at all. If you're shopping for new boats, you may have noticed that there are no builders who specify in their literature what range of operations their boats are fit for, though there is a move underway to require them to do that. Presently, it's strictly caveat emptor, up to you to determine whether the design of a particular boat is suitable for how you use it.

If you're a newbie or even moderately experienced, this can pose serious difficulties in trying to decide what's what. You may even be under the impression that all boats are more or less seaworthy for the normal range of conditions that people normally use them. That would be a mistake, for there are many boats on the market that are unseaworthy for anything but calm water operation and finding out which is which requires an expert.

Tragedies at Sea

The following true stories will illustrate my point. I am intimately familiar with these two stories because I was the investigator hired by the insurers of those two boats. In both cases, I concluded that both vessels were unseaworthy for the intended voyage and it was aggravated by operator error. Neither were aware of the acute limitations of their vessels.

These stories are not related to gratuitously scare you, but to illustrate how cavalier the boat building industry can be, along with public attitudes toward recreational boating. Plus I relate them because very few of such stories ever make into the major media and almost never the boating publications. There is a very common misperception that because a boat is built by a large company, it must be okay. All too often it is not okay. All too often basic issues of seaworthiness are severely compromised in favor of marketing decisions. All too often, fundamental quality issues are compromised in favor of price.

All too often people buy boats that they know, in their own words "are not very sea worthy," yet they buy them anyway with the rationalization that "I won't go out when the weather is bad." Of course it is highly likely that the day will come when a nice day suddenly turns bad and they get caught in conditions they didn't expect to have to deal with. Happens all the time with more than a few paying a high price.

Both of these stories illustrate what a healthy respect for the sea is by illustrating what a lack of respect for the sea is, wherein respect is something born of experience or knowledge of the risks the sea imposes:

To the Out Islands

A middle aged couple from North Carolina bought a new 45' boat in South Florida and headed to the Bahamas from Florida, with another couple of the same age. I'll call them Smith and Jones, with Smith being the boat owner. This couple had quite a few years of experience with smaller boats in the North Carolina area in protected waters, but almost no oceanic experience. They purchased the boat in South Florida with the idea that a Bahamas cruise would be their maiden voyage, followed by a return trip to Charleston. This was poor judgment to begin with for a new boat that hadn't been tried and tested. The couple was both in their late 50's as were the Joneses, the couple they invited along.

The first demonstrable lack of respect for the sea was that this trip took place during hurricane season, which is almost half the year. There's nothing wrong with that so long as a voyage is planned in such a way that safe refuges are always close at hand. That was not the case here. Instead, this couple was heading to the out islands, into the open Atlantic with safe harbors too far and few between for comfort. Big mistake number one.

Mistake number two, the worst of all, is that they misjudged the weather reports which showed a tropical depression passing what they thought was well to the south. Though predicted to continue heading west and away from them, that was not the way things turned out.

Thirdly, both couples failed to assess their own physical abilities, or lack of same. Although fairly robust middle aged folks, they weren't athletes and did not possess the physical stamina necessary to deal with weather emergencies at sea. What was anticipated as a pleasant, relaxing vacation of fun in the sun, white sand beaches, crystal tropical waters and margaritas on the aft deck at sunset, instead turned into a nightmare. Not their worst nightmare, because they had never imagined that such a thing could happen. It simply did not occur to them, and their ignorance nearly killed all four of them.

It turned out that this early season tropical depression did not follow its predicted path, nor did it remain a depression, but instead became a tropical storm which made an abrupt 90 degree turn south of Cuba and headed north to the Bahamas where our relaxed vacationers were caught completely off guard.

The fourth and final mistake was that the vessel was by no means sea worthy for the kind of conditions they were about to experience. The design of their 45 foot motor yacht ANGELINE was little more than a floating condo with a very high superstructure and center of gravity. It was one of those slick-looking price boats that sold for about half of what a good sea boat would sell for. Making matters worse, it was not equipped with adequate ground tackle. By the time our vacationers realized that the storm had turned and was heading toward them, it was already too late.

It wasn't the tropical storm that caused the beginning of their troubles, but a thunderstorm. Caught out on the Bahama Banks in choppy seas, apparently the motion of the boat kicked up water that was lying in the bottom of their fuel tanks, for first one engine, then the other, quit and would not restart. Then the generator died.

The single pulpit mounted Danforth anchor was dropped, one that had six feet of vinyl coated chain and a mere 150' of 3/4" line. At this point, the storm center was 150 miles south and moving north at 11 knots but winds were picking up to around 20 knots and seas getting pretty ugly. Smith was by now aware that they had about 10 hours before coming under the direct influence of the storm. It is not known exactly how it happened, but a gust of wind hit the boat broadside. Everyone on board heard the loud crunching sound as the bow pulpit was torn away, which is where the anchor rode was attached. The anchor held for about an hour until the rode sawed through on the rough edge of the broken pulpit, setting them adrift. Both Smith and Jones tried to protect it with rags, but the boat motion was so bad that they couldn't stay on deck for long. Had they a reserve anchor, they might have prevented what was to come but, alas, they did not.

They called the USCG for assistance and were referred to a private towing company since the owner was not calling a Mayday. The towing company did not come to a quick decision whether they would assist. An hour later, BASRA (Bahamas Air Sea Rescue Association) a volunteer group, overheard the radio calls and offered help. They were about three hours out from ANGELINE.

Meanwhile, ANGELINE continued to drift eastward and they maintained near constant contact with the BASRA rescue boat until the batteries completely died and then they lost the radio. The batteries went dead without their understanding why. They still had a cell phone and were able to patch in through USCG Miami and back to BASRA.

Now the storm was down to five hours out and the direct effects were now being felt. ANGELINE was drifting almost sideways, rolling severely and everyone was violently ill. The interior was a shambles as furniture broke loose and was hurled about. A flying door hit Mrs. Smith in the face, breaking her nose. Mrs. Jones was incapacitated with a sprained wrist and seasickness. Mr. Jones was sitting on the aft deck, relieving himself of breakfast, when the poorly supported hard top came crashing down on him, putting a four inch gash on the side of his head and knocking him out. Smith had a very hard time trying to pull Jones out from under the wreckage, but eventually he got him into the salon. The cell phone, which was in Jones pocket ceased to function after getting wet in the rain. Now our vacationers were adrift without communications with the storm bearing directly down on them.

ANGELINE was now in the outer bands of the weak storm as was the BASRA boat which was forced to turn back. ANGELINE'S last reported position was thirty miles north of Nassau and 15 miles east of the Berry Islands, but now drifting north-north west at probably a good 4-5 knots meaning that they could have drifted another 20-25 miles in five hours. BASRA notified the USCG which initiated a helicopter search at roughly the time ANGELINE was in the storm which remained a weak tropical storm with 50-55 mph winds. ANGELINE had by this time drifted well into the Northeast Channel with its famously confused seas. Exhausted, battered and all but incapacitated, the four unfortunates were plucked out of the water by the rescue helicopter, very lucky to still be alive.

Afterward, Smith's most poignant comment was, "We just didn't know how bad things could get. It was just one thing after another went wrong." I recount this story not to try to scare you, but to demonstrate what lack of proper respect for the sea can mean. And also because the boating media does not like to publicize stories like this; they hurt the image they are trying to promote. It is, essentially, the regard of every day on the sea as a care free holiday without awareness of the risks. Mr. Smith broke every rule in the book and paid a severe penalty. There's more to boating than just having fun, so that if fun is all that you are interested in, perhaps you should take up golf.

It's one thing to buy a fancy cocktail barge and be willing to confine yourself to protected waterways. The problem many like Mr. Smith have is that they want their cake and eat it too, thinking that it won't hurt once in a while to venture offshore and hope that they don't get caught by bad weather. Some are lucky that way and get away with their indiscretions for a long time. Others like Mr. Smith get nailed on the very first day out. And that's something to think about.

Closer to Home

Granted, most owners of mid sized boats will never venture far from shore. Of course, many when they first buy a boat have no intentions of going very far, but then one day something prompts them to go farther afield. Perhaps an invitation to join a group cruise or some other boating activity that is not usual for the boat owner. Such was the case of Mr. Able Baker (fictitious), the owner of a 36' express cruiser that was 14 months old.

Baker was an attorney in a law firm where two other lawyers were boaters and avid fishermen who told Baker that kingfish were running strong and convinced him to take the next day off and go fishing. Not being much of a fisherman himself, he decided to give it a try and the following morning, he and the two other lawyers and a secretary hopped aboard and headed out into the Gulf Stream. Seas were running about two foot or less with a light swell from the north and it was altogether a very pleasant day, typical of spring time in South Florida.

They did, indeed, catch some fish and after more than a half day of trolling, they were hot and sunburned and decided to stop for a swim. At the time they were about two miles out in the deep, indigo blue waters of the Gulf Stream. The wind had fallen off and the water was even calmer than when they started out with a light swell from north.

Too deep to anchor, they threw a couple of trailing lines out for safety and drifted. All four of them jumped in the water and were frolicking around when they noticed very big swells passing from the southeast, probably about four footers. The boat was also oriented with the stern to the southeast.

Unknown to them, these swells were the wake of a passing super tanker that was long out of sight. They were unaware that such wakes can travel for dozens of miles from ships that are far out of sight, appearing without warning like rogue waves which, in a sense, they are.

What one of the more experienced lawyers noticed next alerted him to a possible danger: The stern of their boat was heaving up and down in the swells and the open transom door was going far under water with the water rushing well up into the cockpit. This happened several times. This fellow hollered that they should get back aboard and check it out, which they did. As they started climbing aboard the swim platform, they couldn't help but notice that it was now nearly submerged, whereas before, the platform was a good six inches above the water line.

Water was now washing into the cockpit with every rise and fall of the boat on the light swells. The first person into the cockpit was horrified to see that one of the deck hatches had floated out of position, and water was now pouring directly into the hull. This was a rear engine, vee drive boat, so the water was going directly onto one engine, the one directly in front of the transom door. This more experienced boater/lawyer immediately comprehended the danger they were in and so went to start the port engine because he knew that if they lost power, they would lose the radio and the bilge pumps since it already looked like the batteries were going under.

Unfortunately, the battery selector switch was located in a bad spot, low in the engine compartment, so that it was already underwater, shorting out the system. So were the engine start circuit breakers, a common situation of this type of boat. The engine would not start, but the radio was still on and he managed to get off a mayday with their position before it, too, quit.

By the time the last person had climbed back aboard, it was clear that the boat was going down as the cockpit was now awash. They tried to hold the hatch covers down, but the surging water within the hull caused air pressurization that kept blowing them up and out of place. Realizing that there was no hope, Baker said that the life preservers were located under a berth in the forward cabin and the lady went to go get them and bring them out while he continued to stand on the hatch cover and hold it down. She no sooner disappeared through the companionway when another swell heaved the stern up, then down for the last time. Baker floated away, out of the cockpit while the others, panicked with the realization that the woman was trapped in the cabin.

The boat was now floating bow up with water up to the windshield. One of the men valiantly tried to dive down through the open door and bring the woman out, but the surging motion of the boat rammed his head into something very hard, almost causing him to black out. At this point the cockpit upholstery cushions had floated to the surface and to which all were clinging.

This story has a less than tragic ending because the boat did not completely sink due to a large amount of air trapped in the bow and some real heads-up thinking by one of the men. The bow hatch was partly above, partly below the water as he swam around to try to look inside because he could hear the woman frantically pounding on something. He could actually see her arm flailing around in front of the hatch, but he knew that as soon as he opened the hatch, the boat would go down completely as all the air escaped. He also knew that there was another hatch down deeper.

He shouted to the woman, who could hear what he was saying, telling her to open the lower hatch which was about four feet beneath the surface. He knew that opening the hatch that was below the water would not let the trapped air out that was keeping the boat afloat. That was real heads-up thinking that saved the woman's life. After much struggle, this hatch was opened and they got her out.

The story does not end here for naturally the lawyer/owner wanted to sue the boat builder, maintaining that the boat was unseaworthy, which it certainly was. So did the insurance company that paid a total loss on the boat. Unfortunately for him, he got a really good deal on the boat from a dealer that told him they were "clearing inventory" because they were dropping that builder's line of products and taking on another. That wasn't exactly true: the line was dropped because that builder had just gone bankrupt. He could sue if he liked, but he'd have to stand in line with the rest of that company's creditors for what little was left of an insolvent company.

In recent years there have been very few turly good sea going boats built in the US with the standout exception of sport fishermen and a very limited number of others. The vast majority of boats built today are fair weather flyers, boats designed primarily to attract the numerous newcomers too boating, along with the chronically inexperienced with their attraction to trendy styles and appeals to luxury.

The days of the more seaworthy pleasure craft that were designed by naval architects, such as those boats by Hatteras, Chris Craft in its heyday, Bertram, Pacemaker, Egg Harbor, Trojan, and many others, came to an end in the 1980's, replaced by boats basically created by people trained on CAD machines and in slick marketing tactics and who know little about boats. In the never ending quest for profits, the skill levels of the people who actually build the boats is nowhere near what it was just two decades ago. Twenty years ago the writing of this book would not have been necessary; today it is. The lack of experience and proper training displayed by boat designers today is a central theme of this book for the purpose educating boat buyers so that they may be alert to such deficiencies.

Portrait of a Happy Boat Owner

One doesn't have to be rich to own a boat, but one does need to be able to afford what one owns in terms of size, price and cost of ownership. The people who get the most pleasure from their boats are those who get into boating not merely for fun, but as an avocation or hobby. They're eager to learn as much as they can, and they understand that you don't just buy a boat and become an instant expert because you own one.

A boat owner should be a mechanically inclined person who has some interest in things mechanical and electrical and is not afraid or disinclined to learn more. Far too many boat owners today are the sort who have no interest in things mechanical, are not good with their hands, and who attempt to rely entirely upon others to see to it that their boats are kept in good condition. And more often than not, such people will attempt to pay their maintenance people as little as possible because maintaining a boat is costly. The faulty logic in this should be painfully obvious. In all things in this world, we basically get what we pay for, so that if we pay for cheap help and service, that is what we get.

The bottom line is that people who get the most out of their boats and boating are the sort who love boats for all that they involve, including the work, the adventure and the dangers. They see a challenge in every aspect, from fixing a bilge pump, to painting the bottom, to learning the art of navigation. If this describes you, then the odds are high that you'll love boat ownership and boating.

"There is nothing so fine as just messing around with boats." - Anonymous

"Ya gotta be nuts to own a boat" - An opinion expressed by thousands.

"A boat is a man's first love and first wife. Second loves and wives are optional and ill-advised." - Barnacle Bill

Definition of BOAT: *Break Out Another Thousand*

Insurance

It has been my experience over many long years that far too many boat owners rely on insurance to cover for their lack of diligence. Please be aware that all insurance policies that I have seen contain what is known as a Due Diligence clause. Due diligence simply means that the insured is required to exercise a similar degree of prudence common to that which is performed by other knowledgeable boat owners. For example, if you leave your boat unattended for six months and it sinks, that is not due diligence but gross neglect and your claim for damages could be denied on that basis.

Similarly, no insurance policies cover the failure to maintain a boat properly. If you don't change the engine oil and the engine goes BANG!, this probably won't be covered. Should the boat sink due to a failure to maintain, that may not be covered either.

Understand that boat insurance is intended to cover accidents, primarily events from without the vessel. Insurance is not intended to cover maintenance issues or any other issue that is the responsibility of the manufacturer. Insurance is not intended to cover events occurring from age, deterioration or mechanical breakdown. However, marine insurance policies can vary greatly on these points. Before you buy insurance, I strongly recommend that you obtain sample policies of those you propose to buy, and then READ THEM.

The Cost of Boating

Getting a handle on the cost of boating is not easy because it presupposes you know what the expenses are likely to be. In most cases we know some, but mostly not. The obvious ones are the cost of the boat itself, the cost of finance, insurance, dockage, and fuel. Repairs and maintenance is where we have trouble.

When it comes to fuel, we almost always underestimate how much we'll spend, so figure it this way: Estimate how many hours per year you will use the boat and divide that by two. This approximates the actual amount of time the boat is burning fuel. Then multiply that number times the number of gallons per hour both engines burn at cruise speed. If the engines burn a total of 34 gallons per hour, and you figure you'll use the boat 100 hours per year, divided by two gives you 50 hours of burn time. At 34 gph, that comes to 1700 gallons — enough to fill a small swimming pool. At $1.27/gal., that will cost you $2,159.00, not exactly pocket change.

Estimating the cost of insurance is easily accomplished by calling any marine insurance agent who can give you a general idea of what the premium would be. The same applies for dockage, just make a few phone calls to marinas in your area.

Estimating other costs is a bit more difficult. Estimating repair costs is not similar to cars, wherein new cars rarely ever have anything serious go wrong with them (at least in my experience). When it comes to boats, that's not true. Again, look in that owner's manual package and note all the equipment that you expect to work perfectly for a long time and you'll get an idea of why this is true. Sure, the warranty will cover most things for the first year, but even then, you've got all those warranties to deal with. The fact is that we don't know if or when something is going to go wrong with anything. The product may work perfectly for a decade, or it could crap out the day after the warranty expires, we don't know.

Therefore, the best way to get a handle on repair costs is to apply a composite average. We can do that by applying a percentage of the boat's value, adjusted for age. Based on experience, I recommend applying the following percentages on a per annum basis:

Boat Age	Percentage*
1-2 years	2%
3-4 years	3%
5-7 years	6%
8-10 years	10%

* Warranty coverage not considered

The seventh to tenth year is estimated to be the most costly because this is the time period when major engine repairs are most often encountered, though in reality these costs are usually spread over a period of years. That is to say, that as there are people who will only replace tires on their cars one-at-a-time as they wear out, so most boat owners will only make major repairs/replacements one at a time. When one engine wears out and no longer will run properly, most often only one engine gets rebuilt, even though the other will not be far behind. The reason for that is clear; many people simply can't afford these major expenses and so try to cut corners.

Another expense that is difficult to estimate is the cost of fitting the boat out. Fitting out means providing everything you need to use the boat the way you want to use it. This can include everything from galley utensils, to towels and linens, tools, cleaning supplies, hose and so on. One can easily drop up to $2,000 into general necessities without getting extravagant. This is also included in my percentage for early years.

Beyond extra equipment which we include in the cost of the boat, we have everything from electronics to anchors, there are other needed items which you will probably be adding piecemeal. These can include anything from a boat hook, to extra fire extinguisher, portable spotlight, fenders, extra lines and a list that is nearly inexhaustible. If you think of furnishing a new home, you'll find that buying a boat is not much different; the cost of buying a home is one thing, but the cost of making it the way you want it is something else again. And though it is very hard to put a price on this additional spending, we can be sure that the cost is significant. Moreover, as with a home, these purchases, alterations and additions usually go on year after year, so adding an additional 1-2% annually for discretionary spending items is not unreasonable.

Partnerships

Some people resort to various forms of partnership arrangements, from those merely between friends to those that are more or less business arrangements. Few of these ever have happy endings since buying a boat is not unlike getting married. Boats are simply much too personal to subject to all the problems of joint ownership. The usual complaint is that one partner is not carrying his load, or is abusing the boat and not treating it with adequate care. Something very costly happens and the acrimony begins. Think long and hard before getting involved in one of these situations.

Charter Arrangements

Charter ventures have been around for a while, but I've never heard a good word about one that involves mid size boats. Charter deals can and do work for much larger yachts, wherein the objective is to try to offset the huge ownership costs, plus such yachts have much better argument of on the legit business expense angle. For the average guy that owns a forty footer, that raises eyebrows at IRS. The reason that such arrangements exist is primarily due to a tax angle, yet many actually have visions of profiting. The reason that they don't work well is that there usually isn't enough income generated to cover the costs plus management fees. What they usually end up with is little income and an abused or at least badly worn boat with higher than average repair costs.

If such ideas have crossed your mind, I'd suggest you rethink, or at least talk with a few others who have had experience with such deals.

The Nature of the Industry

The issue of quality and the reputation of the builder is one that the novice or first time boat buyer needs to pay close attention to. As mentioned earlier, due to the harsh environment in which they spend their lives, boats need to be built of high quality materials with consummate skill. Otherwise, the boat will deteriorate rapidly and the boat owner will end up seeing his investment deteriorate at an alarming rate. In order to understand the nature of quality in boats, we need to have a basic understanding of the nature of the boat building industry.

The shortcomings of boat building industry essentially boil down to matter of money and the effect that has on resources. The boat building industry is unlike most other major industries that produce large, expensive products. As industries go, it is smallish and remarkably undercapitalized, unlike the auto industry, and which makes for a useful comparison. The auto industry is very consolidated and limited to little more than a dozen giant international corporations with revenues in the hundreds of billions, each with a worldwide dealership network of thousands of dealers. The gross revenues of a General Motors or Toyota are greater than that of many nations. As for boat builders, their revenues may number from a few million to a few hundreds of millions; up to barely a billion.

At any given time there are around 1200 boat builders offering products in the US. Imagine if you had 1200 auto makers to choose from! That the boat building industry has not consolidated and generated a "big three" (though it is not that some have not tried) is due to the fact that it is highly vulnerable to recessions and economic downturns. When the economy slows down, boat sales come to a near complete stop because pleasure craft are not a necessity like cars and appliances or homes. Every time we have a serious recession, about half of all builders go bust. Hence, few who understand this industry are willing to invest in it, for it is far too risky, thus making it extremely difficult for a builder to raise capital by means of selling stock. It is even hard for them to get bank loans. The recent demise of OMC during boom times is a good case in point.

Yet another problem affects the small boat industry: per unit profits are so low due to strong competition that it becomes almost impossible for these companies to survive economic downturns. This is a case where competition tends to lower prices to the point of extinction. While it appears to buyers that boat builders are getting filthy rich, through what appears to them to be outrageous prices, the truth is that most won't make enough to survive the business cycle. I have personally witnessed this seven times in my own lifetime, and there is no reason to believe that these cycles will not continue, or that the industry will fundamentally change in any way. The fact of life is that boat building is a marginal industry.

This situation causes problems that inevitably seriously affect product quality and reliability. First, boat builders either can't afford, or won't hire, the kind of experienced high priced engineering talent that is needed to assure high quality and reliability. The truth is that boat building pretty much fits that old saying about watching sausage being made. If you could see it, you probably wouldn't want to eat it.

Boat building now, as in the past, suffers from a serious lack of R&D, product testing and engineering skill. And now that it has entered the realm of high tech plastics chemistry and composites, the engineering skills required have become even more complex. Yet the industry continues to make-do as it always has on the basis of trial and error. Unfortunately, much of this kind of product testing is done at the consumer's expense, with the boat buyer as beta tester, which helps explain why the industry as a whole has had such a poor record of customer satisfaction.

The truth of this could not be more forcefully demonstrated than by a large number of boat builders returning to an idea that failed in the 1960's when it was first tried. This involved the use of cores in boat bottoms. A core is a method of attempting to increase strength and reducing weight, while at the same time reducing the amount of costly materials by substituting cheaper materials. A core basically makes a sandwich of a cheaper material such as balsa wood or foam between two layers of fiberglass. What this does is essentially create a truss that is stronger in certain situations, but not all.

The great risk of this method was the risk of water getting into the core since the materials used are porous and contain large amounts of air space. And when water gets into the core, boat bottoms begin to fall apart. It was a bad idea 40 years ago, and is a bad idea now as cored bottom boats are now meeting the same fate as they did back in the 1960's and 70's.

Consider another point: Automobile models typically sell in units of hundreds of thousands and up into the millions. Boats don't come anywhere close to that. A boat model that sells a total of 500 units is a lot in this industry. The larger and higher priced the boat, of course, the lower total unit sales will be. What this means for the consumer is that very few boat models are in production long enough that whatever shortcomings they may have will not have had the time to be perfected, assuming that as problems are discovered, the builder corrects them. Obviously, the longer a model is in production, the more likely it is that it will become perfected as problems and weaknesses are discovered over time, and then get the opportunity to be corrected. This used to be common wisdom with car buying: *never by the first year of any new model*. This maxim can be equally well applied to boat buying today.

From year to year in the auto industry, chassis and engines tend to remain the same, while it is only the shape of the outer wrapper and interior that is changed annually. In large part this is why the auto makers have become so large and prosperous. Thus the fundamental and most important part of the car has the opportunity to become highly perfected. Boat builders do not have this advantage. The boat hull and deck is the chassis, and thus major model changes forces major changes in tooling. Hence, model changes are very costly and builder's profits suffer, as does product reliability.

Finally, for the most part, boats are hand made items. There is very little in the way of robotics in boat building. Some have criticized the industry for being primitive and backward in this respect. However, they fail to realize that the market simply will not support this kind of huge capital investment. And besides, no one has yet figured out how to design a robot that can lay up fiberglass.

With these things in mind, it only makes good sense to be careful about from whom you buy. Just because a company has been successful in promoting and selling its products is no guarantee of quality and good service. Just because a company offers what appears to be a good warranty is no guarantee that the warranty will be honored, especially if a recession hits and the company goes out of business. To show you that this is no idle threat, consider that in the recession of 1989-92, over 50% of all boat builders went bankrupt, including many of the industry's best known names like Bertram and Viking. When bankrupt companies get sold, typically only the assets are sold, without the liabilities, which means warranty liabilities. So, even though the brand name continues to exist, the legal obligation to honor warranties given by prior ownership usually doesn't.

Dealerships

If the boat building industry suffers from serious problems, it naturally follows that their dealerships end up suffering the same slings and arrows of misfortune. Owning an auto dealership can be like owning the keys to a gold mine. That is decidedly not true for boat dealerships since the nature of the product is so different. Boat builders and their markets are simply not large enough to support the kind of dealership networks and profitability that would result in dealership stability. Plus, as you already know, auto sales are the largest and longest running major league scam in the world. With their power, auto manufacturers can manipulate prices in ways that other industries can only dream of. If anyone else engaged in these practices, they'd go to prison for fraud, collusion and antitrust violations. The boat building industry has no such political/economic power, and therefore cannot manipulate prices and sales practices to ensure their survival.

The history of boat dealerships is that they come and go rather like the seasons. Very few have shown any staying power, and those that do seem to change their product lines like they change their socks. That's because manufacturers (both boat and motor) are not very kind to their dealers; they do not instill dealer loyalty, and lacking that loyalty (or other economic motivation) dealers feel free to change whenever a better deal comes along.

Dealerships suffer from the same economic vulnerabilities as builders do, plus one more; in most parts of the nation it is a seasonal business. This factor alone results in a large reason for customer dissatisfaction. With a large part of the business rush coming in just a few months, it is impossible to meet demand and keep all customers happy. It's also hard to attract and keep skilled personnel, from salesmen to engine mechanics. Highly trained people are rarely available for part-time or seasonal jobs.

When you look around at dealerships, you'll probably find that the ones that have been around longest are those that operate marinas where their revenues are not completely dependent on sales and service. To be successful, and survive economic slow downs, a dealer has to have a revenue source other than sales and service. Dockage, storage and other services usually help them turn the trick, particularly when the water is frozen a good part of the year.

Quality Issues

The idea of always shopping for the lowest price may be without risks for many other kinds of products, but it is very risky when applied to boats. In fact, it is downright imprudent. When it comes to boats, lowest price means *de facto* lowest quality. If you would buy the lowest quality boat, you might as well seek out the cheapest lawyer and the lowest priced doctors and surgeons. How about a cheap printer, toaster or vacuum cleaner? You've been there, done that and know that what you get isn't going to last very long, and that in the end you will end up buying the same product over and over. How many cheap toasters will you buy over a life time, and will not the cost of all those cheap ones end up exceeding the cost of just one good one? (I'd guess I've had at least six or seven.) There are some things for which it is not wise to make selections based on lowest price, and boats are surely one of them.

Millions of people fall for the well-planned trap of buying new cars every few years because they just have to have the latest and shiniest vehicle. We see that gleaming new vehicle sitting in their driveway, but what we usually don't see is the mountain of accumulated debt they've run up just to make themselves feel good. People may get away with this sort of vanity buying with a car, but if you value your future, you surely don't want to do that with a boat. And beware that boat dealers are now trying to mimic the auto industry by getting people to do just that by coming up with clever ways to "trade up."

Falling for the trap of buying a new boat with a trade-in is akin to taking fistfuls of hundred dollar bills and throwing them out the window. You don't stand a chance of getting a fair price for you current boat.

In the eyes of the buyer, issues of quality often take a back seat to style, luxury and interior accommodations. There came a time when the boat building industry stopped building just "boats" and began creating "consumer products." There was a time, not too long ago, when most boat builders were in the business for the love of boats. A time when making money did not reign supreme. Those days are largely gone, and most of boat building today is just corporate business turning out corporate products, though there exists a fringe market of custom boats and a handful of high quality boat builders. Though the prices on their products are often stunning, they provide a good price contrast between high quality boats and the consumer market quality boats. Indeed, I can think of no better way to grasp the huge differences in quality than to carefully examine a custom boat.

The term "consumer products" translates to mean that boats are no longer designed and built to serve the functions that boats heretofore normally served, but instead are designed by marketing types to create vanity sales. Along with a chicken in every pot and two cars in every garage, their goal was to put a boat in every garage and dock. It didn't matter whether it was a fat chicken or diseased chicken, so long as that chicken looks really good. Never mind the effect on the consumer if the chicken is fed fat to increase the weight and therefore profits. Why should they worry that the customer dies of cardiovascular disease when the population continues to grow regardless, so they never perceive a potential shortage of customers.

The new design philosophy is sex appeal and status symbols. Not to worry whether a boat is a practical vessel designed to navigate the waters with; what the consumer wants is a status symbol and fashion statement; the practicality of a boat is deemed irrelevant to getting them sold in large numbers. The marketing types know that if you can create a style trend, the style will perpetuate itself because people are like sheep in that they want what everybody else has as long as it is the latest fashion. So if stylish, sexy looking boats that are utterly impractical become the norm, then that is what people will buy. Vanity became the name of the game. Unfortunately, the marketing people are exactly correct.

This could never happen unless boating could be turned into a mass recreation, and so the industry set about doing just that. Somewhere in the mid 1980's they succeeded and the number of boats in existence reached 22 million by 1990, a high water mark that has since receded to around 20 million. My viewpoint may sound overly cynical, but when you compare any well built boat to the typical entry-level class of boat, I think you'll agree that I'm actually being rather kind.

Part of the problem can be laid at the feet of boat buyers themselves. Far too may people have been willing to spend very large amounts of money without an adequate understanding of what they're buying. No doubt they do so, in part, due high levels of consumer trust in most other products, trust that can be, and all too often is, badly misplaced when buying a boat. Like 401k investing in the stock market, many unknowledgeable people were lured by stock brokers advertising with the siren song of huge profits in high technology, running the NASDAQ up to 5,000. As of this writing, the NASDAQ sits at about 1200, meaning that investors lost over 5 trillion, yes, *trillion* dollars, on an investment bubble created almost entirely by advertising.

If you could sit in my seat, you'd view with amazement at how wealthy men, who are capable of shelling out a quarter million in discretionary spending, are daily taken to the cleaners by boat hucksters. How they swallow some of the most lame-brained excuses by boat salesmen – men who often hardly know the bow from the stern – as to why their expensive new toy is falling apart. How they get the run-around for months until nearly a year later it begins to dawn on the boat owner that he's been had, and that the manufacturer isn't about to make good on his highly touted warranty. This is a daily occurrence in my office and I've got the e-mails to prove my point. It's truly amazing some of the things that intelligent men will put up with.

Today, the industry and its leading association, the National Association of Marine Manufacturers, is deeply worried that too many first-time boat buyers have become last-time boat buyers. New boat sales are declining, year after year, even in boom times. Boat owner surveys show that customer satisfaction rates are poor and going lower. Dealer satisfaction rates are even worse. If all this reminds you of the pickle the US auto industry found itself in the mid 1970's, with Japan stealing its market right out from under its nose, you'd be right-on, the result of unbridled arrogance and greed. The problem we have is that there is nowhere else to turn for boats because the fact remains that, although often highly flawed, no one does it better than Americans. Sure, there are a few imports that are superior to US products, but how are you going to find out about them when it proves exceedingly difficult trying to find out about American boats?

Yet another part of the problem with high cost and poor reliability stems from increased complexity and sophistication of the product, combined with increased luxury and equipment that is no longer optional but standard. When the buying public demands all the bells and whistles, all the luxury and pizzazz combined with a myriad of electronics -- and all at an affordable price, too -- the net effect is to drive quality and reliability down as the builders struggle to keep prices down.

So why can't we have our cake and eat it too? Let me lay it out in fast format here.

- Boaters want "reasonable cost," luxury and every amenity imaginable. There's no way you can have a reasonably priced boat plus good quality plus all the bells and whistles. Something has to give, and that something will always be quality.

- Largest Interior Spaces. The shape that would provide the maximum interior space that so many people demand would be a square or rectangle, though I trust you understand why square boats might be a problem. To yield best performance, a boat hull has to have a certain shape. That shape is not conducive to achieving floating hotels or patios. Hence, the majority of boats perform poorly even under moderate conditions.

- Boaters want fuel economy. The type of hull design that is most fuel efficient is also the one that is least sea worthy. Flat bottom boats will go fastest with the least horsepower and lowest fuel consumption. It also yields a ride that's like driving a car on a rail road track.

- Boaters want to go fast, at the same time not spend a fortune on fuel. Therefore, they opt for diesel engines, not knowing that squeezing high horsepower from a diesel drastically decreases reliability.

- Boaters want low maintenance. Low maintenance is achieved by using highest quality materials with a minimum of complexity. That flies in the face of low cost fanciness and luxury.

In other words, what most boat buyers really want is a contradiction in terms, even an oxymoron, but that doesn't have any bearing on wanting it. However, if you understand this, you're now better equipped to make more intelligent choices.

Warranties

Many people make product selections based on warranties. This is in contradistinction to those for whom the primary criteria is the assessment of product quality prior to purchase. Warranties are nice, assuming the manufacturers ability to deliver adequate service. This is often a false assumption in the marine industry. Taken as a whole, the track record of the industry in honoring warranty claims hasn't been good. Too many try to squirm out of resolving serious claims, too often forcing boat owners to hire legal counsel.

This situation seems to ebb and flow with the state of the economy; during downturns claims tend to be more strongly resisted apparently based on the builder's financial health. Then, too, there seems to be a correlation between the amount of defective product a manufacturer has and how much resistance he puts out to claims. When manufacturers make big mistakes across the board, they seem to put up much more of a fight.

Another part of the problem is based on economy of scale. The vast majority of boat builders have only a regional, not nationwide market. Many are so small that their primary area of distribution is only a few states. The fact is that only the very largest builders even come close to achieving a nationwide dealership network that is capable of handling warranty claims with the degree of service most have come to expect.

So what do all the other builders do? Well, they are forced to either job warranty work out to subcontractors, or demand that you return the boat to the their nearest dealer. Such situations can cause major hardships for the customer. If you are one of those who intend to rely heavily on a warranty, it's a good idea to investigate the builder's ability to provide the kind of service you want before you buy.

Many builders, or at least their dealers, will make extravagant claims about warranties. I strongly recommend that you read the warranty from beginning to end; this may prove very enlightening as to what "limited warranty" really means.

A "life time" hull warranty sounds great until you realize that most builders won't survive long enough to make good on such extravagant claims. Bear in mind that when companies get sold, it is most often only the assets that are sold, rarely the liabilities. Warranties are liabilities, and so the new owners are unlikely honor the claims against the previous owners who are nowhere to be found. The sad truth is that customer satisfaction with warranty service is generally abysmal in the pleasure craft marine industry.

New -vs- Used Boats

Used boat sales outrank new boat sales by well over a 10:1 margin. The reason is because new boats are so expensive and used boats are truly great values. First time boat buyers are prone toward purchasing new boats. Their reasoning is usually that they don't want to "buy into other people's problems." Their thinking is that if they buy a new boat, they won't have any problems. That is unlikely.

Experienced boat buyers have a different philosophy. Theirs is that the first couple years loss in value isn't worth the price; that if they can buy a late model boat for half or two thirds of the new boat price, they are thousands of dollars ahead, even when the used boat may have problems to be fixed. For example, consider a boat that sells for $100,000 new and $80,000 two years later. That $20,000 saving could cover a lot of repairs with many thousands left over.

True, with a new boat you have a warranty but the question becomes one of how much is that worth? If the product doesn't have a certain degree of quality, a warranty becomes like a Band-Aid over a wound. It's trouble enough taking a car back to the dealer for warranty work, but with a boat, this can be a lot more troublesome when the dealer is not located nearby.

The fact of the matter is that used boats are usually tremendously good values, so if you find yourself stretching the limits of your budget to get what you want out of a new boat, you'll probably be able to get all that you want out of a used one without breaking the bank or stretching yourself too thin.

What to Expect From a New Boat Purchase

Being hand made items, and generally being rather complex, it had long been expected that new boats will have some "bugs" to be worked out. As with all other products, boats are not extensively tested after they are finished. Like it or not, that job falls to the buyer. With larger yachts a process of "fitting out" is planned for. The larger the yacht, the longer it takes and the more things need to be dealt with. But with larger yachts, there is always a captain and crew who deal with most of these issues, not the owner. In the mid size boat range, rare is the owner who can afford a paid professional, so he's stuck with doing it himself.

Depending on boat size and complexity, one should expect that there will be a small number of problems and defects that need to be corrected. But since you're paying big money for a product, the number of problems and defects should be small. Even so, many of these glitches are going to pop up over a period of time, and you should expect that and be prepared to deal with them. To give you a general idea, the typical new forty footer usually takes about a month to accomplish fitting out, which includes installation of additions and options. During this period of time, if the owner is around much, he'll discover shortcomings and get them corrected while the service people are still working on the boat.

The usual process is that the owner takes delivery of the boat, operates it for about a month and then makes a list of all the problems. When the list is made, he calls the dealer who then sends out a crew, or the boat is brought back to the dealer where the problems are fixed. You should not expect that the boat will be delivered to you half finished, or without a final check out to insure that the boat is ready. See Chapter fourteen *The Art of the Deal*, for more on this subject.

Chapter 2

Boat Types: Which is Right for You?

*No one can appreciate truly good design
until he thoroughly understands
the nature of bad design.*

There are two basic types of boat owners besides the avid fishermen; the dedicated yachtsman and the weekend warriors. The main difference between the two, is that the cruising yachtsman likes to – what else? – go cruising long distances. Whereas the weekend warriors typically confine their boating to the travel radius of what they can do on a weekend, usually not more than 50-75 miles round trip.

Cruising yachtsmen are usually the ones that have the toughest time choosing their boats because their boating activities can vary widely depending on their free time. Naturally, the cruising yachtsman lives for those one or two longer range cruises that he can squeeze in each year or so. In the mean time, he's boating weekends just like weekend warrior. It is at those times, his longer range needs tend to conflict with his weekend boating style.

The greatest difficulty in attempting to find the perfect boat, comes first in realizing that there will be numerous contradictions amongst our desires. The old saying that all boats are a compromise is no myth. Actually, it's not the boat that is the compromise; it is your desire to get everything you want in one neat package, and all at a price you can afford. In past decades, boaters pretty much accepted the fact that a boat can't be everything they wanted it to be. The attitude today is different; many people want it all. But to get it, they often end up sacrificing aspects that, due to inexperience, they aren't aware of until they become experienced. That's usually the point they decide to sell and "move up."

If you are new to boating, there are two approaches you can take. The usual approach is to bear the additional cost of starting with an entry-level boat and move up to something better later, or you can try to get it right the first time, which is likely to save you tens of thousands of dollars, if not more.

Sea keeping, performance and economy are three aspects that are compromised by what most people want in the way of accommodations and style. Yet another is low maintenance versus luxury and sophistication. One of the first decisions you need to make is one of common desires or vanity versus practicality. Listed below are ten positive aspects that are in contradiction to each other. The whys and wherefores are discussed in much greater detail in the remaining Chapters. Seeing it laid out in this format may help you to better understand why we can't have our cake and eat it too. Performance, sea keeping and fuel economy issues are discussed in detail in chapter six.

> Sophistication versus practicality
> Low maintenance versus luxury
> Spaciousness versus sea keeping
> Weight versus fuel economy
> Weight versus sea keeping
> Sea keeping versus fuel economy
> Price versus quality

The basic boat types break down into the following list of fundamental styles that define boat types, and are not builder model names even though many builders will use a generic style as a model name:

> Express
> Open
> Aft cabin
> Convertible
> Sedan
> Flying bridge sedan
> Double Cabin
> Tri Cabin
> Trawler
> Flush Deck Motor Yacht
> Pilot House Motor Yacht
> Cockpit Motor Yacht
> Long Range Cruiser, a.k.a. Trawler
> Down Easter

All of the above styles can or may be modified by further descriptive adjectives denoting design differences, and will be technically correct. The following terms are trade mark model names that are tending to fall into common usage, yet do not do much to indicate

Fig. 2-1. Known as the Hatteras 43 Motor Yacht, it is a classic example of the double cabin style with separate staterooms fore and aft with salon amidships. The flush deck and low bridge makes her very easy to get around on. Great for folks who are tired of climbing around.

a particular boat style, and should not be used except when referring to a model name:

> Sport cruiser
> Super Sport
> Cruiser
> Family cruiser
> Command bridge
> International
> Picnic boat
> Mediterranean
> Weekender
> Sundancer
> Sunbridge
> Sundeck
> Mid cabin
> Voyager

Fig. 2-2. To call this boat top heavy is probably a bit of an understatement. A 35 footer referred to as a "motor yacht," it is the typical floating condo designed to attract the uninitiated. There are so many different levels crammed into this 35' space that spending a day aboard is like spending the day on a jungle gym. Out in moderately rough water (3 footers) the sea keeping characteristics are appalling, rather like trying to pilot a balloon in a hurricane.

The reason I make these distinctions is that when people start using trade names as style names, no one understands what they are talking about because the trade or model name has nothing to do with style. Thus, if you use the term "open" every one knows what style boat that is. Whereas if you use the term "command bridge," or "sunbridge" the listener isn't likely to have a clue as to what type of boat you're talking about.

Mrs. Boat Buyer

This section is written especially for the Chairman of the Board, the CFO, the Lady of the House, A.K.A. Mrs. Boat Buyer. If you are having trouble with the spouse wanting to compromise sea keeping for interior accommodations, I suggest that you have her read this section.

Far and away the biggest problem men have with trying to select a good, seaworthy boat, is the battle between husband and wife between practicality and luxury and spacious accommodations. The marketing departments of boat builders are all too aware of this conflict so that nearly all go out of their way to please the wife's desires. This has the very unfortunate result of creating boats that are not very good on the open water. In fact, the majority of mid size boats are not very good on the open water.

It's a fact of life that open water is a harsh environment and unless a boat is designed to handle that there are going to be darn few days in which you'll want to venture far from the dock. If a boat pounds, takes excessive spray over the bow, rocks and rolls unmercifully and is hard to control in a following sea, then it's unlikely that you'll want to spend much time cruising. Meaning that all that money you spend for a boat could end up being pretty much wasted.

Unless you simply intend to use the boat as a floating condo, it's a mistake to compromise a boat's performance for a spacious and currently stylish interior because you'll not likely be able to get the kind of use out of the boat that you expect. The first criteria should be that the boat be properly designed to handle the kind of conditions that most often will be encountered. And as I pointed out earlier, the best sea boats do not have the most spacious interiors, nor the largest flying bridges.

A boat is not a vacation house, condo or hotel suite, and no one boat can have everything to please every one. Though many designers make this attempt, the end result usually pleases no one after a little experience is had with these hermaphrodite designs. What follows is a discussion of the pros and cons of various areas of a boat to give you some ideas of what to expect.

Boating Life Styles & Layouts

The use to which a boat is put is one of the more important criteria for style choices. There is a great deal of stereotyping about what kind of boat should be used for a particular type of use. For example, the express is usually considered a great choice for the day sailor and weekend warriors, but usually frowned on by the cruising types. As one who has done a great deal of cruising in express boats, other than their tendency to have shallow bottoms, the express makes for as good a cruiser as any other.

The same applies to the sport fisherman; not usually considered suitable for long range cruising, few are aware that sport fishermen often spend long periods aboard their boats. Sport fishermen often make for excellent cruising boats. Conversely, I personally find the trawler, which is reputed to be among the best cruising boats, to be the most inconvenient, returning from voyages with a lot of bumps and bruises and physically exhausted from climbing all those ladders and negotiating narrow doors and passageways. While that's a matter of opinion, the bumps and bruises aren't.

The most important criteria is whether the boat is well suited for what you do and your usual number of passengers. Boats such as motor yachts with high sides are not well suited to water sports such as scuba diving, swimming and snorkeling, where ease of boarding from the water must be considered. The same applies to fishing; to be reasonably good for fishing, you need to be fairly close to the water and not have overhead restrictions on fishing rods.

Fortunately in the mid-size boat range many builders offer more than one layout plan for a basic model, so whether you're considering new or used boats, it will pay to look into what plans are or were available. It is equally fortunate that more and more late model boats are more oriented to the level of the water in recognition that water sports are a primary activity even for the cruising yachtsman. Gone are the days of the two foot wide teak transom platform, replaced by integral platforms that are often up to four feet wide. The following discussion will give you some basic ideas to consider.

Dual Controls

Twenty years ago, most mid size boats had dual control stations, located in the lower house and on the bridge. Today the only dual control station boats are trawlers and sport fishermen with towers. This is unfortunate for northerners who get stuck out in the cold while Mom and the guests are staying warm below. Nowadays, you have to rely mainly on soft enclosures to keep from getting wet or frozen.

Head Room

If you are 6'2" or more, headroom is something you need to be alert to, although head room has increased dramatically in recent years usually allowing up to 6'2" with no problem. Naturally, this can be more of a problem in smaller than larger boats.

Sleeping Accommodations

The most common criteria applied is sleeping accommodations, and it is here that our needs run into budgeting problems. Very often a buyer comes to a purchase with the criteria that "the boat needs to sleep six comfortably." When using such a criteria, we need to define what we mean by "comfortably," for any boat that truly sleeps six comfortably is going to be sized and priced toward the upper range of our size category. Does "comfortable" mean a full sized berth in a private cabin? Or just not stacked up like cord wood?

Another issue is separation of quarters such as sleeping and cooking areas from social areas. This is purely a function of boat size so that the smaller the boat, the less separation of spaces there will be. In the vast majority of boats in the mid size range, the salon will not be separated from the galley, and one or more sleeping arrangements will be in a common area simply because boat size is too small to allow for separation of quarters.

The maximum a designer can get from a forty foot boat is three state rooms, two of which are going to be very small, and the third only modestly sized. For a thirty footer, this drops down to two, both of which will be very small, and not have what we would call full sized berths. In a boat, a full size berth is slightly smaller than a twin bed. Full size means that an average size adult can lay down full length, without restrictions.

Fig. 2-3 & 2-4. The interior of this Riviera 40 Express offers a large fully functional galley; in return for this the overall social area is on the small side, particularly with the large queen size cabin forward. The head compartment is also quite large. Riviera offers good value while sticking to more traditional styling with some very nice woodwork. Easy cruising for two; a bit crowded for four adults. This identical layout is found in many of the Tiaras including the older 3600's.

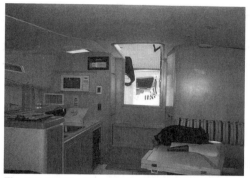 

Fig. 2-5 & 2-6. The interior of this Bertram 30 Moppie is laid out for maximum area of unfettered movement. These two views are looking forward and aft without distorting lens. This is an amazingly large cabin for such a small boat. Except for the head, there are no private areas. Sleeps 4 in one, large open area.

Contrast this with a vee berth which is very wide at one end and usually comes to a point at the other. While vee berths may tend to look full size, the reality is often that for two people they are uncomfortable.

Ultimately, we have to make decisions about social spaces versus sleeping spaces: which is most important? For people who use boats strictly for social purposes and don't do any overnighting, obviously the choice is clear. But those for whom both are important meet with a dilemma. These are the ones that are most often budgetarily challenged because their desires demand a bigger boat than they can afford. Something has to give, so which will it be? If one absolutely has to have both, the only options are to rob a bank or buy a larger, older boat at a lower price.

If that isn't palatable, then we have to choose between social and sleeping spaces. The reality of boating life is that many boaters tend to overestimate the importance of sleeping accommodations, and the frequency with which they will use them. In other words, they don't end up overnighting as often as they anticipate they will, so let's take a look at the various sleeping arrangements available.

If you look at enough boats, you'll eventually get the idea that even designers do not place sleeping accommodations at the top of the priority list. That's why we have so many "convertible" sleeping arrangements such as dinettes and lounges. The convertible dinette actually makes a very good double berth, as do many lounges. Of course, when they're upholstered in vinyl, you need to have a fitted pad made to avoid the problem of sweating when sleeping on vinyl.

Yet another factor is Mrs. Boat Buyer. How well will she adapt to what amounts to more luxurious camping? How well will she really adapt to showering in phone booth and sharing personal spaces with others? Many men deceive themselves by thinking their wives will adapt when they know quite well that they will not if they were honest with themselves. What they end up with is a wife that will go out for day trips, but not for overnighting and thus end up with a boat selected for accommodations that never get used. In fact, I would say that about half the boats I survey under 50 feet show no signs of having been inhabited by a woman. And the vast majority of power boaters not only do not cook aboard, but don't seem to even make sandwiches. This is quite easy to discern by the lack of accouterments on board.

Social Spaces

For most casual boaters, having adequately sized socializing space is more important than sleeping arrangements because socializing is what they do most. This is more of a problem in the under 40' class than for larger sizes. Here we often run into the problem of designers cramming too much in too small a space. For almost all boats except trawlers we have both inside and outside social areas to consider. This is where the typical express cruiser, when thoughtfully designed, excels, for you usually have both an adequately sized interior and exterior spaces owing to the large cockpit areas.

Ultimately in any 35' and under boat, the salon (not saloon; a saloon is a western style bar) has to serve the dual and even triple purpose of galley, social area and with convertible sleeping accommodations. The skill of the designer determines how well these multiple roles are going to work out. A convertible lounge can have for its emphasis stylish design, or alternatively, a more important role of serving as a comfortable berth; all convertible lounges are far from being the same, so if sleeping comfort is more important, pay attention to how well the lounge converts.

Fig. 2-7. This Mainship 35 or 390 has a layout reminiscent of many trawlers with salon, galley and lower helm all conveniently located in the deckhouse. The flush deck layout eliminates a lot of the climbing around one has to do on typical trawlers. Note how spacious the galley is even with a full size gas range.

Another important criteria for social spaces is ease of movement. If an area is filled with seating without leaving adequate room for moving around, it's not going to be comfortable no matter how many it seats. If you're planning for six passengers, then figure the space should comfortably seat four with two moving around. Note here that a lounge that is six feet long can seat up to four people, but if you note the way people behave, no one ever wants to sit in the middle, just like that those middle seats in theaters or airplanes. Figure a lounge seat, no matter how long it is, comfortably seats two.

Built-in seating is usually preferable over any kind of chair because chairs take up so much space. Thus, a boat with two or more built-in seating arrangements – say a dinette and a convertible lounge – will easily offer very comfortable seating for four with a possible maximum of eight.

The Galley

Judging by the number of stoves I see on used boats that have never been used, not many boaters actually do much cooking aboard, particularly on the smaller sizes. However, once boats get over 35' more often than not they will have a reasonably useful galley. Those of you who cook know that having adequate work space means the difference between a tolerable and intolerable experience of cooking. Galleys can have

Fig.2-8. With the flying bridge sedan many builders offer a galley-up or galley-down arrangement as shown here in a Sea Ray 370. This is about as good as it gets in a 37 foot boat. Although the floor space is small, there is a large amount of counter space which is all important when food preparation is an issue. Lots of cabinet space, too.

Fig. 2-9. If a galley is important to you, this is a good example of a poor layout in this Tiara 3100. What could have been a decent sized counter top is ruined by a 3/4 height reefer. The four foot long counter has a hot plate and sink in it, leaving virtually no room to even make a sandwich.

all the modern appliances but still not have adequate space even for making a half dozen sandwiches, so if you're going to be doing any kind of food preparation, you'll want to check out this important factor. What you'll find in the way of galleys runs the gamut, from the sublime to the ridiculous throughout most boat size ranges.

A well-designed and adequately sized galley is always going to require a compromise of other spaces. Here is where we begin to see more definition between boats designed for weekend warriors and those that give more emphasis to the cruising yachtsman. The typical express boat will tend to have a galley that is more of a sandwich board than one that is intended for serious cooking. The most people do with mid-sized boats is grilling steaks or fish on the dock, while micro waving some potatoes and vegetables, or the common spaghetti dinner that involves only a sauce and boiled noodles. Convection ovens in late model boats have all but disappeared while the microwave is omnipresent.

Throughout the range of sizes and styles of boats, I have found that there is no consistency for well designed galleys. A thirty five footer may have a great galley, while a forty footer may have a terrible one. Trawlers, which are considered by many to be long range cruisers, often have some of the worst galleys imaginable and sport fishermen some of the best. Yet quite a few express cruisers often have galleys with abundant counter space, plus their layout is conducive to well-placed appliances.

Therefore, in addition to a reasonable amount of counter space – and consider a cover on top of a double basin sink part of that – you will want to assure that there is at a reasonably sized two-burner cooktop plus a mid-sized microwave. Note here that 125 VAC electric cook tops do a poor job of boiling water, taking darn near forever to boil. To do much beyond frying an egg you need a 250VAC cook top.

Under counter refrigerators may seem like a convenient placement, that is, until you get tired of getting down on hands and knees to see into the frig. Some builders have lately

Fig.2-10. In sharp contrast to the boat in Fig.2-12 left, this Tiara 3600 devotes a lot of space to a great U-shaped galley with large double basin sink and plenty of counter space and overhead cabinet. They don't get much better than this. Of course, one has to give up something to get it, and in this case it was additional sleeping accomodations as this 36 footer only sleeps four, which would be fine for a lot of people.

been resorting to either tall uprights or placing the frige above counter top level, either of which I prefer over crawling around on the deck. Under counter makes for a more spacious appearance, whereas tall reefers of those hung from the overhead make the space seem smaller. The same amount of space is taken up regardless of where it is placed!

Eating

Dedicated dining arrangements beyond a dinette in this size class are rarely found because there just isn't space for this. This is what makes the convertible dinette, no matter how old-fashioned that may seem, so darn useful (a dinette is the same thing as a booth in a restaurant). Comfortably seating four in this size class, they are good for sleeping, eating and socializing such as good game of cards. Dual purpose bar/counter tops with bar stools in front are a reasonable option, though those stools will often be in the way and end up falling over at sea. A better option is the L-shaped lounge with hi-lo table in front, though the major draw back to this arrangement is that the L-lounge doesn't make for as nice a double berth as the dinette does.

Dinette tables should have sea rails on the perimeter to keep things from sliding off; many don't.

Heads

Yes, we still call the restroom or lavatory in a boat the "head." Technically the marine toilet is the head, but we also refer to the compartment by that name also. The great news here is that in recent years the designs of head compartments have improved by leaps and bounds.

Rare is the late model boat that doesn't have a full fiberglass liner. The benefits of this are that these are very easy to clean plus you can easily shower in them without the risk of causing water damage to components that shouldn't get wet, like nearby woodwork. At the smaller end of this size range, the heads are usually smallish and don't have a dedicated shower stall; the entire compartment is the stall. Boats over 38' will often have a dedicated stall, though the small size of some of these makes them less convenient than if they not had one.

The only thing you should watch out for is heads with electric motors at the base. When the entire compartment is the shower stall, it should have a vacuum head that doesn't have a pump motor attached that will get wet and damaged.

Older boats that don't have a fiberglass liner will have mica over plywood and the problem here is one of wood rot that could be extensive.

Cockpit Areas

By far, the most important consideration for cockpits is the ease of movement. This is where the most people spend the most time, and also where docking, piloting and other operations take place. For that reason, it should not be cramped or have a convoluted traffic pattern. The usual culprits contributing to clumsy cockpits are long helm seat benches and oversized lounge modules. See the chapter on decks for more detailed discussion on this topic.

Flybridge Sedan

This is the base style of the flying bridge sport fisherman with the only significant difference between the two being whether the boat is fitted out for fishing. It is often referred to as a convertible when it has a bridge. The sedan is distinguished by a raised house section which can have a bridge or not. Aft is an open cockpit that can be of

Fig. 2-11. Without all the fishing paraphrenalia this Hatteras 36 is a flying bridge sedan, also called a convertable. The FBS is one of the oldest pleasure boat styles.

Fig. 2-12. The Bayliner 3870, 3888 is an unusual departure from the usual Bayliner line-up. Traditionally styled on a very sea worthy hull, she boasts a solid fiberglass hull. Termed a motor yacht, she's really a fly bridge sedan style. Still a "price" boat, it was in production 1983-'94 and has proved to be good value.

various sizes. The style was widely popularized by Egg Harbor, Pacemaker and Chris Craft throughout the 60's and 70's. This is a traditional design type that has been morphed into a number of variations denoted by proprietary model names such as Sun Bridge, Command Bridge and so on. Today the style is more closely represented by the likes of the Hinckley Picnic Boat and other "down east" styles.

Express Cruiser

The modern express doesn't have any superstructure to speak of, though the term express is often used rather loosely. In the past, the express was typified by a low trunk cabin forward, followed by a raised deckhouse. Some builders still produce similar boats such as many Albin boats. It is the most popular type sold today and is usually distinguished by having a large expanse of foredeck, no raised deck house, and a large open aft cockpit. In years past, the express had a low profile raised house forward, distinguished by shallow vertical windows along the sides. This is often replaced by a bubbled up foredeck to increase headroom in the cabin.

The modern Express style is typified by a low, sleek appearance, and very often a reverse sheer line. All cabin quarters are located forward up under the fore deck, except in larger models where a faux aft cabin is usually carved out under the forward cockpit

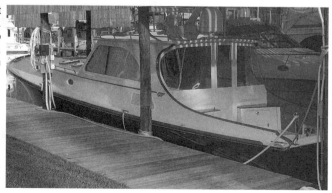

Fig. 2-13. The Hinckley Picnic Boat exemplifies the original express style. Note the complete lack of similarity to what is called an express today. Today, this style would be called a sedan cruiser.

area, an area that usually does not have full head room and is often referred to as "the cave." The other predominant feature is a large aft cockpit that is often half the length of the boat, and normally contains substantial seating and other social amenities. The emphasis of most express styles is social over any type of water sports.

A common drawback of many express offerings is the overwhelming urge of designers to put too much in a too small space, or to take an adequate space and turn it into an ergonomic nightmare just to be able to say the boat has everything. And because the Express is the most popular entry level boat style, builders can get away with this.

When this happens, what could have been a decent cruising boat becomes an ergonomic nightmare. It's no fun to spend long periods of time in a badly cramped boat. Thus, in consideration of the express style, one of the things the reader should focus on is his primary usage of the boat. Bear in mind that any lack of seating can be made up for in a boat with more open spaces by simply adding folding deck chairs; whereas in a cluttered cockpit, one cannot remove permanently installed components so as to make for better cruising or water sports activity. Once you have a cluttered party boat, that's all it can be comfortably used for.

The newcomer to boating will have a difficult time appreciating the need for good ergonomic design. Just remember, the ocean, lake, river or bay is not a perfectly safe place, and that from time to time, stressful situations will occur in which people will need to move about the decks freely without excessive hindrance. A boat is not well, or safely designed that does not provide adequate provision for safe boat handling. This also means that one should not be expected to climb over windshields, negotiate 6" wide catwalks or stand on rounded decks to perform docking or any other necessary boat handling function.

The hulls of Express boats are almost universally designed for protected water to light onshore navigation. The emphasis is almost always on speed and fuel economy over sea keeping. Express boats often have rather poor sea keeping abilities, what with their emphasis being primarily social.

Fig. 2-14. This Albin 31 Express is an interesting departure from the crowd of cookie cutter boats. The basic style is traditional, embodying the better aspects of older designs. Quality is above average and she is more pragmatic in that she lacks most of the eye candy so common on boats today. This is a boat worth looking at if only from the stand point of contrasts with others.

One of the reasons the Express is so popular with young families is that the boats are divided into only two major areas, the cabin and the cockpit. And being all on almost one level, it's a lot easier to keep track of young children, whereas flying bridge boats can be something of a problem in this respect. There is no doubt about it. Express boats are considerably safer when you have small children. In the early 1990's there were a few builders who came up with the bright idea to make an express more water sports amenable, they would eliminate the transom altogether, or of putting double passageways in the transom with no doors. These are not only dangerous to children but adults as well. It's like standing on the trunk of a car while the driver accelerates.

Trawler Style

The modern trawler style yacht retains only vague similarities to real trawlers, mainly because few people appreciate some of the more negative characteristics of true trawlers, namely very slow speed and its rolly-pollyness. Most so called trawler styles have modified planing hulls that are capable of far more than snail paced displacement speeds. That's a good thing, too, because very slow speeds lend to less comfortable motion. The trade off for speed and more kindly motion is greatly increased fuel consumption, though one line of thought suggests that if you can't afford the fuel, then you certainly can't afford the boat.

Trawler hulls are often referred to as "semi-displacement," though in my view that is a misnomer. All boats displace water, but what they mean by semi displacement is that the hull is capable of planing. With enough power, ANY hull can be made to plane, even a supertanker or tugboat! Therefore, we can take this term to mean that a hull will plane when enough power is applied, but not very well, plus the fuel consumption will be very high. What we should seek is either a full displacement or a planing hull as something in between the two offers the worst of both worlds, not an ideal compromise.

The most distinguishing characteristic of the trawler are the multiple levels of superstructure, the typical Grand Banks design being one of the most common. Here

Fig. 2-15. Even the classic Grand Banks 42 is not a true trawler but is actually built on a planing hull with cruising speeds up to about 20 kts. depending on power. It is still enormously popular after more than 40 years in production. The original design was first built in wood.

you have a fully raised house amidships with lower trunk cabins fore and aft. Trawler styles almost always have flying bridges, though some few are found without.

Trawlers are the style of choice for those many who propose to go long range cruising, though the way most modern trawlers are designed today, it's hard to see how they have any great advantages over any other sea worthy type. Hard chine, keel boats predominate whereas the traditional round bilge hull is much in the minority. Interior layouts are usually tri cabins, consisting of staterooms fore and aft with the salon (some people call it a saloon, which is probably appropriate if it has a bar and piano) amidships usually containing the galley, a dinette or settee, as well as a lower control station.

This style can be quite commodious in boats forty feet and over, but in the thirty foot range, breaking the interior up into three to four compartments (with head) can be very cramped. Moreover, getting around on these boats is often akin to climbing over piles of boxes. Doors are usually half-height and hard to get into, not to mention leaky. Ups and downs between levels are often extreme (3-5 steps) with as many as four different levels to negotiate. In terms of comfort, they can leave a lot to be desired and no couch potato is likely to cotton to one. People who are attracted to trawlers tend to be traditionalists. Cruising in a trawler, whether slow or fast, contemporary or modernistic, delivers much more a of a sense of old fashioned seafaring.

The typical trawler hull type today is a warped plane vee bottom with a keel; they are fully planing hulls and not displacement hulls. Common speeds go up to 20 knots. It is appropriate that the displacement hulls of the past be discontinued as there are few advantages anyone would want today. The round bilge trawler hulls of the past were designed that way primarily to carry large cargos of fish, Since they towed large trawls, stability was not much of an issue.

Exceptions to the rule are a handful of true trawler types, such as the Kady-Krogen designs. True trawler designs tend to be confined to larger boats as the hull style is not particularly amenable to smaller boats. One of the problems of the round-bilge true

Fig. 2-16. This Mainship 390 is billed as a trawler. While it has certain features of a trawler, its hull shape is anything but and cruises at 18 kts with a single engine.

trawler in the smaller sizes is that hull lengths are not long enough to make for truly good use of the larger interior volume created by the deep hulls. To make use of both fore and aft spaces, it is usually necessary to have at least two passage ways (staircases) that in themselves gobble up interior space, and tending to make these boats very cramped indeed.

It's not until hulls get up to 45' and over that full advantage of the hull depth can be taken advantage of. This is where the faux trawlers have them beat hands down, for the shallower hulls mean that after spaces can be made accessible by a mere set of two or three steps, without losing all that space that a larger staircase takes up.

The primary advantage of the modern trawler hull is higher speed and the dampened rolling moment that deeper keels and chines give. Some say the keel offers protection to the propellers, though this is surely not much. Typical of most trawlers are uncluttered walk-around decks that are usually about 16" - 18" wide. Also typical are badly cramped engine rooms on most older models that makes maintenance more difficult.

Many single engine trawlers are to be found in the under forty foot range, while twin engines predominate above forty feet. At issue here is the extra comfort of having a second engine and fear of single engine failure. This is no frivolous concern when long range cruising. This is especially true in light of the fact that the higher the horsepower, the lower reliability becomes.

The majority of trawlers in the US are Taiwan built and the quality levels runs the gamut, though I'd venture to say that overall, most are lower rather than higher quality, despite an abundance of shining, but usually inferior quality stainless steel. More than a handful of trade names have dreadful reputations resulting from inferior materials and engineering skills. Among other problems, Taiwanese boats are famous for horrible cases of blistering that results from low quality plastic resin and excessive use of chopped strand mat or chopper gun. Inferior grades of plywood, stainless steel, the use of iron fuel tanks and wooden window frames are other complaints. Electrical systems tended to be pretty good, while plumbing systems often leave much to be desired.

If you're seeking to purchase a Taiwanese trawler, I strongly recommend that you consult with an expert about the problems and quality levels of the various trade names and importers.

Naturally, the higher fuel prices get, the more popular trawlers become. This has been an obvious factor ever since 1974, but as soon as fuel starts getting cheap again, people want to go fast. In recent years trawlers are being given increasingly larger engines, which drives fuel economy down and begins to blur distinctions between the trawler and other types.

Sport Fisherman

This style includes both the "Open" and "Convertible" types. No one really seems to know where the term "convertible" comes from, though Richard Bertram seems to be the first to have used it as a model name. Most likely it refers to the ability to convert interior cabin seating into sleeping facilities, such as dinettes and settees, as these were distinguishing features of most early sport fishermen all the way back to Earnest Hemmingway's "PILLAR" back in 1934.

The modern Convertible Sport Fish is virtually the same thing as a flying bridge sedan, though the later term is rarely used anymore. The word sedan seems to conjure up images of a horse drawn carriage for some, though it is the proper name for this style. This style is one of the most underrated by the cruising crowd since it has many characteristics well suited to the cruising yachtsman. The one drawback is that virtually all the sleeping quarters are located forward and will not have windows. People who don't like this style say it's like sleeping in a cave, which is quite true. But it's also very quiet.

It is important to point out here that unlike almost all other boat types, the sport fishing boat benefits from having the most experienced and talented designers. The designers and builders of these boats tend to really care about their products, not the least of which stems from the fact that they are all avid fishermen themselves. Thus, they are people who actually use and refine the products they create and sell. This fact nearly always stands out in the boats themselves. There is an economy of design that doesn't add anything that doesn't need to be there, plus nothing that needs to be there is missing, all by virtue of the fact that everything has been thought out, tried and tested over many long years.

Amongst all other cruiser types, the sport fisherman usually has the best all-aspect sea keeping abilities. Typically a deep vee hull, or a modified vee hull with very deep entry,

Fig. 2-17. The Blackfin 32 Flybridge is clearly a sportsmans machine as compared to the Tiara 3100 on facing page which is a multipurpose boat. Though similar, the cockpit of the Blackfin is not designed for comfort. Note the very low profile to enhance sea keeping and proximity to the water from the cockpit.

one of its greatest strengths is the ability to take on head seas at considerable speed. Keep in mind that in the mid size boat class, there are no boats that can take on true four footers at high speed, but there are quite a few that can smash down three footers with relative ease.

One of the questions I am most often asked is whether the high aspect ratio and deep vee hull doesn't result in excessive rolling. My answer is no; the hulls are more than adequately ballasted by heavy diesel engines, generators and fuel tanks. Of all vessels, the sport fishermen are designed to spend long periods at trolling speeds in lousy weather. I put them right up there with a well-designed trawler in terms of sea kindliness. See chapter Six, *Performance and Sea Keeping* for additional discussion on this subject.

The sport fishing category is where you'll find most of the highest quality mid sized boats. This is by reason of the fact that fishermen tend to be more experienced boaters and therefore more discriminating. Bertram, Hatteras, Viking, Blackfin, Cabo, Albemarle and other U.S. builders are famous for their quality — and equally steep prices. However, as used boats they offer superb values.

A convertible sport fisherman, minus all its fishing paraphernalia, is a flying bridge sedan cruiser. This point is often overlooked by those seeking cruisers. Small F.B. Sedans don't make for particularly good cruisers, primarily due to the fact that the forward quarters tend to be cramped. But the FBS or convertible in the mid to larger sizes is a leopard that changes its spots as the ability to fit reasonably good sized staterooms up under the foredeck increases.

However, there are a number of older used boats, such as the Bertram 33 and several Hatteras models that have low, but extended deck houses with very comfortable accommodations for their size. Again, I stress that fish boats are not party boats and most are designed for people to spend longer periods on board so that many offer superior cruising appointments, it's just that some people can't get past that word, "fishing." Take a look, you may be surprised.

Fig. 2-18. Tiara 3600 Open decked out as a sport fisherman with marlin tower. Note that it still has the large cockpit seating modules and swim platform.

The advantages of the Convertible are better quality and sea keeping, better visibility from the flying bridge, separation of social from sleeping quarters, and strong long term resale values. The type never goes out of favor and styles tend to be classic and long-lived. Negatives include smaller staterooms and having to climb high ladders to the bridge and not being good for people with small children.

Sport Fishing From Other Types

Many people approach the purchase of a boat with the idea that they're going to do a little of everything from their new toys, including a little salt water deep sea fishing, particularly from express style boats. It's one thing for the guy who only plans to drop a couple lines overboard and hopes he'll catch something, but won't be crushed if he doesn't. It's something else again for anyone who is fairly serious about it. I've tried trolling baits from an express cruiser fitted with outriggers and the experience would have been laughable but for the high frustration levels. From breaking rod tips on a backward leaning arch to getting a fish on and stumbling over molded-in-place steps sticking out from the side of the cockpit and almost falling overboard, party boats by no stretch of the imagination can double as fishing boats and it's foolish to expect them to fill the bill.

The biggest problem is boarding a fish over the gunwale when that gunwale is far too high. With a fish as small as thirty pounds, it's near impossible. Many expresses have transom doors, many of which are too narrow and too high and the door opens the wrong way (out). Fishing from boats with stern drives is equally impossible because one finds it almost impossible to keep the lines out of the drives. If you are serious about sport fishing, then you need to be equally serious about your selection of a boat, for it's irrational to think that the boat has nothing to do with catching fish. And yes, I'm very much aware of the predicament many men find themselves in with their wives who, under no circumstances, want anything to do with a fishing boat. That's where most men get forced into compromises they'd rather not make, so we'll take a look at what multi purpose style boats have to offer.

Fig. 2-19. What makes this a multipurpose style are the seating modules that are nornmally offered as optional equipment. Without the seating you have a large open cockpit suitable for water sports and a cocktail cruiser.

Multi Purpose Styles

The only type that could truly be called multi purpose is a design that is taken from a dedicated sport fishing hull and modified to incorporate more social conveniences. These are boats that are often designated as "open" styles and they may more or less resemble express boats, but most similarities stop there. Compared to an express, they'll have larger cockpits, shorter forward cabins, less seating and upholstery. They will not have arches but often pipe frame tops and even mini towers that double more as a flying bridge than a tower.

The so-called open sport fish can be included in what I am increasingly finding myself calling a multipurpose style. An older boat that many are familiar with is a good case in point; the Tiara 3600 Open. Though somewhat similar in appearance to the express and sometimes called such, a multi purpose or open style has major differences, including deeper hulls, better sea keeping, very often higher quality and emphasis on water sports over social activity.

The open or multipurpose style easily morphs between an express booze cruiser and a fishing boat. The major difference is what you put into it, how much is put into it, and how well the fishing aspect has been thought out. This is particularly true after Tiara deepened up their too shallow hulls to make them a little more sea kindly in the mid 1990's. Pull out some fancy seating and the wet bar, replace it with outriggers, fighting chair and tackle center and one type becomes another. Well, sort of, for in many instances the layouts are not well thought out for the fisherman's taste, but are more attuned to partying and half-hearted fisherman. Yet only a few add-on items have actually changed for we still have the same hull, deck areas and cabin layouts.

In more moderate climates, the express cruiser makes for both a great cruiser and a party boat, but when one can rather quickly change from booze cruising to cruising and

Fig. 2-20. The Tiara 3100 (1997) has a very large cockpit that is taken up with a lot of seating though it can, and often is, used for less serious fishing. Not visible along the transom is another bench seat that is removable. This boat has much higher hull sides giving it a greater internal volume though the amount of cabin space is similar. The extra high windshield provides good protection from spray.

fishing, you have what is truly a multipurpose boat that fulfills multiple purposes well without ending up looking like a bastard stepchild. Instead of being a jack of all trades and master of none, it is truly far closer to being the master of many. It's about as an ideal compromise as you'll find in boat design.

One of the more important things to look for is how well the cockpit area can be enclosed. Tiara has been the long-time master of practical design by always providing a tall windshield that is of near equal height to the radar arch. This provides plenty of head room and good visibility forward, which solves two serious problems with many open boats, namely that from low headroom to the convertible top, your head will cook from hot sun radiating through. Nor do you want to have to hunch over so that you can see through the windshield to see where you're going, nor have the windshield so low that when the bow rises up, you can't see where you're going.

The multi purpose boat category, which includes the likes of Tiara, Bertram, a handful of older Hatterases, Blackfin, Luhrs, Cabo, Albemarle and quite a few other more limited production builders, spans a wide price range and quality level, though generally multi-purpose boats tend to be considerably higher quality, as once again the marketing thrust is toward the more experienced boater. As of 2002, even Sea Ray has hopped on the band wagon with a couple models which give credence to the notion that a committee is a horse designed by a camel.

The wide span in pricing primarily comes about by virtue of the entry level type builders occasionally dabbling in this market and undercutting the quality name builders. Their products almost never rival the quality nor good design of the competition, and so they tend not to stay in the market very long. Sea Ray, a builder with a reputation of catering to the plushie crowd, has also repeatedly tried over the years to break into the sport fishing market with a number of spectacular failures, turning out boats that had all the right gear, but not a clue as to proper design and construction. These boats provide excellent examples of what a lack of designer expertise can accomplish.

Albin, which switched from Taiwanese imports to a U.S. built line of sport fishing/ multi purpose boats that are certainly worthy competitors to the big name U.S. boats. They are very pricey but the quality is commensurate.

The advantages of the multi purpose boat are numerous. In addition to making decent sport fishing boats, they are equally good for social gatherings and make for decent cruisers for one or two couples. A large dinette or settee in the cabin is a common feature that is usually convertible to a berth. The negatives include the fact that these boats usually are not as deep and tend to suffer in sea keeping a bit. There is little or no separation of sleeping from social quarters; there is little in the way of separation of the galley from the salon and typically will only have one head, though usually with a good-sized shower stall.

True multi purpose boats will not have the sort of cavernous interiors that you find in most Express styles. That's because the hull is going to be deeper, and therefore somewhat narrower. And unlike the Sea Ray Express boats, they do not have extremely full, almost spoonbill bows. The open hull is often derived from a sport fisherman hull.

Motor Yacht

This designation is more of a generic term than anything else, and is one that mid size boat builders have taken great liberty with. Traditionally, the term yacht is reserved for larger vessels, whereas their smaller cousins are referred to as cruisers. The term is usually accompanied by a subcategory such as Raised Pilothouse MY, Cockpit MY and Flush Deck MY. In any case, the simple term "motor yacht" doesn't really tell us much other than the fact that it isn't a sailing yacht.

The pilot house motor yacht is distinguished by a raised pilothouse, i.e., the deck of the pilot house is at a higher level than the main deck, usually just a few steps. If the helm area is not in one way separated from the other quarters, then it is not entitled to be called a pilot house motor yacht. The Navigator 55 is a good example of the former while the Carver 500 the later.

Bloat Boats & Clumsy Design

This is the pejorative term that has come to be applied to certain builder's products that pander to people for whom interior volume is far and away the most important criteria used in boat selection. Most builders have been guilty of it to some degree, while a few others carry the bloat boat to extremes. Some of these boats, loaded up with tear drop windows to resemble automobiles, produce loud snickers from experienced boaters. These builders pander to the inexperienced and first time boat buyers with siren songs of sex appeal, status, glitz and glamour. But beneath the surface, the beauty is usually only skin deep and very often hiding some truly terrible design.

Fig. 2-21. Welcome Aboard! This little beauty takes ignorant boat design to new heights. It's one of the worst the author has ever seen. The main deck is five feet above the dock and there is virtually no way to board from an ordinary dock.

Fig. 2-22. This ungainly looking arch was created because the cockpit deck is so high and the windshield too low to be of any value. The problem with this design is that the soft enclosures turn the cockpit and helm area into an oven on a sunny day.

So what is a bloat boat? Well, it's an otherwise ordinary style boat that the builder stuck an air hose into and ballooned it up! Figuratively speaking, that is. It's wider and higher profile than her contemporaries and is often very peculiarly shaped. In fact, so peculiar that whatever style it has is more like too much facial make up on an elderly person in a misguided attempt to disguise age.

Aside from being extraordinarily clumsy looking, bloat boats usually have more serious problems than an ungainly appearance. Having a very high beam to length ratio and high centers of gravity, they tend to suffer from overall poor performance. Not only do they rock and roll, but pound more and are usually very fuel inefficient. All that high windage creates a lot of drag. Some even look like three story buildings, their aspect ratios are so high. Often the exterior designs present a nightmare for moving around on the weather decks and can often pose serious boarding difficulties because of their high sides. Bloat boats often go by the name "motor yacht".

Fig. 2-23. Peculiar designs that create clumsy looking boats have a tendency to result in poor resale values. This Carver 410 has two stairways up to an extremely narrow bridge and an arch that looks like it was tacked on because the builder had a surplus of arches laying around.

Fig. 2-24 & 2-25. The 1977 Bertram 35 left and the 2001 Bertram 50. Notice how little difference there is in the overall styling after a quarter century. Good styling withstands the test of time and works wonders on resale values, too!

The most serious problem for boats with trendy, clumsy, ungraceful design is that they may appear to look very stylish on the showroom floor, but a few years later as styles change, the shortcomings of the design will become glaringly obvious to all. That wouldn't really be a problem but for the terrible effect that this has on resale values. As I said earlier, style shouldn't be everything, but it is important.

To get an idea of how economically important this can be, we can look back in the past and find examples of boats that are good quality, such as Bertrams and Hatteras, that were ugly ducklings. While the boats held up well, the resale prices did not because the style became less desirable year after year. Conversely, there are boats that are a quarter century old that still look good today, and people still pay top dollar for them because classic design always looks good.

While nobody can really explain what constitutes good style design, most of us know it when we see it. Classics become classics because, though the style may not be current, the lines remain pleasing indefinitely. Good design withstands the test of time.

High Sided Expresses

There are a fairly large number of high side express cruisers that nearly qualify as bloat boats, though no express is going to be a three-story affair. If it was, it wouldn't be an express. By raising the sheer line up higher, a designer can create greater interior volume. Even if it is only vertical space, the visual effect is to make an otherwise cramped interior appear more spacey.

However, there are some unfortunate prices to be paid for mere appearance. Structurally, raising the sheer up inevitably results in weakening the hull-to-deck joint because instead of having a 90 degree angle at the deck (which makes it much stronger) now we have a

Fig. 2-26. Careful inspection of this very high sided express reveals the fact that the only way to board the boat is via the transom. That's fine if the one is always docked at the right kind of dock. This is a mind numbingly foolish design.

parallel lap joint which is very weak. High sided expresses tend to be leakers because it is impossible to seal this joint when so much flexing occurs.

Another, equally serious problem is that a high sheer makes it more difficult for boarding and usually very difficult for docking operations. Usually these boats have extremely narrow or no side decks at all, being replaced by a windshield walk-through. So what's wrong with that? Start with a leaking windshield that usually fails to line up properly. There is a reason why yacht designers for nearly a hundred years have designed boats with side decks: it's because one needs to be able to move along the sides for docking and other reasons. A windshield walk-through does not make up for the lack of side decks and is often more dangerous to move through because one has to climb up and over the helm and where there are few, if any, hand holds.

Finally, high sided expresses are particularly bad for any kind of water sports as the only way to get close to the water is via the stern platform. Try recovering your hat that blew overboard from the stern! These boats may be fine for people who get in the boat and stay in the boat, but they are not fine for most normal boating activities. Note here that climate will play a large role here. In cold climates, many boaters would probably prefer to stay as far from cold water as they can get, but in the southern U.S. a boater's desires are far different.

Double Cabin

This style designation is usually virtually the same layout as a tri cabin. Double cabin refers to having two staterooms. All such boats have a third cabin area, the salon, which may be either separated or included in a galley/dinette area, hence it is sometimes called a tri cabin. The style used to be known as DCFB, for double cabin, flying bridge.

The typical traditional double cabin has a fairly deep hull, flush deck with superstructure more or less centered amidships. Very often there is a trunk cabin forward, though usually not aft, which is about all that separates the style from the typical Grand Banks faux trawler. Double cabins typically offer large volume interior spaces that are usually overfilled with accommodations and appliances. Many will have dual control stations, which makes them particularly popular in colder climates.

Most have moderately good sea keeping abilities as they are designed for medium range cruising.

Down Easter

Down Easter is a unique boat style. Derived from New England lobster and fishing boats, and often referred to simply as "work boats." The Down Easter is distinguished by a rather old hull form that has a sharp entry, round bilges (sometimes tapering into a hard chine aft) and relatively flat bottom sections aft. They most always have large keels. The mid point of the hull, where the bottom meets the waves, is usually a fairly deep vee section, so these boats have a well-deserved reputation for good sea keeping abilities. The transom is wide and flat but the bows very pointy. which points up a short coming in the minds of most week end warriors:.

Down Easters are usually superbly performing boats, and one look at her lines tells the story to the experience eye. The beam to length ratio is low, they have narrow but deep entries, minimal wetted surface area for less drag, and rather low profiles that offer less wind resistance. These boats tend to perform extremely well in steep, short chops, but do well in higher seas also. They are found in both single and twin engine installations. For the economy minded, the single engine down easter is hard to beat for low fuel consumption. And with their great efficiency, there is little loss of speed just because it has only one engine.

The negatives consist of greater rolling moment, a hull shape that doesn't allow for voluminous interiors, deeper drafts because nearly all have deep keels to retard rolling, but at least you do get some propeller protection. Docking single engine boats is difficult until one relearns how to handle a single engine boat.

So what about single engine reliability issues? If it really bothers you, most of these boats are available with twin engines. However, with lower powered diesels, engine reliability is considerably greater. Even so, with a single engine, the risk of system failure

Fig. 2-27. The Down East or New England workboat style is slowly gaining popularity as its primary virtues of seaworthiness and fuel efficiency become increasingly important. This boat, even with single engine power, still cruises at 22 knots. What it lacks in glitz and glitter is more than made up for in quality and durability. At 18 GPH, fuel cost savings over the years become very substantial. So does having only one engine to maintain.

is always present and so one should probably not venture too far from the prospects of immediate help. Certainly this is a no more significant problem than that faced by the floating condo fleet.

Other Basic Design Considerations

The Death of Practicality

It is sad but true that there are so many newcomers to boating that the majority of boat builders end up pandering to the inexperienced rather than the experienced whose numbers seem to be diminishing. This has resulted in a situation where there are more boats on the market that look like Buck Rogers space ship than boats of practical design. Whereas twenty years ago, the majority of boats were practically designed, based on function rather than form and style.

I point this out because it is getting truly difficult to find boats that aren't designed by the ignorant for the unknowing. And this is but one reason why the ranks of experienced boaters continues to decline. This is not merely my observation or opinion, but is reflected by several boating industry polls. So much so that the stock of older, more traditionally designed boats has been holding its values very well. The industry is simply not building the kind of boats experienced boaters want except in the very high priced segment.

It is not until a person has owned about three or more boats that he really begins to understand the importance of good design, for by then he's learned all about bad design the hard way. Those tend to be awfully expensive lessons. My purpose is to get you look past the style of a boat and help you avoid making big mistakes by pointing out problems and showing you what to look for beyond the racy styling that is often the main marketing angle that deflects attention from more important design issues and to look at sound boat design principles.

Fig. 2-28. Superfluous styling often comes with a high price, literally and figuratively. In this case, the large sliding doors curve inward and cut over two feet from useable salon space while adding greatly to the cost of the boat since curved doors likely cost quadruple what a normal door would cost. If not curved, many boats feature inward leaning doors. It's odd that at a time when interior space is deemed everything, designers would chop 2-3 feet off a salon for this silly design feature.

Fig. 2-29 & 2-30. Form follows function, or form follows trendy fad? At left this top and windshield design leaves a huge expanse of glass and clear enclosures. At right, the poorly placed arch (that looks exceedingly awkward) creates the same situation where sunlight heats up the enclosed area to temperatures that are intolerable. The black window covers were added to minimize sunlight damage to senstive stuff like electronics and upholstery. This begs the question of the value of a design that has to be protected from itself.

Interior Ventilation

One point that few boat buyers ever think about is what happens when the power goes out, possibly for an extended period of time. These days a lot of boats are designed without any opening windows or any other forms of ventilation, apparently relying on the mistaken notion that the air condition system will always be working. Anyone who's been around boating very long can tell you that dependable air conditioning on a boat is a pipe dream. Here's a short list of the problems that can terminate the use of air conditioning:

> Major land based power failure
> Dock wiring system failure
> Onboard circuit breaker failure
> Shore power cord failure
> Shore power receptacle burns up
> Generator failure
> Cooling pump failure
> Loss of freon
> Compressor failure

So there are nine ways that one can lose air conditioning that might occur in multiple combinations that keep the air conditioning off for a considerable period of time, forcing you to leave the boat because it has no ventilation and it is 115 degrees inside.

Boats with no opening windows may be fine in Michigan or Massachusetts, but they are anything but fine anywhere in the southeast, the Bahamas or Caribbean where a boat with fixed windows and no working air conditioning is uninhabitable. Take it from one with a lot of experience with fixed window boats, most are uninhabitable when the AC doesn't work. That means that you have to get off the boat or sit outside until such time as the AC is restored which, in the case of AC system failure, may be the day after tomorrow or next week.

For this reason alone, I recommend against boats with all fixed windows; it's a dumb mistake that can make life miserable when you expected to be having a good time going boating on your very expensive new toy.

Express boats with no superstructure are among the easiest to air condition because they have no windows to speak of. However, when the AC fails, they become the most difficult to ventilate because of this fact, but the lack of window glass and outside water temperature will keep them cooler than most other boats, so the lack of opening windows is much less a consideration.

Directly related to this are issues of the amount of window glass and how well the boat is insulated. Excessive amounts of window glass frequently allow so much sun radiation into the interior that the air conditioning cannot overcome it. This tends to be more the case with low price boats that often lack any insulation at all, as well as being deficient in air conditioning capacity. While window dressings can cut down on the amount of radiation, all too often that's not enough.

This can be a difficult issue to evaluate unless you just happen to be checking out a particular boat on a very hot day, so one should be generally alert to the amount of window glass a given boat has relative to similar boats. It's also worthwhile to check on

Fig. 2-31. Modular, all-fiberglass head compartments were first seen in the early 1990's and are a vast improvement over wood construction which had rot and mildew problems. Fiberglass makes cleaning a breeze but also greatly adds to the cost of a boat.

the number of AC units as well as the capacity of each, bearing in mind that "price" boats have lower prices because the builder has cut corners. Reducing the number of very costly AC units is a good way to keep the price down by thousands of dollars.

Deck Areas

There's nothing like trying to move from one end of the boat to the other along a six inch wide deck studded with cleats and other nifty hardware. Particularly when there are no railings, and the only available hand hold is the flimsy convertible top. Unfortunately, this describes far too many boats.

Keep in mind that docking operations usually require ready access to all areas of the exterior, and not infrequently under panic conditions as when wind and current make docking difficult. Normally, it is not you, but other members of your family that will be subjected to these dangerous conditions, so I suspect that you might want to give this a moment of reflection.

You might want to think about what it's like trying to get up to the bow to handle lines or even an anchor on a rocking, rolling, bouncing boat. Is it a good idea to expect your wife or daughter to climb up over the helm and through a windshield to handle a bow line? Do you really want her negotiating the six inch wide side deck with no hand holds?

Probably not, so keep in mind that this is usually what you get with boats where the overemphasis is on style and accommodations at the expense of practicality.

Area Sizes

Newcomers to boating are often prone to look at boats as though they were houses, especially when the lady of the house has a lot of influence in the selection of a boat. I know this is a very touchy issue for many people, but I'm going to address it anyway. Most women are primarily interested in the interior, and that fact alone drives the selection of a huge percentage of boats. Boat builders know this only too well and do everything they can to exploit this fact in order to sell the most boats. They'll do it even knowing that it makes a boat utterly impractical and all too often at the extreme expense of performance and sea keeping.

You can probably guess the names of some of the worst offenders as their names and absurd designs are constantly bandied about: Sea Ray, Carver, Cruisers, Silverton, Mainship and many others. Boat designs that devote the most attention to providing spacious, roomy interiors usually do so at the expense of practical exteriors, resulting in what is facetiously referred to as the "bloat boat."

Because the exterior shape of the boat is blown up and puffed out, this usually has a very negative effect on practical exterior design that makes it hard to get around on the exterior of such boats. Despite those gorgeous interiors, more people spend more time on the outside of their boats than they do inside, at least in warmer climates. Such designs might be fine for Seattle or Portland, Maine, but they're a lot less fine for other regions.

If one just plans on using such a boat as a weekend retreat on a fairly infrequent basis, such issues may be of little concern, but they'll become a serious problem in direct proportion to how much one uses a boat. On cruises, whether it's a weekend cruise or a cruise of several weeks, you will be spending a lot of time climbing around on the exterior. If those spaces are not well sized to your body size, and in consideration of how many people you have aboard, moving around becomes a hassle.

Flying Bridges

The term flying bridge derives from large ships wherein long, winged extensions are added onto the sides of the large, high house structure where the pilot station is located. These are so that the pilot can see beyond the large structure to the sides and aft section of the ship. At one viewpoint, they do sort of look like a bridge. While the flying bridge on a yacht bears no resemblance to the original, it still serves the same function, so that is what we call it.

Fig. 2-32. Be wary of excessive upholstery on flying bridges for upholstery has to be maintained. The lounge at right absorbs huge amounts of water and is on its way to becoming a soggy mess. Another point, the helm panel is set far too low so that the boat can only be operated sitting down, a mistake you might not think of until it's too late.

Fig. 2-33. Just because the boat is small doesn't mean it can't have a good sized bridge. This 36 footer with "island" helm has a spacious helm area with seating for six including two pedestal chairs without cramping, displaying the typically superb design of most convertibles.

The area and layout of the flying bridge should be an important consideration, for it is here where you, the owner, will spend most of your time. In warmer climates, so will most of your passengers so long as it is designed properly. Otherwise, you may end up spending a lot of your time alone while everyone hides below.

In boats 35 feet and under, there is a limit to how big a bridge can be and how many people it accommodates comfortably. My criteria for good design is not how many people it can hold, but how many people it can accommodate without them falling over each other in order to move around. This is one instance where less may be more. Much depends on the styling of the boat. One can create very large bridge areas when the overall boat design generally disregards good styling and is instead a big, clunky looking box. For flying bridge sedans and sport fishermen, one shouldn't expect more than 5-6 people, and in most cases this is enough. For even though you may have more people aboard, not everyone usually wants to be up on the windy bridge.

One of the more important points is the space around the helm seating. Whenever we have a couple of helm chairs crammed together behind the helm with inadequate space forward and back of the chairs, this creates a serious problem for the pilot, both when he, and anyone else sitting there wants to move. Sometimes the layout is so cramped that it can actually interfere with the operation of the boat. More thoughtful designs avoid this problem, but always at the expense of less seating in other areas. In most cases it is better to have less seating but good ease of movement as you'll discover come time for docking operations.

Tops and Enclosures

Soft enclosures have been a fixture of boating for decades. They consist of a flexible clear plastic usually sewn into a panel of the same fabric as the soft top. Most boats have soft or convertible tops though many builders offer hard tops as an option. Soft enclosures have a limited life span due to stress and wind strain as well as the lack of durability of the plastic. Total life span runs about 5-6 years with good care, much less without.

Fig. 2-34. Zippered enclosures allow one to open up and get some breeze fast. Without them one has to go through the difficult task of removing the whole panel. Good design avoids using overly large expanses of clear panels so as to avoid the greenhouse effect. To achieve this, the windshield, arch or hardtop heights have to be properly balanced at the same time while trying to avoid giving the boat clumsy lines. Some builders have designers that recognise this while others don't.

The best types contain what are called smilies, U-shaped zippered sections that allow them to be zippered open rather than taken down. The object is to open the panel without removing it. Naturally these cost quite a bit more than non zippered types. About the last thing one wants to do is to fight with large panels with zippers scrunched in behind bars that are darn near impossible to reach.

The quality of the material and stitching plays a huge role on how long these things last. Most builder supplied enclosures are usually poor quality and you'll be lucky to get three years from them. It is usually money well spent to order the highest quality material from local shops. Double stitching is necessary for strength, so you can judge any single stitched product as being inferior. Top frame bars are almost always stainless steel, though on some smaller boats you may find aluminum, which, I can assure you, it not worth the price you pay for it.

While boat-matching colors are the most popular, I can assure you that maroon, green and blue tops become extremely hot and can make life under them unbearable. White is the only sensible choice unless you prefer frying your brains just to be stylish, as the top of your head will probably spend hours situated a few inches from that 150 degree dark-colored top.

The experienced boater places a great deal of emphasis on how a bridge is or can be enclosed. Bridges are up high and exposed to wind. Even in fair weather, modest winds combined with boat speed can make long periods on the bridge uncomfortable. Even in Florida we find that bridge enclosures are normally taken down or rolled up on an as-needed basis. In other words, you don't put them up as needed, but take them down. The distinction here says a lot about the importance of soft enclosures.

Recently much more thought has been given by boat builders to creating good designs that facilitate good enclosures, whereas in the past it was more of an afterthought, if any thought was given at all. As you travel about, make it a point to note how well tops and enclosures match up. Tiara seems to have been one of the forerunners in the creation in good design, as it was hard not to notice the tall windshields that always lined up well with a radar arch that made for good- fitting tops and enclosures. While the windshields made the boats somewhat clunky-looking, the trade-off was superb head room, great visibility and easy put up and tale down enclosures.

Usually we don't understand this until we have had a bad one, and then move onto a boat where it's no trouble at all. I can tell you that not infrequently do I go aboard boats where either we can't get the enclosures off at all, or if we do, we can't get them back up.

The important thing to look for here is how well the forward-most support bar of a convertible top lines up with the windshield top, for this determines both whether you have adequate head room (so that the top of your head doesn't fry because it is too close to the hot top) and whether enclosures can be created that fit well and are easily removed or preferably zipped open. This is primarily a problem for express cruisers. You can test this for yourself by simply opening or removing a panel section yourself to see how it goes. What you don't want are enclosures that you have to struggle with to get them off or open.

When the radar arch and windshield are at the right height, this allows the top to line up in such a way that there is a sizeable panel between the two, that improves vision and prevents one from having to hunch down to try to see through a low windshield. If that's what you have to do, you are looking at a lousy design.

For flying bridge boats, all this is much less of a problem because there is usually just a vertical drop panel and no windshield line up issue.

State Rooms

Newcomers to boating usually concentrate on how many a boat can "sleep" and are often perplexed by the very small sizes of enclosed sleeping compartments called "staterooms." We take a lot of liberty with that term, for many such are nothing more than cubicles, little bigger than closets. If you're new to boating, you should probably ask yourself what you expect from a boat. Do you and Mrs. Boat Buyer expect deluxe hotel room accommodations or are you prepared to do a little "roughing it?" For, unless you are very rich, boating mostly involves roughing it and more than a little discomfort. If maximum comfort is your criteria, you should probably be thinking in terms of cruise ships and not small pleasure craft.

With a little experience, we quickly learn that stateroom size is not all that important because we spend so little time in them, and besides, for most of that time we are unconscious and sleeping, so what difference does it make. Therefore, it certainly makes little sense to devote precious space to little-used areas.

Fig. 2-35. Being up high provides a nice, scenic view. It also puts you at the end of a long pendulum arm on a top heavy boat, which is not so nice for those who don't like rocking and rolling. Boats like this draw snickers from the experienced, particularly when you see her flat bottom.

As to how many a boat sleeps, a novice is apt to think that the more the better. Most designers would agree that you don't need more sleeping accommodations than the number of people the boat can accommodate comfortably. Where we run into trouble is with people who want to use boats mainly as floating vacation motels rather than boats. It's one thing to have a crowd aboard for an afternoon, something else again for more than a day. Most experienced boaters feel that two couples are enough for even a forty footer. Mom, Pop and two kids gets cramped even aboard a thirty-five footer, what with kids being underfoot most of the time. Adding another couple to the mix begins to get real uncomfortable.

If you're planning to be carrying more rather than less people most of the time, overnighting with six or more becomes unrealistic for most boats in the mid size range. Therefore, it's usually better to think in terms of adequate day-time space; not about enclosed staterooms but good convertible sleeping accommodations such as dinettes and settees. The problem with too many small staterooms is that often – we call them berths, not beds – a stateroom berth is too short and too narrow and probably hard to get into, such as over/unders. Vee berths can get real interesting, being very wide at one end and tapering down to nothing at the other so that your feet get tangled up with your bunkmate's.

Convertible dinettes make for some of the nicest double berths and so often do convertible lounges or settees. What you lack in privacy is made up for in size. Though differences in layouts abound, they are all more or less variations on the same theme. Whatever your style of boating, you are going to be faced with a choice between your desires for interior accommodations versus the practicality of the design and quality of the rest of the boat. Ultimately, highly experienced boaters end up placing interior design lower down in the order of importance, since there are other issues that are far more critical. Again, if all you are looking for is a floating condo, then none of this matters and you can go ahead and choose the one with the interior that most suits your requirements.

Dizzy Desgin and Loony Luxury

Last but not least in this chapter I want to address an issue that I refer to as loony luxury, loony because it involves the gratuitous addition of luxury items in places that should not be on a boat. The forms this can take are nearly endless, but one good example I ran into the other day was built-in, upholstered seats and a stereo system on a swim platform. Obviously, there are many people who find nothing wrong with such silliness. Yet, from a practical standpoint, such things are just plain crazy.

Many boat owners have to learn what crazy means the hard way, a lesson that invariably takes place at resale time. We look at these larger yachts that cost upwards of a million dollars or more and say to ourselves, ah, well, the owners can afford such craziness. The truth of the matter is that come resale time, most of these things are deteriorated and/ or broken because, as I said, such stuff shouldn't have been there in the first place because it was doomed to become damaged. But the fact remains that when such things go bad, the owners in most cases DO NOT repair or replace these things.

Why not? Couldn't they afford to? When the boat goes to survey, they surveyor ends up with a long list of things gone bad. Then comes negotiation time wherein the sellers fight like hell to avoid reducing the price for all the deficiencies that add up to more than just petty cash. Often times deals go down the drain because there were a lot more deficiencies than the owner expected and the buyer isn't interested in a restoration project.

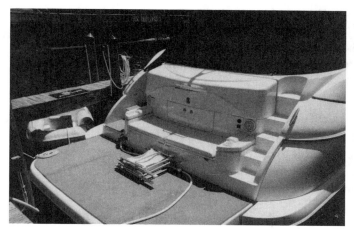

Fig. 2-36. The back portch. The only problem is what the station wagon effect, dragging along diesel soot and salt spray, will do to this upholstered lounge replete with stereo system.

All of this belies the notion that the rich owner can afford it. One would think that if he could, he'd keep up to date on maintenance. But the simple fact is that (1) people tend to go overboard financially on boats and, (2) they underestimate maintenance costs because they haven't adequate experience with larger boats. They aren't aware that maintenance costs rise exponentially with the increasing size of the boat.

So it is that they allow deferred maintenance to pile up, knowing very well that the costs aren't petty. That list of "little stuff" can add up to thousands upon thousands. But the third and final reason why it all got out of control is simply loony luxury. All that delicate luxury stuff that looked so cool at the boat show when it was all bright and shiny, but now is rotten and corroded . . . . well, they just didn't know.

But now I'm telling you and you do know. There's no magic to understanding this; boats exist in a very harsh environment and there is no place for delicate luxury items on the exterior of the boat. I strongly recommend that when you go looking at boats, you do so with a critical eye as to the durability of what you see.

There is one gadget that has probably caused more trouble and cost boat owners more money than any other in boating history. That is the hydraulic boat lift, the kind that were first installed on the backs of Sea Rays and now many other boats. So what's wrong with those things? Namely that they are constructed of aluminum and are submerged. They also involve huge lever arms that place tremendous strain on the boats structures and usually seriously alter the trim of the boat and therefore affect performance.

I've had Sea Ray owners with these things, whose boats run along with the nose pointing toward the sky, swear that the lift has no effect on his boat's performance! Believe that and you probably trust the politicians, too.

Unconventional Boat Design

It is often stated that the introduction of the computer into boat design freed designers from the constraints of traditional design that the use of wood posed. True, but in many cases it also freed inexperienced designers from the constraints of common sense, or at least marine common sense. Free-wheeling design occasionally goes beyond the bounds of mere common sense and borders on lunacy.

Boat design has, in recent years, changed very rapidly. While not inherently a bad thing, the down side is that it takes the general boating public years to accumulate knowledge. The reason that builders have been able to do this is because there are so many newcomers to boating who quite simply don't have much knowledge and experience and so they are more susceptible to falling for the latest fads in design.

There's a darn good reason why the vast majority of boats are designed along the lines of conventional shapes, and it's not merely a matter of tradition or conservatism. It's because those are the shapes that have proved to function best over the years. For this reason I want to warn you about boats that incorporate far out designs.

A good exercise in contrasts is to take a look at the designs of multi million dollar sport fishermen and compare those designs to what is happening with low cost motor yachts. What you'll see is that the highly experienced sport fishing guys are increasingly gravitating toward more traditional designs. Here we see overall styling of the latest boats being only slightly refined from those of forty and fifty years ago; far out designs simply don't exist in this class of boat.

Instead of getting more complex and cluttered with details, these boats have become increasingly simplified, many to the point where, if an item isn't absolutely necessary, it doesn't get put on the boat. That's not to say that these boats are spartan in terms of luxury -- far from it. But the luxury is on the inside where it belongs. Many of these boats are true maintenance marvels, so much so that we can all learn a great deal from them. This is so because many of these owners are on their 10th or 15th boat and they know just about everything there is to know about the costs of ownership, what works and what doesn't.

Another very important factor is that we don't find them sacrificing machinery spaces for interior spaces. With most of these big fishing machines, the engine rooms are overly large, and, get this -- many have a dedicated pump room, a place where the myriad of pumps are located so that they can be easily service. Experienced owners understand that equipment that operates with salt water requires frequent maintenance; to put that equipment in a place that is hard to reach causes the cost of maintenance to increase dramatically.

Yet another consideration is that very experienced owners know that it is very hard to keep a captain on a boat that is a maintenance nightmare. Captains try to avoid boats like that, so there's an additional incentive toward ease of maintenance. For those of you with limited budgets this is even more important. It proves the maxim that less really can be more -- more money to spend on having fun instead of maintenance.

Anatomy of Frivolous Design

The photos on next page illustrate one of the most foolish yacht designs that I've ever seen. It is included here, not as gratuitous criticism, but as illustrative of just how far removed from sea worthiness, safety and practicality some builders will go in an attempt to lure the unknowing into a vanity purchase. There were so many aspects of amatuerish

Fig. 2-37. Bad hull design. Contrast the bow of this Silverton with the bow of the Hatteras seen in the background. Even worse is the steeply sloping foredeck.

Fig. 2-38. Welcome aboard! - if you can get aboard.

design on this boat that I could have written a small booklet on it, but a brief summary here will have to do.

Probably the most serious fault is in the basic design which has a hull freeboard of six feet aft, but only four feet at the bow. but then there is a three foot long pulpit that brings the nose down to 3'9" above the water. What will happen here when heading into any kind of sea should be painfully obvious; it's going to stick that pulpit right into a wave and probably tear it right off, possibly even separating the hull from the deck in the process.

As if this weren't enough, then they add a searchlight onto the end of the pulpit, where, if a wave doesn't rip it off, a bow or anchor like will. Then there is that fancy railing which, because the bow slopes downward at a seven degree angle, the railing is too high and is so weak that it felt like I could tear it off with one hand.

Walking downward at a seven degree angle on this deck was an interesting experience, but not nearly as interesting as trying to sit on that built in bow seat that is what, play pen? I couldn't quite figure out what that is.

Boarding this boat is a challenge. The yacht is backed into the slip, as it must be if you are to have any chance at all getting aboard. The design appears such that it is intended that the boat be boarded from the swim platform which is right down at the water's level, meaning that one has to jump down. The alternative is to try to climb up four feet from the dock and board through the 16" wide gate in the weather rail. The owner doesn't want to bring the boat close to the dock because the rub rail is set in what looks like the middle of the hull, simply being screwed onto a flat panel which is very weak. If the boat bangs against a piling, this would be very likely to cause damage, so the owner moors the boat well off the pilings, making boarding possible only for the very agile.

The relatively inexperienced boater should be very cautious about "cool", far-out boat designs. This one-year-old boat is for sale with few takers because the owner learned the hard way that just because it looked good to his eye, didn't mean that it was good. The boat becomes a hard sell because the initiated immediately see and understand what is wrong with it, whereas the inexperienced do not.

Once again, issues like these point up the vast gulf between entry-level boats and those types of boats that will appeal to the experienced boater. Price is but only one aspect of this big divide.

Chapter 3

Old Boats, New Boats and Quality

There is a very common notion amongst some would-be boat owners that they can beat the high cost of boating by buying a much older boat and fixing it up. It's a notion of which I want to disabuse anyone who holds it.

The sort of person who comes to this line of thinking is usually one who desires a much bigger boat than he can really afford. He's also usually a person who is good with his hands, has a number of skills that can be applied to boat restoration, and thinks he is capable of fixing up an older boat at a cost he can afford.

He's also usually a person who has little experience or involvement in what owning an old boat is all about, because if he had, he'd know better. Possibly he has had some experience in home renovation or restoration of old cars or other such projects. But more often than not he has little such experience but very grand notions that he can find himself the proud owner of a larger boat at considerably less cost than everyone else.

The truth is that very old boats typically will end up costing nearly as much as new ones, if not more. It is no different than restoring old homes; it's usually cheaper to build a new one than to restore an old one. As mentioned elsewhere in this book, one reason why boats are so expensive is a function of the hard environment in which they exist. It is necessary that superior quality materials and engineering expertise be utilized to withstand that environment. And because of cost considerations, boat builders are always juggling the issue of longevity and quality versus price, with the former usually losing the battle.

While the hull and structures of a fiberglass boat may last a very long time indeed (though the way boats are being built nowadays casts some doubt on this), the machinery, systems, hardware and numerous other components certainly have a more limited life span. It is the cost of replacing or overhauling engines, the various other systems, equipment, and finish items, when added to the likes of upholstery, interior and enclosures replacements, that the cost of fixing up that old gal begins to approach the cost of a new or at least much newer boat.

Then there is the issue of labor hours. A typical forty footer requires about 3600 labor hours or more to build it. This equals 90 man-weeks, or one man nearly two years. That does not include design time nor the time involved in the myriad support operations. Since restoration includes undoing and then redoing, there will be more time expended than for the original construction.

Obviously, anyone who works full-time for a living can't begin to devote the time needed to complete such a project. This leaves the only viable option for such a project the hiring of various contractor services, which raises the ante in terms of cost. Yet another thing to be considered is whether such skilled people are available at reasonable cost. In many, if not most areas they are not.

There are those who have tried to use labor from the building trades to perform marine work, but the results usually aren't up to marine standards.

None of this is to say that restoration projects aren't economically possible. They are, but only when both the size and age or condition of the vessel serves to keep the cost of the project down. That is to say, the boat isn't too big or too run down.

Note: In the following discussion, the presumption is that all restoration work is done to a standard of equal or better than the original standards.

Service Life of Pleasure Craft

How long should boats last? That's a question I don't hear discussed very much, perhaps because boats last as long as they do. Being so costly, most people can't treat boats like ordinary consumer products that, as we all know, are designed so as to force you to buy another one fairly soon, automobiles being the one example we are all most familiar with. The auto industry is one vast scam intended to get people to buy a new vehicle every three years. They do it by constantly changing styles and engineering the things to look bad because of all that plastic that soon turns to dust.

Some boat builders have tried to do much the same, but have not been completely able to get away with the planned obsolescence thing because boats cost too much to change them like dirty socks. When engineered properly, it is possible to create boat structures that would last far longer than we'd probably want them to. We know that many of the heavier boats built back in the 1960's are still going strong, and could go on for another forty years but for the fact that they'll be so stylishly out of date that few would want one.

We can look back to boats like Chris Craft, Pacemaker and Egg Harbor and see mid level quality boats that give us a good idea of what a reasonable service life should be. Why is service life important? Because, as with a house, we are less owners than short term occupants. Both boats and homes generally last longer than people own them. We care about longevity because we are interested in resale value. Longevity is important to us because it is of even greater importance to the next owner. If the condition of the boat at resale time isn't such that other buyers will not find good value in it, they will not want it, and so the resale value flies out the window.

We see that some boats built in the sixties will last indefinitely; we see that many built in the 1970's have lasted 25-30 years and are now ready for the grinder. We now see more than a few boats from the early 1980's that aren't making it through to the present day, being ready for the grinder in twenty years or less. The current generation of boats built in the 1990's don't seem to offer any relief, as these are more plush and delicate than any that have gone before.

When it comes to entry-level boats, which are the majority in production today, the average service life spans will be dropping dramatically. The life spans are shorter less because the structures deteriorate, but because of delicate luxury materials and electronics that are very costly to replace, and therefore won't be replaced or renewed. Thus, resale values drop rapidly and recent generations are ready for the grinder much sooner than their predecessors.

Styling is yet another factor. Classic styling remains pleasing almost indefinitely. Trendy styling doesn't, and like shoestring ties and leisure suits, bubble boats – those with excessively roundish styling, will soon fall into the undesirable category just as soon as this trend passes into history, which probably is not far off.

The Economics of Older Boats

First off, I must make the assumption that anyone with a desire to get involved with an old boat expects to end up with a reasonable rate of return for whatever he invests in an older boat. No boat is an "investment" in the sense that one expects to profit from it. However, to most people, resale value is important; they expect to recover a high percentage of the amount they expended.

Fig.3-1. It is not uncommon that electrical systems in older boats end up like this. This is not only dangerous, but extraordinarily costly to straighten out. When systems get this bad, total rewiring is usually the only option.

Over my 35 year career of surveying pleasure boats, I've heard many boat owners make the dubious claim that they made a profit on the resale of a boat. Except during the 1973-74 Arab oil embargo, which drove up prices of used boats because the cost of resin made new boats very expensive, I've never believed such claims simply because the economics of boat ownership make that almost impossible. I've known people who tried to make a business of buying run down boats, fixing them up and reselling at a profit. None of them have ever succeeded because the cost of restoration was too high, and buyers are too skeptical of such boats.

With first hand experience in such projects, and having known many people who have done it, I would estimate that the average rate of return on sums invested in older boats is approximately 50% – that is, they got an average of half their money back on resale. At first glance, that probably seems like a horrible loss. Yet when we compare what the average resale value of a new boat is sold for 4-5 years later, the amount is about the same, so it really wasn't a foolish investment. However, one will definitely not be rewarded for one's personal time spent performing or managing the project. You either do it as a labor of love or forget about projects.

Estimating Costs

Estimating the cost of fixing up older boats is extremely difficult even for highly experienced professionals. To make a reasonably accurate estimate of such costs would be a project that could take an expert a week to complete. It also presupposes that one has a large collection of marine equipment catalogues with current pricing. Barring that, here's a rule of thumb that can be applied that is fairly accurate: *Subtract the current market value of the subject boat from the price of a comparable new boat* and you will have a very good idea of just how much deterioration and depreciation the subject boat has undergone.

Say for example, an older run-down boat is purchased for $100,000. This boat has a new replacement cost of $500,000. The theory is that this $400,000 difference represents a true amount of depreciation over the years. And with a 25-30 year old boat, it will be certainly true that if all the systems have not been replaced, they will need replacing at this time. It is equally true that our example can be returned to at least fully operational and serviceable condition by spending less than $400,000. There are limits, of course, to how many times one can keep repairing old equipment until the reliability factor becomes unacceptable.

This later point is the view point that most prospective buyers of your restored boat will take. It's one thing to have an old boat where major systems have been replaced, but entirely something else again for one that has been merely patched up. Both instances will be viewed differently and valued differently. Old boats are hard enough to sell, even when well maintained, but when subject to patch up jobs, become nearly impossible to sell.

Bear in mind that all restoration costs have to be done at *current prices*, not the costs at which it was originally built. Moreover, restoration costs more because restoration involves the labor of *undoing* and then *redoing*, which means more labor is involved over the original construction cost. With this in mind, it's not hard to see how that $400,000 difference can quickly disappear. Shown in the table in next page is a summary of the actual amounts expended on a twenty two year old 43 foot sport fisherman refit project in 1999. This run down and neglected boat was restored to first class condition, both cosmetically and mechanically with all major systems undergoing either overhauls or

Fig.3-2. This aging 46 Bertram Motor Yacht is looking good and holding up well on the outside due to a lot of repairs and replacements. But her basic internal systems have been jerry-rigged and patched up for over 25 years so that she needs a serious internal systems overhaul at this point, something not many people would want to tackle.

Cost of Refit

Urethane paint exterior	35,000
Overhaul two diesel engines plus transmissions	37,000
Replace generator	9,600
Replace mufflers	2,700
Replace engine room insulation	4,000
Refinish aluminum window frames	4,400
Plumbing replacements	9,000
Upgrade electrical	12,000
Replace damaged salon paneling	2,100
Replace two A/C systems	9,840
Replace head system	5,675
Replace appliances	6,700
Replace all exterior upholstery	6,620
Replace Bimini & Enclosures	4,815
Repair damaged rub rails	7,735
Remove excess bottom paint, repaint	4,500
Replace carpet throughout	3,267
Replace anchor windlass	6,849
Salon furniture	3,400
Bedding	1,985
Misc. renovations & upgrades	11,000
Day Labor Paid	7,630
Total	**$195,816**

Table 3-1

replacements as needed.

The work was done partly by the owner and partly through subcontractors with full-time owner supervision and a great deal of thriftiness. Only the bottom work was done in a boat yard. The used purchase price was $140,000. Adding the $195,816 refit cost, the owner's net investment came to $335,816. The new replacement cost of a comparable was approximately $600,000, or he could have gotten a late model used for around $450,000 to $500,000. I'll leave it to you to decide whether it was worth the effort. Upon completion, the estimated fair market value of his restored boat was $250,000 to $275,000. In the end, it actually sold for $262,000.

Why was it not worth the amount that he put into it? Because it is still a twenty year old boat, and no matter how good it looks and no matter how good it is, the average person is going to be highly suspicious of any boat that age, and rightly so. People will certainly pay a premium for well restored older boats, though the increase in valuation never equals or exceeds the cost of the refit.

One of the main problems with older boats is not merely deferred maintenance, but substandard repairs, alterations and additions. It is very typical of boat owners to seek to make repairs and/or replacements by the least expensive means possible, and this often involves poorly skilled do-it-yourselfers and Mac the Jack of All Trades who know how to fix things around the house but not on boats. By the time a boat is twenty years old, it can have accumulated a great deal of jerry-rigging and substandard repairs that becomes very costly to set right.

Yet another problem older boat owners encounter comes in the form of the insurance surveyor, who is a lot like your local zoning inspector. The insurance surveyor is going to be looking at the boat through the eyes of the ABYC Standards for Small Craft. Unfortunately, when he runs across all those substandard repairs (like the garden hose fittings used on underwater plumbing, swimming pool filters in place of proper sea strainers, and substandard wiring, the new owner may well ending up footing the bill for the thriftiness of the former owners.

Approximate Service Life of Boat Components

The table 3-2 on following page is my estimate of average useful service life of various components on inboard gas and diesel boats based on historical experience. Naturally, with superior care most components will last longer. Useful life also depends on product quality which can range from poor to excellent. Poor quality components are likely to last even less than that indicated.

Life Expectancy of Boat Components

Gas Engines	Years	Diesel Engines	Years
Alternators	6-8	Alternators	6-10
Exhaust risers	4-6	Exhaust insulation	8-10
Water pumps	6-8	Water pumps	6-8
Manifolds	10-12	Fuel pump	8-12
Exhaust piping	8-12	Mounts	8-10
Mounts	8-10	Mufflers	10-12
Heat Exchanger core	8-10	Piping	12-15
Oil cooler	6-8	Heat exchanger core	10-12
Trans cooler	6-8	Fuel lines	8-10
Engine room insulation	4-6	Fuel lines	8-10
Engine Rm Insulation	6-10	Trans cooler	6-8
Fuel pump	8-10	Injectors	4-8
Carburetors	8-10	Shaft couplings	8-12
Shaft couplings	6-10	Turbo chargers	6-8

Table 3-2

From table on facing page we can get a general idea that the typical entry level type boat is going to be ready for a lot of repair and replacement work after only ten years or so, while for a superior quality boat this is likely to be closer to twenty years.

Selecting the Right Boat for Projects

There are some people that truly enjoy boat restoration projects. To them it is not hard labor but a challenge, and maybe even a labor of love. The people who successfully complete such projects are usually those with considerable skills in the physical arts, or those who are very good at managing others, such as building contractors, or anyone with a good sense of materials, mechanics and electrics.

Life Expectancy of Boat Components

Components	Years	Components	Years
Air conditioning	10-12	Plastic through hulls	3-5
Sea cocks	8-10	Sea cocks	10-14
Sea Strainers	5-6	Sea Strainers	12-15
Rudder sleeve	8-12	Rudder sleeve	10
Sea hoses	3-4	Sea hoses	6-8
Exterior upholstery	10-12	Exterior upholstery	5-8
Enclosures	10-12	Enclosures	3-6
Stove	8-12	Running lights	6-10
Ice makers	6-10	Antennae	8-10
Fans, blowers	6-8	Electronics	6-8
Anchor windlass	8-12	Veneer paneling teak	12-20
Steering system	15-18	Veneer paneling oask, ash	8-12
Battery charger	6-8	Veneer cain soles	8-10
Circuit breakers	5-8	Carpet	4-5
Batteries	2-3	Aluminum windows	10-20
Battery cables	6-10	Exterior plastic parts	3-5
Bonding system	8-10	Exterior finish	5-12
Water makers	5-7	Painted features	5-6
Switches	5-10	Freezers	4-6
Bow thrusters	6-10	Trim tabs	6-10
Electric davits	6-12	Electric search lights	4-5
Hydraulic platforms	4-6		

Table 3-3

It's one thing to throw money at an old boat out of love and nostalgia for old boats so long as you understand that the return on your efforts isn't going to be anywhere near what you put into it. To be economically successful at restoration projects requires a certain knowledge of the market and those older boats which are most popular and in demand. Good examples are vintage Bertrams or Hatterases. Many of these boats were so well built, and of such timelessly good design, that they are still very much in demand despite their age. Which, of course, means that they command superior prices.

These are the kind of boats that offer the best potential return on investment in restoration dollars. However, one must understand that this is true only when the caliber of restoration quality equals or excess that of the original. And even then, no one gets back what he put into it. It is not advisable to put a lot of time and effort into any entry level boat simply because no experienced buyer will pay a premium for such a boat, no matter how jazzed up it is.

New -vs- Used Boats

The fact that 90% of all boats that are sold every year are used boats tells a lot about what experienced boaters think of both new and used boats. Used boats are an incredibly good value as compared to new ones. No doubt we are all familiar with the rationale in the automobile market that most people use for buying a new car versus a used one. People want a new one because "they don't want to buy into other people's problems". Since we all know about planned obsolescence, there is some rationale to this, though I

Fig.3-3. Aging price boats pile up in the back lots as the cost of repairs pile up beyond the owner's ability to meet the demands. Note the engines on the ground and missing drives.

doubt boats are planned by designers to deteriorate rapidly. Simply making them cheap will do it, without having to plan for it.

The reality is that most people want to buy something new as opposed to used is mostly a matter of ego; we want the latest style and to be perceived as being able to afford a new one. When it comes to boats, the premium between new and used is very a steep price to pay, so much so that 90% of all buyers recognize it as such and do buy used boats. However, somebody has to buy the new ones or we won't have any used ones around in the future. The question we deal with here is whether you are to be that person.

For all the reasons described previously, it is patently untrue that new boats are more reliable than used ones. It is true that things break down and quit working at an appalling rate on both new and used boats, which is something we all have to chalk up to not being able to afford highly reliable equipment and systems. If you could compare the quality of engineering and systems in multi-million dollar custom yachts as compared to middle class production boats, the reason this is true would become immediately clear.

The real issue with the choice between new and used boils down primarily to one of economics and personal desire. If you can easily afford a new boat, and that is what you want, by all means go for it. But, if you're pushing the financial envelop just a tad, you'll find yourself miles ahead if you go for the used one. Just be sure to toss out the rationalization that a new boat will cost less because it will be more reliable.

Depreciation of New and Used Boats

The average mid sized used boat, in a calculation of boats based on ages one to fifteen years, sells for approximately half of its original cost. That should dispel any faulty

Fig.3-3. This oid Hat 36 is also still going strong after fifteen years.

Fig.3-4 & 3-5. From 33' (above) to 60 feet (below), vessel complexity increases exponentially. So, too, do the costs of keeping it all in good order.

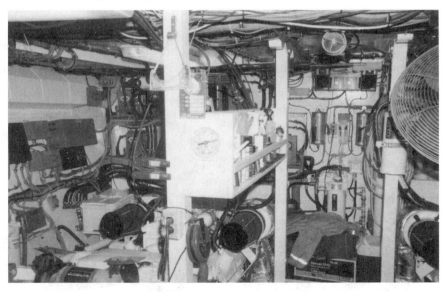

notions about the economics of new boats. As with automobiles, the first couple years depreciation on new boats is horrific, and all out of proportion to the amount of physical wear and tear they receive. That's one reason why used boats 1-3 years old tend to be very hot items on the resale market. This is more true of entry level boat than for high end boats.

We are not able to apply any rule of thumb first year's depreciation to newer boats because the rates vary widely, primarily based on the caliber of quality. There is also a correlation to the original price wherein the higher the original price, the higher the first year's depreciation rate is likely to be. In large part that is due to the fact that the greater the cost, the fewer wealthy people there are to buy them, and thus more expensive boats have a generally smaller market. Then, that steep first few years depreciation curve flattens out.

By the time the higher quality, higher priced boats become five years old, their resale values remain very steady for a significant number of years thereafter. Again, the reason for this is market economics: Now that the boat has lost half its value, it has fallen to the point where more people can afford it, and the more people there are bidding up the prices.

Entry level boats tend to have a depreciation curve that is opposite of what I have described above. Because they are lower quality, physically they deteriorate more rapidly. Yet, because they are lower in cost, there is more demand for them which may have a tendency to keep prices up a bit. But as they advance toward middle age, increasingly fewer people want those older boats, and so they tend to decline in value more rapidly at that end of the scale. As with everything in life, there are exceptions to the rule, and boats are no different. There are some cases in which a certain type or style of older boat, for reasons of peculiarity of increased popularity, become more desirable and in demand. Thus, their resale values rise above the rest, or at least don't decline as rapidly. Such types are few and far between and we generally need not be concerned with them here.

If we were to value the things we own based on the amount of use we get out of them, surely boats, unless we manage to spend every week end of the summer on them, will rank the lowest. They are one of the most costly purchases people ever make, and yet are the least used. This is yet another factor that makes used boats such a good value to most buyers.

Quality and the Mid Size Market

"One man's trash is another man's treasure" is an axiom that is all too true for most of us. The truth is that our opinions about quality are largely governed by our wealth. The less we have of it, the lower the quality we tend to tolerate by sheer economic necessity.

That's a lesson I've learned the hard way in writing boat reviews; if you tell the truth about a low quality boat, you'll end up with a lot of ugly reaction and people who try to shoot the messenger rather than face the reality. That's the reason our mothers told us, "If you can't say something nice, don't say it." That is also the answer to all those of you who are disappointed by your inability to find accurate reviews on boats, particularly those in the lower price categories.

For the fact is that we all know good quality when we see it. Now, I'm going to say something that probably most of you who are shopping for boats in the lower price ranges probably don't want to hear. The reason you are looking for boat reviews of "price" boats is to try to get confirmation of your hope that you can find good quality at a low price. Having said that, I will trust that you can now see the error in your thinking, and will leave it at that. For reasons I've already explained, in the marine business you are lucky to get what you paid for; getting more than you paid for is an exercise in wishful thinking.

It has been a sad thing to watch over the years, as one quality builder after another either got out of the small boat market, or folded up. One of the most frequent questions I am asked is why there are so few high quality boat builders anymore. This has been a result of the trend of the boating industry to turn boating from a fairly elite activity into a mass recreation. Since high quality boats will naturally cost much more, the market for them necessarily remains smaller as there are fewer people to afford them. With ever increasing competition from lower price competitors, those few builders who did choose to remain dedicated to high quality boats, found it increasingly difficult to survive.

There is also the issue of size. Just about everyone wants a larger boat, so that somewhere around 95% of all buyers would choose a larger, cheaper boat over a higher quality smaller boat. What the market wants is what the builders try to give them.

And so it was that one-by-one, most of the quality boat builders either went out of business, or sold out to the large corporate builders who then cheapened the product in order to establish market share. This has created a huge demand for older boats like Bertram, Hatteras, Blackfin, Viking and a few others, and one of the reasons why there is brisk activity in refitting these quality older boats. The fact is that there is very little in the way of high quality, late model offerings in the mid size boat class. Those that do exist, seem to be more outrageously priced than ever. It says a lot that the smallest boat now built by Hatteras is a fifty footer, and though Bertram still offers couple of smaller boats, the prices of these are very high.

On the opposite end of the scale, there has been a huge proliferation of very high end outboard and small, primarily fishing boats. Why just fishing boats? Well, mainly it is because sport fishermen, who are generally more experienced than the average boater, want higher quality boats. And because they are small, there are more of these people who are able to afford them, thus spawning a resurgence in this market. There are some signs that this market for high end fishing boats is beginning to expand from small sport fishing boats into a bit larger multi purpose boats, such as open express types and a smattering of flying bridge sedans or "convertibles." If unusually high quality is what you are seeking, these are the kinds of boats where you're most likely to find it.

Old or New, Which Is Better?

Companies like Bertram, Hatteras and Viking were pioneers of the fiberglass production boat industry that have managed to survive to this day. We hear it all the time, "Man, those old Bertrams and Hatterases were built like a tank." Unfortunately, this common myth really isn't true. Neither is the myth that quality boats built thirty or forty years ago were much better built than boats of later years or even today. The reality is simply that today there are a lot more offerings in the price boat category than in the past.

As one who has had continuous involvement with fiberglass boats right from the very beginning, I can tell you that old fiberglass boats aren't necessarily better built then than now. Although today regarded as top-of-the-line boats, we need to keep in a proper perspective about what that means. We're talking about top-of-the line *production* boats, not custom or semi custom. These builders had to compete with all other builders, and so their products, while engineered to be a cut above the rest, were certainly not built like tanks, nor are their structures "bullet proof" as some say.

The structures of these boats were undeniably well engineered yet by no means were any of those builders liberal with the use of materials. Many people are surprised when I tell them that the hull sides of a 46' Bertram are only 1/4" thick. My view of the quality level of these older boats is that they had overall good quality of a level we would like to see all boats built.

It was true that right at the very beginning of the fiberglass production boat, there were a few builders (namely Chris Craft) that overbuilt hulls because they did not fully understand the material, its strengths and weaknesses. But rest assured that that ignorance did not last, and it did not take them very long to skinny down laminate thicknesses to the most profitable level. So, yes, there are a very tiny handful of overbuilt hulls out there, but these are very few.

Have low quality boats become a lot more expensive? Actually not. What we perceive as even the lowest quality new boats being terribly expensive is a reflection of the tremendous amount of additional luxury and additional systems and equipment that buyers demand now than in the past. Even people in the industry complain about today's high prices, little realizing that it is buyers themselves that have pushed the prices up.

For example, if we were to take any 2002 boat and compare it with a 1970 Chris Craft boat, we'd find that the degree of luxury and sophistication has increased dramatically. If we were then to remove as much of that luxury as possible to make the boat more closely resemble the 1970 model, and then reset the price to reflect this, adjusting for inflation (which is about 600% since then), we'd find that the cost has only risen slightly. Most of this would be due to improvements in productivity, as well as in economies of scale. In 1970 Chris Craft was still casting their own chrome/bronze hardware. There isn't a single builder that does that today. Chris Craft even built their own engines! Needless to say, those were not cost effective operations; the problem was that what they needed was not then available, so they had to do it themselves. Today we find that there are usually three main competitors for just about any manufactured item we can think of because there is sufficient sales volume to achieve this economy of market competition.

What Does Quality in Boats Mean?

The answer to this question is a more complex issue than one might think. Quality begins with the education and experience first of the boat designer as well as the builder. And since the vast majority of boats are built by corporations, which are collections of individuals, headed by business executives . . . . and almost never by boat builders, most of the products are corporate products, not products by dedicated boat builders. In other words, boats are built by men and women in suits, not overhauls. True, men in overhauls do the actual work, but they are controlled by men who typically care more about profits and stock prices than the boat they are building.

These statements aren't intentionally derogatory; that's just the way it is in the business world. It has been a very long time indeed since the heads of boat companies cared more about product quality than profits, salaries and stock options. Boat building today is not what it was in 1970 or even 1980. The days when men built boats for the love of boats are gone.

Boat quality is essentially meaningless unless we define our terms. What we need to do is to describe to ourselves what quality means to us. For most of us, we can begin the definition by stating that quality means that the boat has been designed in such a way as it will fulfill the purpose we have in mind for it safely and reliably, and also without falling apart, having excessive breakdowns or unacceptable rates of depreciation.

There, that was easy, wasn't it? Ah, but now comes a harder question; safely and reliably for *how long?* How long do we believe that a boat should last? How long should it be before we have to start replacing things that go bad? More specifically, how much maintenance should we be expected to do to keep in good, operating condition? And then, since we all know that nothing lasts forever, least of all boats, how long do we expect major components to last, components that we know will have to be replaced at some time or other?

We can start with the easy things like the exterior finish of the boat, hardware, soft goods like upholstery and tops and enclosures, and on down the line to the hard things like engines, generators and so on. And, oh yes, how about the hull and other structures? Will those hold up as we expect? An entire chapter, *Power Options* has been devoted to the discussion of machinery.

In the table on preceding pages I gave you my experience with average useful life on average quality components. When it comes to lower quality products, the average life span can be cut in half. To new boat buyers, the useful life span of a boat is of little concern except insofar as overall quality affects maintenance costs and resale value. It should go without saying that low quality and priced boats suffer from more rapid deterioration and therefore depreciation. But to used boat buyers the anticipated life span of a boat becomes of paramount importance, particularly when the subject boat is not a late model. That is because as a boat ages, the rate of deterioration increases; it increases relative to overall quality and it increases relative to how well it has been maintained.

However, there is no escaping the fact that lower priced boats are purchased by the kind of people who are least able to afford them, a point which has a serious affect on the reason why "price" boats tend to depreciate in value more rapidly. That's because owners of price boats are far more inclined to avoid maintenance or to perform substandard repairs than the better healed owners of higher priced boats. You'll see the owners of Silvertons and Bayliners doing things that you'd never find an owner of a Hatteras, Bertram, Viking or Tiara doing. This is what leads to a more rapid declination of resale values. Thus, when a boat's systems are all clapped out, the finish is gone and all the windows leak, that's the point where the cost of ownership becomes too great and the boat falls into disrepair, eventually getting shoved off to a back lot somewhere, or a dock way up the river where it quietly fades into history because no one wants it anymore.

In contrast, the better quality boats, while their systems will only last so long, and have to be replaced at some point in time, are far more likely to have those systems be completely replaced (rather than patched up again and again), so that as the boats get older, a potential buyer is far less likely to be looking at a boat where everything has to be replaced, because some of it already has.

This point is well illustrated by the experience of older Hatteras and Bertram yachts. The basic structures are usually so well done that that basic boat will nigh well last indefinitely, so that the desirability of a particular old boat is primarily based on how well the systems have been kept up. Of course, here we have the problem of boats reaching two decades or more and becoming so out of date stylistically that almost no one wants them. But that's a separate issue.

Ideally, what we mean by quality is that we pay an acceptable price for a product that will last as long as we expect it to last, with the expected amount of maintenance, and will have a resale value that is acceptable. Therefore, our individual definition of quality is that the vessel performs as expected. This has to be in recognition of the fact that good quality costs more, and that it is unreasonable to have those kind of expectations from a product that is priced substantially below other vessels of known quality levels. It has to be in recognition that in this business, there are no bargains, no fire sales, no foolish owners selling for too little, that we're not going to beat the market and get more for less.

I understand quite well that the novice probably doesn't want long-winded explanations for why things are the way they are. What he wants is for me to cut to the chase, so here it is in brief:

Price Boats – These are boats built to attempt to outsell all the rest based on price and style. Typically they are the lowest quality boats of all. By the time such boats reach 8 - 10 years they become suspect; at 15 years will most certainly have serious problems; at 20 years the majority of these will be relegated to the back lots.

Mid-Level Boats – These are boats considered to be a cut above the rest and typically priced considerably higher. These become suspect at 15 years but will often remain in good condition 20 years and longer.

Custom and Semi-custom – These are very hard to predict because they typically lack consistency as a class. Some will last 25+ years while others will succumb earlier for reasons not easily identified. Lacking specific knowledge, it's best not to assume that because it is custom, it has superior engineering. Most do, but many do not. Long-standing reputations usually account for a lot.

One final point. Quality levels in boats tend to run along the line of styles. Express boats tend toward the lower to middle quality range. Sport fishermen strongly tend toward high quality levels. Trawlers tend toward the lower end with a good quality segment notable by their high prices. Motor yachts, such as they are stylistically designated today in the mid size boat market, now tend toward the lower to middle range, which is a big change from twenty years ago. While we can all think of exceptions, my use of the word "tend" means that this will be found true for the majority of boats.

Foreign -vs- Domestic Builders

The United States has long been a leading maritime nation with a long tradition of boat building. Other than a few island nations, we have the longest coastline of any continental country. If the people of this nation do one thing particularly well based on its heritage, it is boat building. Hands-down, the US builds the best production pleasure boats in the world, despite our high labor costs and the havoc lawyers wreak on our economy. That is not to say that a few companies don't build some pretty lousy boats, yet the majority are superior to those of other nations. Economy of scale is one of the primary reasons why. Technology, innovation, communications and organization are yet other advantages we have.

This is a subject that I approach with great trepidation because of the tendency to shoot the messenger with allegations of prejudice. Regardless, I have no doubt that more than a few of the purchasers of this book would be disappointed if I didn't address the issue of foreign builders honestly. For the fact remains that large numbers of foreign built boats in the US have a widely known history of common problems, along with difficulty in getting warranty resolution of those problems. When considering foreign built boats, we should first realize that most foreign builders target the US because, due to much lower labor costs, they are able to greatly undercut the prices of domestic builders. Now, let's consider whether that is a real advantage to boat buyers.

This is particularly true of boats built in the Orient, notably Taiwan which is the number one exporter of boats to the U.S. The Taiwan boat is something of an anomaly since at least half of its sixty-odd boat building yards build boats specifically for American importers. That is, the builder doesn't build and export boats under his own trade name. Instead, it's more of a "build to suit" situation where the importer applies his own name brand. Unfortunately, many importers have business arrangements with the builder wherein they have little or no control over the product, while other importers are either partners or have other arrangements that allow them greater latitude of control. The later, however, are a distinct minority. None actually own a large share of the production facility in Taiwan which does not permit majority foreign ownership.

Historically, Taiwan boats have had a host of similar problems. Among these were low grade materials and inferior design expertise. The use of black iron fuel tanks that corrode rapidly has been a major problem that has gone on for nearly thirty years. So has the use of inferior grade stainless steel for water tanks. The use of plywoods that are not even exterior grade, let alone marine grade, was another. Bad stringer design, poor engine mounting, badly engineered cores and severe bottom blistering almost universally across the board rounds out the list. And, as you can see, these are not minor issues.

Why do such things happen? The history of Taiwan pretty much tells the story. Being a tiny island nation of mostly educated refugees from Mao's revolution in 1949, the Taiwanese turned to copying mostly American products, a nation that went from nothing to a major world player in less than three decades, a feat not before or since equaled, not even by the Israelis who still rely on US welfare payments. No one ever helped the Taiwanese. They started an island nation from scratch, and being so small, there was much they lacked, and still lack. But the biggest shortage of all was engineering knowledge and experience of all kinds; the people of Taiwan did not have a seafaring tradition.

While some few of them knew how to build teak fishing boats in the Chinese tradition, this did not serve them well in the modern plastic pleasure craft business. Hence, you see this reflected in the fine teak interiors of their boats, but not in the art of designing and molding plastics, nor in the basics of naval architecture. Their boats were copies of our boats, often without knowledge of the why's and wherefores as happens with many of their other products, not just boats. Machine tool is another very good example of

Fig.3-6. The worst case of hull failure I've ever seen was with this 55 foot Italian boat with a foam cored bottom. Here they have attempted to repair it but ran out of money. The builder simply did not understand the nature of the materials he was using. It's hard to imagine why anyone would experiment with materials in a product this costly. A 1995 yacht, the builder is no longer in business.

imitation without engineering expertise. Anyone who owns older Taiwanese machine tools will have the same complaints as we do about boats.

Moreover, the problems with Taiwan boats has continued for a long time because they could not be disciplined by the U.S. legal system -- mainly because no one could afford the cost of an international lawsuit. The only party that could be sued was the dealer/importer, who all too often turned out to have very shallow pockets; importer/dealers came and went with great regularity. Thus, the problems festered without getting resolved and the Taiwanese continued in their old ways. Continued, that is, until the market suddenly changed.

Historically, the Taiwanese were heavily into sailboats and slow speed trawler types and when the market for these boats began to die out in the early 1990's in favor of faster boats, for whatever reason they were unable to adapt. Computer controlled machinery may have had much to do with this.

In any case, the number of Taiwan boats marketed in the U.S. today is only a small fraction of what it was, but fortunately those that remain tend to be of considerably better quality than in the past. Further, more of these imports are more closely supervised by their U.S. counterparts. Still, several decades worth of older imports remain on the market, so if you're interested in one of these, I can only suggest that you have it checked out very, very closely.

The next largest exporter of power boats into the US is Italy, and though most of these tend to be in the larger sizes, there are a number of mid size boats to be found. The quality and engineering levels of these runs the gamut from very good to utterly inept with most falling toward the lower end of the scale. These boats also tend to suffer from use of materials without adequate knowledge, engineering expertise.

The aspects that prove attractive to many buyers of Italian boats is sleek styling and the abundant use of polished stainless steel and often a superficial play on "old world craftsmanship". Unfortunately, the levels of quality often ends with the eye candy such as walnut burls, birds eye maple and other cosmetic window dressing. Apparently fine quality cabinetry often is built on a substrate of interior grade plywood that, once it gets wet, falls apart. In the eyes of most surveyors, the engineering expertise of many Italian boats has left a lot to be desired particularly for hull structures, electrical systems, combined with an ignorance of metallurgy.

The point here is not to engage in gratuitous criticism of foreign products, but to show that when we seek advanced, high tech products from nations with very low labor rates, we are looking at a contradiction in terms. Low labor rates necessarily equates lower educational levels and all that goes with that, such as industries that are not fully developed and therefore do not supply the qualities of materials or expertise that most Americans expect of their products. In other words, there is always a reason for that lower price, and it usually isn't a "good" reason.

Chapter 4

Basic Hull Construction

Men prize the thing ungained more than it is
The sea being smooth,
How many shallow bauble boats
Dare sail upon her breast.
                                        – *HAMLET, I,ii.*

When we purchase a road vehicle, few of us find it necessary to give any consideration at all to the nature of the chassis, but when it comes to boats it's best not to be so cavalier. Unlike other vehicles, fiberglass boats don't have a chassis, making it unique among vehicles. As with an aircraft, the boat is the hull which is the frame. This is known as monocoque construction, which refers to the fact that the body and frame are essentially one unit. This chapter gives detailed consideration to all aspects of hull construction.

Of course, I can fully understand why someone who just wants to have fun by buying a boat probably has no desire to go into the esoteric details of hull design and engineering. My experience with many boat buyers tells me that many people who prefer to spend their hard-earned dollars wisely do make the effort to learn as much as possible.

The basic engineering that goes into good hull design is not particularly difficult to understand and can be illustrated by simple, everyday examples of which we all have some understanding. Among these are the box, beam and bridge, to which the boat hull has similarities. Boat hulls traveling at high speeds are subject to enormous forces, first because the boat itself is very heavy, secondly because of speed and finally because of waves.

Anyone who has had the experience of a five ton boat launching two feet in the air off of a wave knows what a bone-jarring experience this is. For the boat hull, this is like doing a belly-flopper off the high diving board. Water has little or no "give" when impacted by a wide flat surface. Boat hulls are also similar to bridges as they are often hauled with lifting straps and then placed on two blocks under the front and rear of the keel, thereby spanning a long length without the usual support of water it normally gets.

But image the load that is placed on the keel and bottom by the entire weight being placed on just those two points! When we think about things like this, it is not hard to see why, unless the hull is designed and built exactly right, problems are going to develop.

Overview of Current Hull Issues

The subject of hull construction is particularly important for used boat buyers by virtue of the fact that only with used boats do we stand a very good chance of avoiding problems before buying into them. Since new boats have not been used, potential shortcomings are unlikely to be evident unless there is a glaring deficiency, which in some few cases there is. For example, there have been quite a few boats wherein just looking at the stringers and bulkheads told me that there was a structural deficiency. There were too few bulkheads or the stringers were obviously undersized.

We would have no need to delve into this subject in depth were it not for the fact that despite fiberglass boats having been production built for over forty years now, there are still problems with boat hulls that should not exist. That it does, is mainly a result of the effort to make boats less expensive by using less material. And in using less material, the end result is occasionally hulls that fail in one way or another. Yet this is a problem we've had to contend with right from the beginning of pleasure boating, even with, and perhaps especially with, wooden boats, so this is nothing new.

We should also be aware that it is possible to damage any boat through abusive operation. There isn't a production boat made that couldn't be damaged by running it full speed into large waves. Any appearance of damage on a used boat does not automatically mean substandard construction.

Despite all the problems we continue to have with FRP boats, these are nowhere near the extent of problems we faced with wooden boats, so we'll briefly take a look at that in order to keep things in perspective. Wood is a less reliable material than man-made fiberglass. So while this is a subject all of us would rather not have to consider, we've at least progressed to the point where no longer do we have to deal with issues such as wood types and planking thicknesses, framing sizes and the myriad details that go into the making of a wooden boat. Since no two pieces of wood are identical, one piece is likely to be weaker than another, a situation that is hard to discern just by looking at it.

With wooden boats, the breakage of hull frames due to pounding was a constant problem. Boat yards did a fine business in the art of frame repair. But the biggest problem was rot. Not dry rot, for wood does not rot without the element of water. Some woods are more resistant to rot than others, and of course those are always the more expensive woods, so we had the same old problem of price versus quality. Add to this the fact that good technical design was far more critical for wood than FRP.

For these reasons, we were more forgiving of hull problems from wooden boat builders. Since fiberglass laminates are at least capable of being far more consistent in strength than wood, we are less forgiving when fiberglass failures do occur since they are more easily preventable. That's because a laminate failure is always the result of human error, not the vagaries in the growth of a tree. Even so, most boat buyers would rather not go into such a large purchase totally reliant upon the manufacturer's advertising claims, particularly when so much is at stake.

The problems encountered with boat hulls are usually the result of three factors. First is the never ending quest by most builders to gain market share based on offering the lowest price. Second stems directly from other cost issues, the fact that boat builders hold down costs by hiring less well trained workers as well as designers. In addition to cost factors, we also have problems with unskilled design, in large part due to the proliferation of computer design programs that have largely removed naval architects from the design of most production pleasure craft, again as a cost factor.

A third factor results from a lack of adequate R&D data and testing standards. "The marine industry has yet to develop a set of tests that yield the right type of data for the marine designer." This is a published statement by a well-known naval architect. I have long been a critic of the kind of overly simplistic testing of materials that has been used for decades, mainly by materials manufacturers and distributors to tout the strength of their materials, often with the intent to deceive.

Thus, when we combine the effort to engineer materials costs to a bare minimum, the problem of inaccurate marketing of material properties, along with undereducated people designing boats, then it's not too hard to understand why, despite forty years of fiberglass boat building, far too many builders end up with less than satisfactory products. The recent disaster that Sea Ray experienced by using balsa to core the bottoms of their larger boats proves my point: The designers apparently were not aware of the risks and numerous past failures of this material application.

We can put the situation into even better perspective when we realize that some few builders *never* have problems with hull failures. The right question to ask is *why?* Why do a few builders always get it right, when so many others don't? The answer is self-evident; those who don't have problems simply make the effort to be sure that their hulls don't fail. Needless to say, the products of those that don't are always priced higher than those that do. So, once again, the issue constantly boils down to a matter of price.

Hull problems are not simply minor problems to be addressed by a warranty. While some builders advertise "life time hull warranty," that won't provide a bit of reassurance if the hull cracks open while you are at sea. This is an issue as serious as wheels falling off cars, wings falling off air planes or trains jumping the tracks. In the end, the warranty provides only after-the-fact relief.

A boat, a house, car or airplane have similar characteristics in that they all have a frame covered by a thin skin or shell wherein the frame is the more important part of the structure. You've seen the Wright brothers first airplane: It has no skin on the body, just a frame. That can't be done with a boat, of course, which makes my point that a fiberglass boat hull is a unified structure in which both elements, frame and skin are of equal structural importance.

FRP is – at least when made correctly – a very strong material, but not so strong that frames aren't needed. Steel and aluminum are even stronger, yet if you look at steel and aluminum boats, you'll find a lot more frames than in any fiberglass boat. Part of this is due to the fact that FRP is more resilient; it doesn't dent or take permanent bends. When it does bend, it will usually spring back into its original position. That is, unless it bends too far, at which point it breaks. But FRP does become weakened, as almost any material does, by repeated bending cycles that can result in ultimate failure over time. Fortunately, this is not nearly as much a problem for glass and plastic boats as it is with commercial aircraft involving aluminum fatigue. Long term fiberglass fatigue failures are not a common problem, and when it does show up, it is usually associated with a design or construction defect.

While we do find that fatigue has become a widespread factor in many older boats – notably those from the 1960's or even earlier – when it does occur this is usually in association with the excessive use of CSM, chopped strand mat, or the use of very lightweight fiberglass fabrics. It has not shown up with heavy woven roving based laminates, though it does appear in lighter weight woven fabrics commonly used in the 1960's but is almost never used since then. Properly designed roving based laminates, which are now up to nearly 40 years old, so far have not shown degradation rates approaching failure. For all we know, well-designed laminates could last a hundred years. Only time will tell.

Basic Materials

A question that I'm often asked is why more boats aren't built of other materials. Why does it always have to be fiberglass, many people ask? The answer here is pretty simple and it begins and ends with labor costs. Anyone with any experience with wood knows first hand why he doesn't want to own a wooden boat; very high maintenance costs.

So What about aluminum and steel? Steel is almost as bad as wood because it rusts. Aluminum, of course, does corrode, but that's a corrosion that can be kept much more easily under control. The fundamental problem with aluminum is that it's too expensive, not so much the material but the process of plate-on-frame construction that is not nearly as efficient as molding fiberglass. Aluminum begins to become cost effective at around 70 feet, mainly because most large boats are custom built anyway, and therefore involve higher than normal construction costs in any case.

The fact is that fiberglass is a near perfect material for small craft construction because it is so versatile and is the one material capable of keeping labor costs to a minimum.

Lamination, the Essence of Modern Boat Building

Fiberglas Reinforced Plastic, or FRP for short, is plastic reinforced with glass fibers, made of the very same stuff that windows are. Glass is one of those materials that in many aspects is very weak, but in one aspect is very strong. When spun into fibers and bundled together it is very strong, particularly in tensile strength. When woven together into fabrics it is even stronger and thus makes an excellent reinforcement material for plastic in much the same way steel rebar is used to reinforce concrete. Even more important, it allows for a degree of flexibility without breaking so that FRP is reasonably good at withstanding repeated stress cycles without failing. Combined with its corrosion resistance, these are the primary reasons that well made fiberglass hulls can easily last 30 years or more with no significant degradation.

Understanding Laminate Strength

If you're ever spilled a large amount of paint on your shirt, you know that when it dries your shirt becomes very stiff. That is the principle behind fiberglass; a fabric saturated with plastic resin. That the material is strong in some ways but not in others is largely due to the ratio of fiber to plastic, as well as the direction of the fibers.

A fiberglass boat hull is subject to three basic loads, tension, compression and shear (impact or side loading. Take a bar of any type of material and bend it and we have both compression and tension, tension on one side, compression on the other. Fortunately, fiberglass is fairly good at resisting both these forces as fiberglass bends quite readily without deforming. But glass fibers are best at resisting tension loads, which is what allows it to bend without breaking because the fibers resist being stretched. They are like the cables that hold up suspension bridges.

However, neither plastic nor glass does very well with high compression loads; plastic tends to deform while glass simply shatters. Think of it as pushing a rope; the fibers have very little resistance to compression loads but plastic does have significant elasticity to compress and return to original shape. Glass also shatters from sharp impact loads. Thus, when the skilled designer designs a boat hull, the orientation of fibers is of utmost importance to him because he needs to take advantage of the strengths of the material while avoiding the weaknesses.

Fig.4-1. Chopped strand mat. Short fibers and the random direction of fibers assures that anything made with this material is going to be weak. Its main use is to bridge the gaps in heavy fabrics that have a coarse texture.

Fig.4-2. A biaxial fabric which is not woven but is sewn together - stitching can be seen to run vertically. Fiber bundle orientation plays a major role in determing laminate strength, as does the glass-to-resin ratio.

Up until about 1985 almost all boats were built with woven fabrics, after which time many new configurations of fabric were introduced. Using woven fabrics with the usual 90/90 degree fiber orientation made the job quite easy. A 90/90 orientation is adequately strong, but if another layer is rotated 45 degrees off the 90/90 he now has fiber directions running at 45 degree intervals in every direction. In other words if we have two layers of roving, one with orientation north/south and east/west and the other turned 45 degrees off perpendicular. This makes the laminate even stronger.

After about 1985 non woven fabrics were introduced. These consisted of bundles of fibers that either ran in all one direction called unidirectional fabric. Other configurations consisted of bi and tri-directional fabrics consisting of two or more layers of fiber bundles that were stitched or sewn to a backing of CSM. This allowed the designer to place the fabric fiber bundles in specific directions to deal with particular loads. Since every good hath its evil, the downside of uni and bi-directional fabrics is that they are very strong in one or two directions, but very weak in others. Thus a designer has to really know what he's doing and be very careful when using these specialty fabrics.

The sequence in which differing fabrics are laid into the hull is known as the layup schedule. With a boat built solely of roving, the sequence is very simple: one layer of roving followed by a thin layer of CSM all the way through the process. No variations, no chance to get things mixed up. That's especially important when dealing with 8-12 layers on a boat bottom. But when a designer starts adding in fabrics of differing fiber orientation, the layup schedule becomes more complex - often much more complex - so that he now introduces a much greater potential for error by the people who are actually doing the work.

What can make a fiberglass hull so strong is the length of the fibers that easily run half the length of the boat, or the beam, or more. In most cases, the length of the fiber is as long as the length of the fabric. The exception is chopped strand mat (CSM) which is made up of random directional short fibers about 4" long or so. CSM is a rather weak material that is not considered to be a structural laminate.

One weakness of FRP is its vulnerability to stress point loading, as are many materials, but only more so. Point loading is a condition in which a high load is applied to a very small area, such as where a stringer or bulkhead is attached to a hull. It is at these points where careful design becomes critical, and where historically the designs of many builders have failed.

A laminate is composed of more than one layer of glass and resin. The process of creating a boat hull is called lay up, and is achieved by placing multiple layers of fiberglass fabric and resin into a mold. The more layers added, the thicker the laminate.

The entire layup process should take place before the previous layers completely cure, which results in the newly placed layer to become infused with, and not merely glued to the previous layer. This is called a *chemical bond*. Its rather like welding. If, however, the prior layer is allowed to completely harden before the next layer is laid in, then only a mechanical bond will occur, which is not nearly as strong. Gluing two objects together usually results only in a mechanical bond. What distinguishes a chemical bond is that the two mated layers are no longer two layers joined together, but literally become one. They cannot separate without actually breaking the plastic, as opposed to simply becoming unstuck as a glue joint can.

The chemical bond takes place in a perfect world, but since we don't live in a perfect world our boat hulls are usually not perfect because things like holidays and weekends, dirt, dust, bad weather, human error, and excessive concerns with labor costs interfere with the ability to create perfect laminations. Therefore, many boat hulls and other molded parts contain a certain degree of mechanical rather than chemical bonds. To put it another way, boat laminates almost always contain many errors and defects of the laminating process. Of course, with strict supervision and expert workmanship, these errors can be greatly minimized. Our affordable boat, however, would become much more expensive, and thus lay up crews are not well-trained, well-paid nor well-supervised.

The way smart boat builders get around this problem is to build in a safety factor to account for these flaws. Thus, the typical boat hull has to be a bit thicker than what our engineering calculation says it should be absent any loss of strength due to defects. I trust you can see where I'm headed with this discussion: If the safety margin isn't sufficient, or the lay up errors are more than normal, we run into trouble.

The boat building industry has long had a lot of trouble in this regard because laminating is dirty, ugly work with a high labor turnover rate that is often left to immigrants. Of all the jobs in a boat building operation, it is the least desirable and ranks right up there with sewer cleaning and chimney sweeps.

High Technology and Boat Building

Thanks to the aerospace industry, which is largely responsible for the development and application of what is widely touted as "high tech "composites, the vast majority of boats today are being built with a wide range of these materials. The pure, all fiberglass boat has largely gone the way of the wooden boat, instead incorporating a variety of other materials as well, a subject which we'll deal with in much greater detail further on.

Boat building, despite most advertising claims, is a relatively low tech industry that often attempts to use high tech materials. Because boats are essentially hand made, the process utilizes a great deal of labor. Since we all know about the relationship between highly skilled labor and labor costs, it naturally follows that if we want boats that we consider to be reasonably priced, labor costs have to be minimized.

The utilization of high tech materials such as Kevlar, carbon fiber, vacuum bagging, and other exotic materials and process runs contrary to the number one priority of most builders – reasonable cost. Many consumers, of course, are greatly attracted by any claim to high tech stuff, and because of this many builders are simply unable to resist the siren song of "high tech." The problem with this is that the vast majority of boat builders do not have the kind of resources needed to conduct adequate R&D on the use of new materials or process.

Historically, those builders who do experiment with new materials usually do so directly in the product line, often with unexpected results. This puts the boat buyer in the position of being a beta tester, not at the builder's expense, but at the boat owner's. The list of builders that have had major product failures resulting from the lack of knowledge about the material or process they were using is a very long one. And all too often, these major product failures either resulted in, or directly contributed to, the company's bankruptcy and the boat owner's loss. Adding insult to injury, many of these builders were loath to make good on their mistakes, often forcing boat owners to engage attorneys to get resolutions that are frequently less than satisfactory.

This is the primary reason why the author is, and the reader should be, skeptical of any and all claims to the use of "high tech" or exotic materials in boat construction. This is not to say that all builder's use of high tech materials is likely to be faulty. Our difficulty is that we have no easy way of finding out. Needless to say, sticking with the tried and true tends to yield the least risk. High tech materials are fine so long as their properties have been tested and proven *before* being used in the product.

Inevitably, some wit is going to ask: Why can't they mass produce hulls with a greater degree of reliability? Why do they have to be handmade? Indeed, Irwin Jacobs of Genmar has been pushing this very idea. However, it overlooks other serious problems, namely that it increases complexity and cost while reducing versatility and the ease by which design changes can be made. Builders tend to like the ease with which the common fiberglass mold can be cut up and modified at a reasonable cost.

Plastics

The fiberglass in a boat has an ideal ratio of 65% glass and 35% plastic. Many people find it surprising that a boat contains glass in a quantity 2:1 over plastic. This becomes quite clear if you have ever seen a burned up boat. Though all the plastic burns away, a huge amount of glass remains that often reflects the shape of the original structure. With the vacuum bagging process, the amount of resin used can be squeezed to as little as 25% and actually result in a stronger laminate. At which point we might reverse the name and call it plastic reinforced glass instead.

The vast majority of all boats are made with polyester plastic, the least expensive of three types that include vinylester and epoxy. The later two are not only more expensive, but have positive properties of being stronger and more impervious to water. A problem with polyester plastic is that it is not impervious to corrosion which can occur when water migrates into a void within the laminate. The blistering problem is actually a form of closed cell corrosion that is closely associated with the use of chopped strand mat, or CSM for short. While it may sound peculiar to say that plastic corrodes, when we understand that corrosion is fundamentally a chemical reaction that forms an acid or alkaline that attacks a material, it may make more sense.

Polyesters break down into two basic types called orthopthalic and isopthalic polyesters, usually shortened to isos and orthos. Of the two, iso is much more corrosion resistant while ortho resin usually goes by the common name of "general purpose" or GP resin that should not be used to build boats. Unfortunately, in the interest of profitability, many builders do use it. Only custom and limited production high end boats are built with epoxy, and only a handful of production boats are completely built with vinylester. The reason is simply that vinylester and epoxy are two and three times as expensive as polyester.

It is very common that boat hulls are built with combinations of high quality and low quality resins. Back in the 1960's fiberglass first began to be substituted in industry for other materials in large amounts. At first, not a lot was known how the material would perform. One of the major lessons learned about blistering occurred in the petroleum tank industry when steel underground gasoline tanks were first replaced with fiberglass. These tanks were large and used huge amounts of fiberglass, so naturally the lowest cost plastic was used. These first tanks blistered so badly that most failed within a few years. This led to a process called tank coating, a process wherein the outer layers of the tank (the part exposed to ground water) were laid up using high quality resins, while the inner layers continued with GP resin. This method worked fine and eventually carried over into spas and boat hulls where it worked equally well.

Later, vinylester and improved forms of polyester called isopthalic polyester resins were developed to help drive down the cost. These two functioned well when used properly, though these are not nearly as corrosion resistant as the better types.

Plywood

Plywood is an essential material used in boat building for nearly a century. In fiberglass boats, it is used for bulkheads, stringers, frames, cabin soles, partitions, seating, cabinets and many other uses including as a core material. It would be very difficult to build a boat without it. It, too, is a laminated material consisting of thin plies of wood with the grain running in different directions. Plywood also has the benefit of being relatively inexpensive because it can make use of defective woods not otherwise useable for most purposes.

Yet, as most of us know, plywood has certain weaknesses, particularly its tendency to absorb water at exposed edges. This tends to make the material vulnerable to rot, most particularly when lower grade material is used.

Plywood comes in a large variety of differing grades. Naturally, when made of more rot resistant woods such as fir or mahogany, the material will not only be much longer lasting, but also more expensive. A 4' x 8' sheet of low grade plywood can cost as little as $15 while a high grade marine plywood as much as $240 for high grade veneers. A typical thirty-five footer will have 600 to 800 square feet of plywood in it. With that in mind, we have good reason to be skeptical of the quality of low price boats. Three-quarter inch plywood can weigh as much as 3.5 lbs./sq. ft., so one can see that plywood can constitute a significant portion of the weight of a boat.

And speaking of gel coat, since we already know that it is not a water barrier, does it make much sense to paint over plywood with it, as many, if not most, builders do? No, it doesn't, and that's why we so often see gel coat peeling off plywood in wet areas.

Quite a few smaller boat builders recently have been advertising that they are building wood-free boats, giving the impression that wood in a boat is a bad thing. Not true, wood in boat construction is only bad when its poor quality and improperly utilized, a claim that can be made for any material. Poor quality plywood is recognizable by its appearance; the surfaces are usually rough, often very rough, with gaps, splits and visible knots apparent even when painted over with gel coat.

Building wood-free larger boats is not economically practical, at least for most buyers, but we do need to assure ourselves that where wood is utilized, it has been properly

Fig.4-3. Cores are intended to stiffen a fiberglass laminate and do not take kindly to bending. When cores bend, they are subject to high internal stresses that often result in separation of core from skins because the core and skins bend at different rates. This drawing illustrates why that happens.

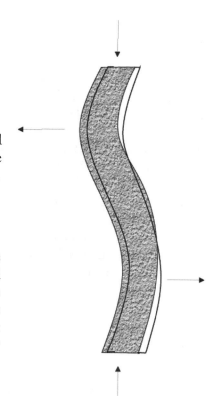

employed. Plywood of most grades will perform well when sealed with varnish or resin, particularly the edge grain. That will keep it from absorbing water.

Composites and Cores

In today's boating industry, the term composites is widely used to mean cored structures. In the real world, composite simply means composed of more than one material. That definition includes basic FRP since it is a *composite* of two materials. I point this out because some builders use this term rather loosely when, in fact, it may signify nothing.

The subject of cores is a hot one these days owing to large numbers of problems with cored hulls both in the past and the present. It is ironic that this is happening again because what we are witnessing is history repeating itself. The use of cores first occurred in production boat building in the mid 1960's. During that time I worked in the shop of a well-known sail boat builder who was one of the first to use an all balsa cored hull, as well as one of the first to be put out of business due to the large numbers of customers who complained that their balsa cored hulls were full of water and weighed thousands of pounds more than they were supposed to weigh.

Fig.4-4. A balsa core plug removed from a large Sea Ray. The outer skin is at the bottom and is only 1/4" thick while the inner skin is 5/8" thick, mostly chopped strand mat. This is either poor laminate design or bad quality control, making the bottom of this boat doomed to failure. See Fig.4-5 & 4-6 on next page.

Balsa isn't the only material used in the early days of FRP boat building. By the mid 1970's foam cores were introduced that resulted in even higher rates of hull failures than balsa did. Aluminum and even paper honeycomb cores were tried, not in experimental, but production boats. By 1980 and through the mid 1990's, the idea of coring was dropped until Sea Ray and a few others picked up on it again in the mid 1990's with predictable results. Sea Ray, for example, started coring the bottoms of all their larger boats and ended up with large numbers of failures and lawsuits, firing of management and so on. So if coring a hull causes so many troubles, why do so many builders insist on trying to use it?

I know of no compelling reason to core the bottom of a hull. Hull sides, yes, but not the bottom. Certainly it does not save the builder any money because it ups both labor and materials cost. However, cores can make hulls significantly lighter, so you can get a bit more speed from a cored hull. Even so, a slight increase in speed doesn't seem a reasonable tradeoff for the additional risk involved.

The need for cores was perceived right at the very beginning of fiberglass boat building when builders sought to eliminate the wood framing that was being used to hold up fiberglass decking. While FRP has many advantages, one of its disadvantages is that it is rather flexible and bends too much to be used on large flat surfaces without framing. Adding a core to a laminate does much the same thing as a roof truss or I beam. In separating the laminates with a light material in between, it becomes much stiffer.

Note that while boat builders will say that cores make hulls stronger, that is not necessarily true. They make bottom panels stiffer and less subject to bending, but they're certainly not stronger in many other aspects, such as impact resistance, shear and cleavage strength.

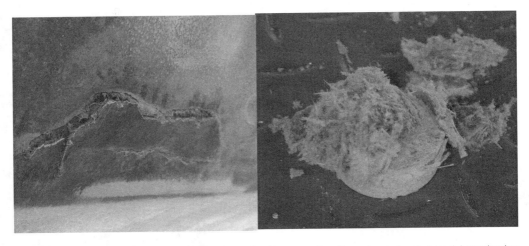

Fig.4-5 & 4-6. The bottom of this large Sea Ray split wide open when it was hauled and shored. Investigation revealed that water ingress into core plus hydraulic errosion had turned the core to mush (above right). The loose material seen here is both pulverized balsa and fiberglass, indicating that hydraulic pressure is capable of destroying a fiberglass laminate as well as a core. The hull of this three year old boat was essentially destroyed.

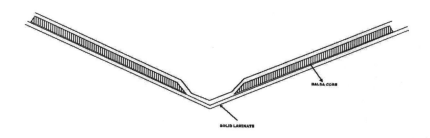

Fig.4-7. Boat bottoms must not be cored around the keel where the weight of the boat when hauled will cause crushing of the core such as show in the photos below. The keel area should be a solid laminate as shown above.

In fact, cored structures are much more prone to being punctured by small impacts and broken apart in heavier collisions. In essence, cores are very good for stiffening large flat panels such as hull sides and decks, but are a lot less good when used on surfaces with compound curves.

There are two basic problems that the boat building industry has with the use of cores in boat bottoms. The first and most obvious is what happens when water gets into the core. When it comes to balsa, the first thing most people are likely to think of is rot. Balsa is wood and it will rot. Fortunately, balsa is fairly resistant to rot, and when we have problems with water into a hull core, rot usually isn't the basis of the problem. Long before the balsa ever has time to rot, yet another problem intervenes. It's called *hydraulic erosion* and requires a rather lengthy explanation here.

Try to neatly wrap a baseball with a piece of paper and you have a general idea of the problem of coring hulls; sheets of core don't fit into a curved mold very well. Cores like balsa and foam have a similar problem with conforming to compound surfaces in that they will only bend so far. In order to bend at all, the core material is made up of small blocks of foam or balsa about one inch square with 1/16" gaps between the blocks . On one side is glued a very thin fiberglass cloth called a scrim to hold it all together. This allows the core to be moderately flexible, but only up to a point. It bends well around a uniform surface, but not so well around a compound curve, especially a concave curve.

Next we have to consider what is called bonding or cleavage strength. This takes into consideration how strong the joint is when the core is bonded to a fiberglass surface with resin. Balsa has excellent cleavage strength because the shape of the cells of the wood is near perfect in that it can draw resin up into the cells by means of capillary effect since the cells of balsa are long and narrow. But foam is different in that it has nearly round cell structure that presents a very poor mating surface that causes it have a rather weak cleavage strength. This is one of the reasons why first use of foam produced disastrous results and hull skins came apart.

To overcome the bonding strength problem of foam, bonding putties were developed. These are simply thick, adhesive pastes intended to provide a better bonding joint. The only problem is that when we're working with very large surface areas, there is always a blind side of the core that can't be seen so that in the application of coring, there is always the risk of having some areas that aren't stuck together. In marine parlance, these are known as never bonds. In fact, in virtually all cored structures there will be a number of voids that are usually small and within acceptable limits.

Now, getting back to hydraulic erosion, perhaps you can see that if there is water ingress anywhere into the core, that water will follow the gaps between the squares of core and migrate throughout the laminate. It will also work its way into those inevitable void spaces and collect there where closed cell corrosion can occur. With water trapped in the core, and with the hull slamming against waves, we have thousands of pounds of pressure compressing that water between the skins of the hull. That causes the water to migrate under high pressure in the gaps between the blocks. These pressures are so great that they will literally turn any kind of core to a slurry of mush, eventually completely destroying the core. And when that happens a catastrophic bottom failure is soon to follow.

Cores would work fine in bottoms if we could be assured of (1) keeping the water out and. (2) assuring that we have good bonding on both sides of the core. Being assured of keeping water out is about as difficult as making a water proof wrist watch. A boat is

Fig.4-8. A graphic example of why foam cores prove so troublesome without using the vacuum bagging process. Here a bonding putty was used to attempt to improve bonding to the skins, but as you can see there is over 50% failure to bond.

immersed in water and that water exerts a pressure on the hull. Everything has to be done just right, plus no one must ever drill a hole or make a faulty installation of anything on the hull, and that includes making proper repairs of damage such as occurs after grounding. The bottom line is that there is just too much risk involved with cored bottoms. Who needs it when a solid glass bottom will do just as well?

Most of these problems can be solved by the process of vacuum bagging. This involves placing a sheet of plastic over the wet layers of fiberglass in the mold, and then drawing a vacuum that compresses the layers together, works out voids and ensures excellent bonds to the core. It assures that the gaps between blocks of core are filled with resin, thus reducing the potential for water migration. Even if the potential for water entry exists, there's no place for the water to go and so hydraulic erosion of the core cannot occur. This also results in a higher glass to resin ratio which makes the hull even stronger. Unfortunately, vacuum bagging adds a lot of labor cost to a boat and the process is only used on custom and very high end boats.

Ultra High Density Foams

A relatively new product, UHD foams do not look like ordinary foams. The cell structure is so fine that the individual cells can't be seen with the naked eye and therefore appears as a light weight solid material. Its initial use is showing up as deck cores and transoms of outboard boats and will probably end up in bow pulpits and as foundations for anchor windlasses.

While my tests show that several samples will absorb water much the same as all glass laminates do, only time will tell if water absorption will be a problem. That will depend on the corrosion resistance of the plastic used. My feeling is that it won't be a problem

Fig.4-9 & 4-10. Cores are subject to layup errors such as these gaps and failure to bond with the outer laminate (top right). These are called "never-bonds" as opposed to delaminations though the lack of bonding are likely to initiate progression of delamination under stress. The size of the void at top may be acceptable while the one below is much too large.

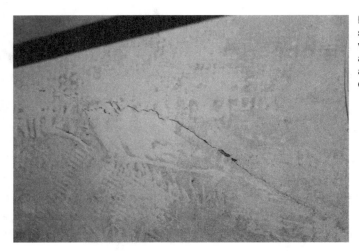

Fig.4-11. This disbonding of a hull stringer has just inititated and visually is hard to see. Tapping around on the laminate will reveal a very distinctive sound of delamination.

and will perform far better than using plywood as bosses and fillets for mounting hardware. It also creates decks that have far less give than any other type of core. The material is quite expensive and as of this writing I only know of outboard boat builders who are using it.

Delamination

This is a condition that occurs with some frequency in boats. It simply means that two laminations of fiberglass separate, for whatever reason, and is also known as ply separation. A similar condition, mentioned earlier, is known as never bond. This occurs when air or gas bubbles cause two plies not to come together, resulting in a void (see above photo). These voids are fairly common and often are sized one to two inches. They are within acceptable limits when the number does not exceed more than two per square yard.

Delamination can occur for a variety of reasons, the most common of which are physical damage and manufacturing errors. Virtually all boats that are not laid up with the vacuum bag process will have some degree of incomplete lamination (which is much the same thing as delamination) within its structure, usually in very small areas usually no more than an inch or so. This is referred to as incomplete bonding, as opposed to any kind of ply separation that occurs after the laminate cures and becomes hard.

Incomplete lamination can occur from a condition called out-gassing in which gas pressure develops while the plastic is curing, thus creating large bubbles between the plies. And it can occur from plies that stubbornly just refuse to lay flat against the previous ply for reasons that are preventable, but require better process and skills than are being applied.

Fortunately, problems involving major delaminations in solid fiberglass laminates are rare. They are less rare when cores are involved because getting every lamination plus the core to all stick together in a mold is not easy. Major delaminations most often occur as a result of interruptions in the layup process. They can also occur as a result of faulty resin catalyzing, airborne contaminates and excessive humidity and condensation occurring in a mold.

Most often delaminations occur as a result of failure to achieve a primary bond. A primary bond is a bond between two laminations that are not fully cured. When a lamination is made against another that is already cured, this is called a secondary bond. The difference between the two is that a primary bond is a chemical bond, while the later is simply a mechanical bond and is similar to a glue joint and not nearly as strong.

Major delaminations of any laminate are most often readily detectable, sometimes from visual distortions, and almost always by physical sounding. Minor delaminations usually go undetected except in cases where they form blisters on the bottom that are obvious. Surveyors are usually most concerned about delaminations occurring on the bottom, in hull structural members such as stringers, and various component tabbing which will be discussed in greater detail in the chapter on hull inspections.

Decks are the area where Delamination most frequently occurs and usually in conjunction with the deck core. Balsa core separations are very rare except when core saturation and rot is involved. With foam cored decks, the relatively weak bond of glass-to-foam can contribute to large area delamination caused by stress.

Putty Cores

Also known as spray cores, putty cores consist of what is usually a polyester putty in semi-liquid or paste form that this sprayed into a boat hull. This putty is really the "hamburger helper" of boat building, its primary purpose is to take up space, or "add bulk" as I've heard people in the industry say. Putty cores are primarily used in hull sides, not bottoms. The material is very much like, and may actually be, the same as auto body fillers – polyester with a high solid content.

The way it is used in most boats, putty cores do little or nothing to increase strength – in fact they do the opposite when putty is used to substitute fiberglass structural laminate. These putties are usually quite brittle when cured. These materials really don't qualify as "cores" and would more appropriately be called fillers. The primary problem that I have found with the material results from very low impact resistance, plus a tendency to disbond.

The time when we learn the most about the strengths and weaknesses of boat construction is after hurricanes when surveyors get the opportunity to examine wrecked boats to see how they hold up under extreme conditions. Shown in Fig.4-13 are a variety of different types of putty cores taken from wrecked boats. The significance of this is that in a number of instances where hard impacts against hull sides were sustained, the entire hull sides were found disbonded from the putty.

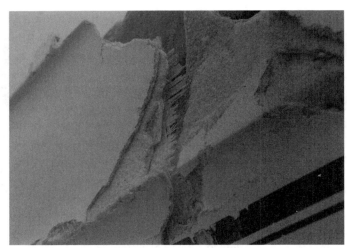

Fig.4-12. Strength is a major issue for boats built with putty cores. Here it can be seen that there is only one layer of fiberglass reinforcement in this Sea Ray hull side. When impacted, it doesn't fracture like a normal FRP hull but actually shatters. Boats built like this cannot legitimately be called fiberglass boats. Composites is the term usually used.

Even worse, as shown in Fig. 4-12 above, it is revealed that the only structural fibers used in a 30' Sea Ray hull consisted of one layer of woven roving and one layer of CSM. The roving was the layer exposed on the inside of the hull where one could see it. The significance of this is that when you looked at the hull from the inside, you got the impression that you were looking at a solid fiberglass hull when, in fact, 50% of the hull thickness consisted of polyester putty! I have no doubts that roving was placed in that position so that it is exactly what people would think.

I have conducted studies of hurricane damage to boats following seven major storms, and a number of minor storms involving hundreds of damaged boats that were examined carefully. Although this was not a formal study, it became abundantly clear to me that boats made with putty or spray cores were vastly inferior in strength to very thin solid fiberglass hulls and even well made cored hulls. I even found that solid laminate Bayliners could withstand much more violent beatings than a putty core boat could. In many cases, even mild impacts against the sides of putty boats resulted in the whole side caving in.

The putty boats were easily punctured by sharp impacts with small objects, whereas solid laminates are not. This could be determined by the amount of battering a hull side sustained before it folded up. With putty boats, it was generally found that very little overall battering occurred before they were holed or fractured, whereas solid laminate boats usually sustained terrible beatings before failure occurred, and often suffered no laminate failures at all.

In one prominent example, we had an old (1979) 38' Bayliner sitting right next to a 1990 30' Sea Ray. The Bayliner was about 23 years old and the Sea Ray eight years. The Sea Ray hull had a putty core and was about 1/4" thick; the Bayliner, 3/16" of solid glass, which is about three layers of roving and one of mat, not much by anyone's

Fig.4-13. Putty cores are the problem of the future as boats made with this material age and reveal the weakness of the material. Here are seven different types of putty taken from seven different boats, all of which broke up but should not have because the hulls lacked adequate fiberglass reinforcement.

standards. The Bayliner was horribly battered from stem to stern on both sides with not a single breach in the hull. In several places the sides were so battered there was no gel coat left in large areas. The Sea Ray showed relatively little battering, and yet one whole side had numerous punctures and was completely caved in. Photos on this and facing pages show how relatively minor impacts resulted in near total disbonding of the putty from the thin glass laminate.

Puncturing was a common feature of all the putty boats that were inspected. In fact, disbonding is becoming an increasingly common problem with putty boats, though it often goes undetected for a long time until the boat is surveyed or becomes damaged. A putty boat with disbonded hull sides is easy to detect simply by pounding on the sides with your fist and you hear sort of a double "clack." First you hear the sound of your fist hitting, followed by the sound of the disbonded laminates striking together.

My view of putty boats is that the material may be fine for a $19,995 sixteen foot runabout. But to spend $50,000 to $100,000 or more for a boat made of this material is to end up on the short end of the stick by reason of the fact that this is very weak and inferior material. While such boats may hold up fine with very light use, I personally would feel uneasy about getting caught in rough weather in one of these light weight beauties.

Unfortunately, none of the literature or specifications of any boat that uses this material that I have seen has ever mentioned its use. While builders are quick to tout "high tech" materials, they're a lot less willing to say exactly what those materials are. So where does this leave the boat buyer in his quest to acquire the most trouble-free boat, or the best value for his money? It leaves him in the lurch to choose only amongst those builders who are willing to specify what their hull construction materials are. But this is no help whatever for used boats where such information is not likely to be available.

Foam Cores

Expanded plastic foam as a core material has been with us since the early 1970's. Its first use in boat hulls generated numerous hull failures resulting in the material getting a well-deserved bad reputation. In theory, the use of foam as a structural core seems like a good idea, that it makes for a good replacement for balsa, which has one serious weakness – its ability to absorb water. Theoretically, closed cell foams don't absorb water, but experience shows that some foams do indeed absorb water, while others deteriorate for other reasons.

Our difficulty in discussing foams here is that foam can be made of many types of plastic and configurations as indeed there are a half dozen common types, and about a dozen less common types currently in use. In addition, foams can be made in different configurations such as cell structure and densities, so what the boating industry has been faced with is a large variety from which to choose, without the knowledge based on test or research data to make good decisions. Nearly all foam use up to now has been experimental. What little testing data that does exist, is often criticized by engineers as being inadequate or the result of manufacturers slanting data to put their products in the best light.

To give you an idea of how some manufacturers market untested materials, consider one foam manufacturer that failed to consider the effects of temperature on one of his products. Used on decks and hull sides in way of hot engine rooms, cored laminates came apart because the foam could not withstand ordinary temperatures. Ultimately, this product was pulled from the market and replaced with something else, while retaining the same name. You probably know it as Airex. Yet others never considered sheer strength and so the foam cores simply sheered apart, resulting in boats that fell apart. A couple of these manufacturers rightly went down the tubes along with their products, taking a few boat owners with them.

The ultimate award for density between the ears goes to the Ft. Lauderdale company that built and sold a few boats with a paper honeycomb core. Yes, you read that right, *paper*. The second place award goes to the company that similarly tried aluminum honeycomb. Needless to say, no naval architects were associated with either of those brainstorms and the companies didn't stay in business long.

One of the drawbacks of foam, unlike balsa, is that the cell structure makes it difficult to bond to a fiberglass laminate, hence its propensity for delaminating. The illustrations on bottom of this page shows the cell structure of balsa and common PVC foam. The larger the bubbles in the foam, the less well it bonds. This necessitates the use of special bonding putties. Of the many problems associated with foam, most have resulted from inadequate R&D with the use of foams. These include material incompatibility, sensitivity to heat, shear and cleavage strength, embrittlement with age, and long term water absorption. In addition, foam panels cut into small blocks result in pockets of resin that cause hard spots that can result in long term surface deformations (the outside of the boat develops an embossed checkerboard pattern.)

The majority of foams used in the marine industry are PVC (poly vinyl chloride). The principle advantage of foam is its resistance to fungicidal attack and its initial resistance to water absorption. Like most plastics, it is not water resistant over the long term. Its weaknesses are that it does not bond easily to laminates, requiring a bonding putty and greater labor costs. The bonding or cleavage strength, as well as the shear strength, is considerably lower than balsa. Moreover, most foams have fairly low heat distortion temperatures and can result in surface deformations when heated up by dark colored surfaces under a hot sun. The relatively low compressive strength means that outer skins need to be thicker than for balsa, otherwise crushing and deformation can occur.

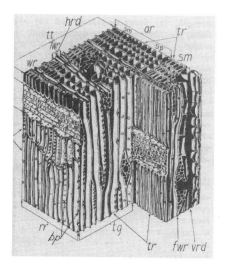

Fig.4-14. The microstructure of wood reveals why it can work well in conjunction with fiberglass boat building. The individual cells are like tiny straws that will suck up resin and make for very strong bonds. Its drawback, of course, is the potential for rot since it sucks up water equally well.

Fig.4-15. The structure of foam cells is more or less spherical and will not bond as well or as strongly as balsa. This foam crumbles easily in your hand. One wonders why any builder would think to use it.

A relatively recent newcomer to the foam market is ATC CoreCell™, a styrene acrylonitrile polymer material I have personally done some casual testing with. The material has a high density but low weight, making it stronger than most PVC foams, along with a high heat distortion temperature. Neither its compressive nor shear strength approach that of balsa (which is 8 times stronger), but it's far better than other foams. The real advantage of this material is its higher shear strength and cleavage strength over other foams, which will reduce two of the most common failure modes of foam, rendering it in my view a near equal with balsa in overall performance.

Surveying Cored Hulls

Cored hulls pose a real nightmare for surveyors. Lacking x-ray vision, we cannot see inside and therefore must rely on imperfect techniques in attempt to evaluate them. Physical sounding of the hull is one method that may reveal delamination. Then again it may not if the outer skin is particularly thick as it usually is on bottoms.

With larger boats hauled out, this poses the problem of scaffolding needing to be erected to reach the upper hull sides. The usual survey does not anticipate this because of (1) substantial additional cost, (2) the problems associated with tying up a travel lift for too long for which the yard will also charge extra.

Plywood as a Core

Plywood has often been used as a core for providing extra strength, commonly in gunwales, particularly around cockpits of sport fishermen, as well as isolated areas for foundations for windlasses, outriggers, towers, etc. Of course, all sorts of hardware gets attached to gunwales that provides the opportunity for water to leak in and rot the core. Plywood has been used in the past for cockpit decks and especially to strengthen hatch covers. The end result is almost always a rotting and failing structure because water ends up going in through bolt holes. Since around 1995, plywood has been rarely used for these purposes, with higher density plastics being substituted instead.

While I could accurately state that there should be no problem with the use of plywood, that statement doesn't take into account the fact that there is a large number of differing grades of the material. There is the matter of the type of wood used to make plywood, as well as the glues and process utilized. In other words, there are endless variations of quality. Marine grades of plywood have almost become extinct because the high grade types of wood used to make them are almost extinct. This causes good quality plywood to be very, very expensive.

The Essentials of Hull Structure

Every boat owner needs to have a knowledge of basic hull structures. Compared to wooden boats, from which the names were derived, the number of parts is rather small. Rather than force you to go to the glossary, I'll outline them here.

Keel

Everyone should know what a keel is. In the days of wooden boats and ships, the keel is the backbone of the vessel. Most plastic boats don't have true keels, although some few do, because the hull is monocoque, a fiberglass hull doesn't need a central spine. The one-piece hull is the nearly complete structure much like an aircraft fuselage. What we refer to as the keel today is simply the point at which the two sides of the bottom meet. It is a location more than a thing because the hull is one piece. Aluminum and steel boats still have keels that are separate parts. If an FRP boat does have a keel, it is always hollow or filled with foam and is there for other reasons than as a strength member.

Whether a boat has a fin keel or not, this is an area that has to be made extra strong by substantially increasing laminate thickness because it carries the entire weight of the boat when it is shored on land. On a survey, the keel area is one area that needs extra careful inspection by the surveyor to check for weakness and damage.

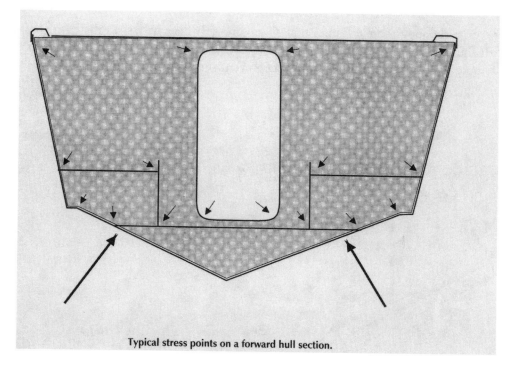

Typical stress points on a forward hull section.

Fig.4-16. Bulkheads carry a major part of the load on a boat's hull. This illustration reveals the major stress points

Go into any boat yard and you will probably see boats suspended between two shoring blocks so that the entire boat rests on those two small points. This is not good for boats and it is easy to see how and why boats end up getting damaged because of this practice. Now imagine a cored hull boat being shored up like this.

Bulkheads

All fiberglass boats have bulkheads, or at least they should. Bulkheads span the width of the hull and primarily serve the purpose of preventing an otherwise flexible hull from twisting. When you put the boat into a hard turn, it is the bulkheads that prevent the hull from twisting. A 35' Cruiser should have at least two full size bulkheads and one partial. The fewer and smaller it has, the more likely the boat is going to be a bit twisty and flexible. When that happens, things have a way of starting to come loose and fall apart. Doors don't close properly and upper structures and decks begin to develop excessive numbers of stress cracks due to excessive bending and distortions. One of the worst symptoms of a twisting hull is leaks, especially leaking deck joins, windows and frames. Bulkheads in pleasure craft are typically plywood, a material that has worked well for over forty years except when it is poor quality material.

Stringers

These are the longitudinal frames that, when properly designed, span the entire length of the hull. In boats over 30' there are usually four of them. Smaller, single engine boats may only have two. Not only do stringers prevent the boat from bending on a fore and

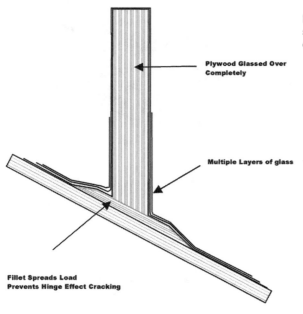

Plywood Glassed Over
Completely

Multiple Layers of glass

Fillet Spreads Load
Prevents Hinge Effect Cracking

Fig.4-17. The basic fiberglass over wood stringer has been in use from the beginning of fiberglass boats and is still used.

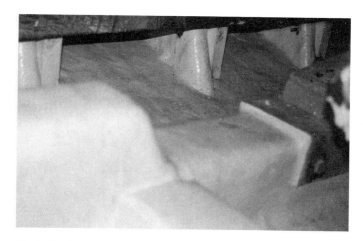

Fig.4-18. Amateur hull design from Taiwan. This step down in stringer immediately behind engine mount (right) makes an already shallow stringer even shallower. In this case the result was stringer deflection and transmission and engine mount damage. Another fault, visible at top of photo, are the fuel tank foundations sitting on the bottom of the hull. These are the type of errors typically found in Taiwan boats.

aft axis, but carry the load of the weight of the engines, as well as the driving force of the engines. Needless to say, stringers are another very important element of boat design and construction. Think of stringers like the girders of a bridge, except instead of being on the underside of the deck, they are on the upper side. Anything you wouldn't want to see in a bridge girder, you also don't want to see in a stringer. That includes doglegs, large holes and steps either up or down.

For the boat buyer, there are a couple of very simple rules of stringer design he should be aware of. Stringers should run the entire length of the hull and fade away at the point where the bow starts to rise. If the stringers end before they reach the ends of the boat, chances are they are poorly designed. Next, stringers should not have major dog legs in them; that is to say, they should not jog right or left, up or down as shown above. The drawing on the next page is of a boat that suffered a major hull failure because the stringers were improperly designed. The boat was literally breaking in half, though it was only a couple years old. The reason was a simple failure by the designer to observe correct engineering principles, most probably because he had no engineering training.

Stringers can be constructed by a variety of methods. The oldest is by means of laying fiberglass over wood, in which case both the wood and glass becomes a composite structure. Some people called them "wood cored," but that is incorrect. When wood is used in stringers, the wood is *the* major strength element and is not a core. The wood used needs to be high quality like fir, spruce or other marine grade plywood. Inferior woods, including low grade plywoods are subject to deterioration. The plywoods used by Bertram Yacht, for example, are known to survive 30 years worth of water saturation without serious degrading. These days, marine plywood has become extremely expensive

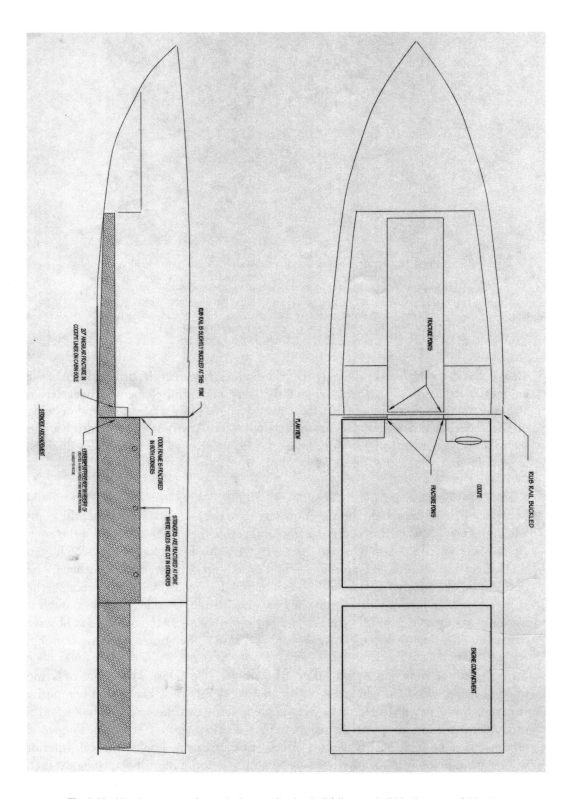

Fig.4-19. How improper stringer design can lead to hull failure as it did in the case of this 41 footer.

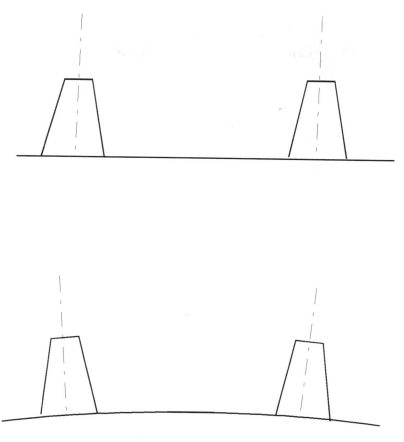

Fig.4-20. This illustration reveals what happens when bottoms and stringers are not rigid but begin to flex. Since the stringers are the foundation for the engines, if they move, the engines also move and will cause damage to the drive train.

and rarely used due to its high cost. Thus, with any late model boat that has plywood for framing, we need to be skeptical. For older boats, it is best to do some serious probing to check for rot and delamination; a professional marine survey is recommended.

The other most commonly used wood stringers is fir plywood which is still not so expensive as to be cost prohibitive. Fir has relatively high rot resistance.

In most recent years there is a drive to eliminate wood from stringers altogether. Thus, stringers can be either solid fiberglass, usually laid up in a separate mold and then glassed into the hull. Another method is to cut foam male formers over which glass is laid while directly in the hull. This common method works well. *The foam is non structural and it doesn't matter if it gets wet or saturated,* so don't worry about it if it is wet. In this application foam is not considered as a "core," though many people refer to it as such. It is simply there to serve as a form, much like wood forms for pouring concrete, but since the foam is on the inside, it can't be removed because it is no longer needed. A peculiarity to this method is that the essentially hollow stringers are very capable of transporting

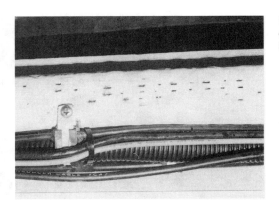

Fig.4-21. Looking down on stringer top. the presence of rotting wood is signaled by the numerous little brown stains of fluid seeping through the FRP fabric.

water from one compartment to another, causing unexplained leaks that baffle many a boat owner.

When inspecting stringers, exposed wood, discoloration, water trails (brown), bulges and evidence of fungal growth are the things to look for, particularly around limber holes. The photo above shows a stringer on a fairly late model boat that has only one layer of roving over a wood stringer. Not all the gaps in the roving are filled with resin and you can see the brown fluid seeping up. In the photo, it looks like a bunch of little staples.

Frames

Frames are transverse members that serve the purpose of stiffening the bottom panels. Unlike wooden boats, FRP boats may not have any frames, or only a few. The basic frame structure is usually fiberglass laminated over wood, very often plywood, or foam. The method works well with few problems.

A true frame attaches to stringers; a stiffener is similar to a frame but it is not attached to anything but generally stands alone. The intent is to stiffen a bottom or side panel that would otherwise deflect. Stiffeners do not appear often because their use involves a fundamental engineering fault. Stiffeners will usually crack at the ends and often break loose completely. No designer who knows what he's doing will use them.

Structural Grids and Grid Liners

Another method of framing out a hull is the molded structural grid. In this method, a mold is made which contains the forms of the stringers and other framing. After it is pulled out of the mold, it is then glassed into the hull. An alternative method, and one of which I remain skeptical, is gluing the structural grid to the hull. Structural grids and grid liners are most commonly found in boats thirty feet and under.

A grid liner is similar to a structural grid with the exception that a liner is a complete shell, it contains the same elements of stringers and frames. The difference is that there

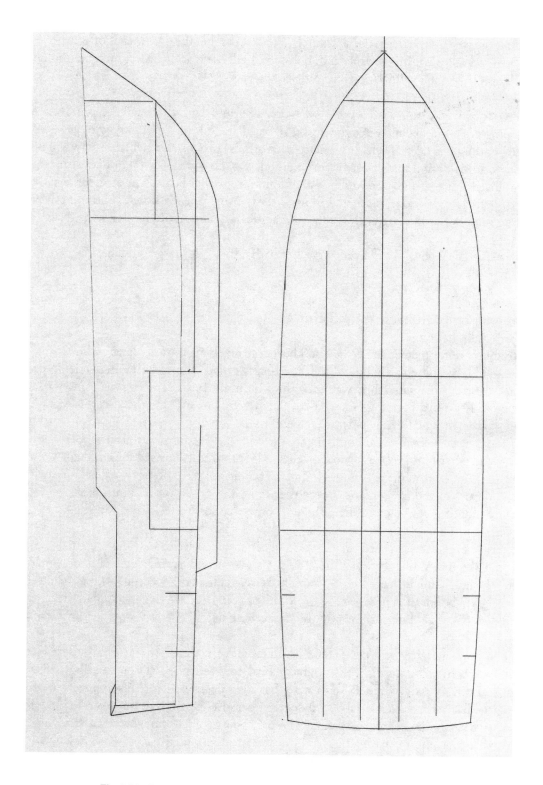

Fig.4-22. Framing plan of a typical sport fisherman or fly bridge sedan.

are no open spaces between the structurals. This means that the only means of attachment is with an adhesive. In this method, buckets of adhesive are trowled into the molded hull and then the grid is pressed into place.

Obviously, if grid and hull are not very precisely matched, there will be problems of incomplete bonding, and once the grid is in place, there is no way of knowing how well the bonding has taken place. It's strictly a hit or miss proposition, which is why I'm not keen on this design and construction method. Boston Whaler is one builder that has employed this method, one which is only found in smaller boats. The structural grid at least gets fiberglassed in place and in my view is a superior method. Both methods are discernible when looking at the interior of a hull as a pattern often telegraphs through.

I've yet to see a power boat over thirty feet with either grids or grid liners. They are not cost effective and pose too many problems.

Tabbing and Taping, a Weak Point

Structural reinforcements, be they bulkheads, stringers or frames, have to be attached to the hull by some method, and that method is called tabbing or taping. The process uses strips of fiberglass fabric wetted with resin in much the same way as using a piece of tape. The term bonding is also used. An attachment of a bulkhead can use one or more layers of tape for this purpose, depending on the degree of strength required. The problem of various internal components breaking loose from the hull has been a long term and persistent problem. Most often this is seen in the bow sections of boats where the stress of slamming is frequently breaks bonds apart. Tabbing is often done with little regard to the tremendous forces that can be imposed on it. Thus, breakage and failures continue to be a problem, though somewhat less so today than in the past.

The type of fabric used can make a world of difference as to how strong the attachment is going to be. And since these are almost always secondary, mechanical bonds, made after the hull laminate has cured, the tabbing is weaker than other laminates. To effectively make good bonds, it is necessary to grind the bonding surface to get adequate strength. Builders of "price" boats often skip this important step.

Tabbing should never be done with CSM. In recent years the more conscientious builders have taken to using unidirectional fabrics so as to orient the load on the fibers to the right direction. And while woven roving has long been used for this application, this material has the weakness of a 90/90 degree fiber orientation that turns out to be quite weak when one of the axis is parallel the part being joined. However, if the roving is turned so that the fiber direction is 45 degrees to the joined parts, a very satisfactory attachment is achieved. In many cases, the tabbing will consist of more than one ply, so that if the fiber orientation is varied, this will also prove satisfactory.

Fig.4-23. When screws are backing out and the rub rail is coming loose, one can be certain that there is a serious problem with the design of the deck join. This photograph of a Silverton is an extreme example.

Broken Tabbing

Surveyors frequently find broken tabbing in boats. In the vast majority of instances the extent of this is limited and does not signal a major structural problem. It does, however, require repair. Many boats sustain minor damage to tabbing after a single instance of slamming off a big wave which is not repeated. In most cases this sort of minor damage is simply and easily repaired at relatively low cost. It will require the expertise of a surveyor to size up the significance of broken tabbing when it is occurring in more than one location.

Note here that there are two ways that tabbing can fail. Either the bond can fail, which is most common, or the fiberglass tape itself can fracture (less common though not rare). Bond failures are more problematical as they require complete removal, grinding and redoing. Tape fractures can usually be repaired by light grinding and merely adding

Fig.4-24. This deck join is a simple vertical lap joint held together with nothing but screws. A few hard hits against a piling and it's bound to break open. The flimsy, plastic molding doesn't help much.

more layers of tape over the existing break and are therefore less work.

Decks & Superstructure

The decks of a boat go well beyond just being a surface to walk on or something to keep the water out: Decks are a major structural element of the hull. The deck serves to stabilize the hull, as when putting a lid on a cardboard box actually makes the weak box stronger. That box becomes even stronger when the lid is securely taped in place. Thus, it should become readily apparent how important the design of the hull-to-deck joint is for a boat. With most of the boats we are considering in this book, the fore and side decks should be a major focal point. To understand the importance of the deck join, in teaching marine surveying classes, I use the analogy of a shoe box. Taking a small lead ingot weighing a few pounds, I place it in the shoe box without the lid and ask someone to pick up the box. The box invariably crumples. Taking another box, placing the ingot inside, I then put the lid on and firmly tape it in place. Viola! The box can be picked up without crumpling.

Next, I ask a student to stand on a medium sized closed cardboard box. Of course, he crushes it when he does so. Then I produce a liquor bottle carton, one that has a dozen dividers or bulkheads that separate the bottles. Closing the lid, the student can stand on this and the carton fully supports his weight. This provides an unforgettable demonstration of the importance of adequate bulkheading and framing in a boat. The deck ties the sides of the hull together and, along with bulkheads makes the whole many times stronger. When well done, it becomes extremely strong, though the hull skin may be quite thin.

A ten ton hull traveling at 20 knots through three foot waves creates enormous stresses on a hull. When the boat bottom smacks a wave, it is force against force, for the wave is moving also. Something has to give, and if it's not the water then it will be the boat hull.

Fig.4-25. Sea Ray has a long history of inferior deck joints as shown in this photo of a boat with chronic interior leaks. Notice how small the lap joint is and that the fasteners are right on the edge of the lip. Unfortunately, there is no good way to repair this because the lap is too short.

The impact sustained on the bottom is transmitted up the sides of the hull, as well as into the interior structure. From the hull sides, the load is transferred into the deck. So now we know that decks are not just something to walk on, but are an integral part of the structure. Or at least they should be, but when the builder hasn't given this critical joint the proper emphasis, that is when we run into trouble.

The molded deck part acts as a horizontal bulkhead. It is not hard to imagine what would happen to a hull without a deck; there would be nothing to hold the upper hull sides which would buckle and be flopping around. As a hull slams down on the water, the impact causes the hull sides to bow outward due to the bending moment this causes. The deck when properly attached strengthens the hull and prevents this.

This also reveals why simply screwing the deck onto the hull as most boat builders do is not a good way of making the attachment because the direction of load sets the hull and deck shearing against the screws. Eventually the screw holes elongate, the screws go loose, the boat's rub rails begin to fall off and serious leakage occurs. Of course, everyone thinks this happens because of hitting the dock too hard, and in some cases that's true, but in most cases rub rails start to come loose because the deck is simply screwed to the hull. The illustrations on next page will help you visualize what happens and why. Deck join trouble is one of the most common but least recognized problems with pleasure craft. Taking a tour of any do-it-yourself boat yard, you're likely to find at least one boat owner struggling with the problem.

Deck Join Methods

Deck joints are strongest when the plane of the hull side is nearly perpendicular or acute angle to the plane of the horizontal deck as illustrated photo below right. In other words, if the hull and deck joint form a ninety degree right or even an acute angle, that

Fig.4-26 & 4-27. RIGHT: This Bertram deck join provides unusually high strength due to its angular shape wheras the parallel sided Chris-Craft joint at LEFT is exceptionally weak. The principle for strength is the same as an angle iron.

Note: In several cases you will find the same photo appearing more than once and may be used to illustrate more than one point. This is done for your convenience rather than have you leaf back through the book.

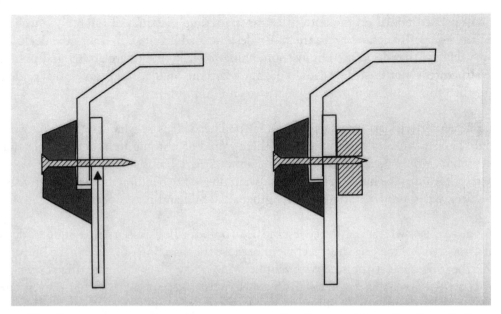

Fig.4-28. A typical screwed together deck join, one without backing strip and the other with. It's easy to see why such a joint isn't very strong when you consider the upward force exerted by the hull side when slamming. Even with the backing, the screw hole tends to elongate.

joint will be the strongest for the same reason that an angle iron is stronger than a flat bar: It resists bending. Conversely, if the deck joint forms a parallel, or obtuse angle, it is proportionately weaker as its degree of obtuseness because the two parts simply lack strength. Thus we find that designers come up with all sorts of angles in their quest for styling that end up weakening the structure. As discussed in the next chapter, this point becomes critically important to whether hull joints end up leaking water into the interior and causing water damage.

As for attaching the deck to the hull, the best method is mechanical fasters plus fiberglassing or bonding the deck to the hull. Not only does this make the joint as strong as reasonably possible, but it also nearly eliminates the possibility of leakage. In the past, this was done only on the highest quality and priced boats. However, in recent years we are beginning to see more and more of it in lower priced boats. The reason why more builders don't use this method is that the deck needs to be designed in such a way as that the interior can be easily reached to accomplish this work.

The second best method is to use bolts to make the joint in conjunction with an adhesive. Bolts have the ability to draw the two parts together and create a clamping action that is not possible with screws because screws can only be drawn so tight before the threads begin to shatter the laminate and then become totally useless.

Third best is to use screws with some type of backing strip on the inside. Hard vinyl strips have worked best, followed by aluminum, solid wood and finally plywood strips working least well. The use of screws will work better when used with a good adhesive,

Fig.4-29. There are two fundamental problems with this hull/deck join. First, it is a vertical, parallel lap joint which, by nature, is fundamentally weak. Second, placing this large window nearby makes it much, much weaker. This deck join is bound to break, along with the window.

but only when the deck is near perfectly fitting the hull, which is unlikely. Simple lap joints, like a box with a lid on it, and being simply screwed together, are the norm in boat building and the type that is found on most low priced boats. It's the main reason why there are so many problems with leaks and loose rub rails.

Yet another design problem results from the design and placement of things like as windows and engine room ventilators in such a was as that these cause a weak spot as that shown in Fig.4-29 above. The large window placed only an inch or so from the deck join/rub rail is doomed to be broken along with a probable failure of the joint itself. *See Chapter Five for more on rub rail issues.*

Deck Issues

For mid size boats, the deck shell is often a one-piece molded part that includes the fore deck, side decks and the vertical part of the superstructure up to, but not including a flying bridge deck which is usually a separate part. The cockpit deck and cockpit liner are also a separate part. Decks are laid up in female molds just as the hull is with the difference that it is a lot easier for the lay up crew to work on, so in most cases we find fewer problems with these parts. If any problems occur, these usually result from poor design rather than workmanship.

The most common problems with cockpit decks are sagging and water saturation of the core. Balsa is most commonly used because it bonds so well, yet great care must be taken in attaching fasteners to a cored structure. Things like hatch hinges and pull handles. If this hardware is fastened directly through the core, it is almost guaranteed that sooner or later water entry will occur. For this reason, bosses, fillets or other methods

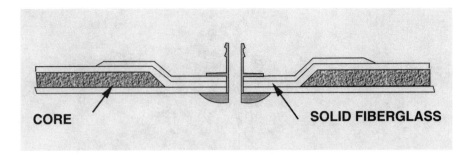

Fig.4-30. A proper fillet for a cored hull or any other structure.

must be used to prevent this from happening.

Since about 1990, both Tiara and Pursuit boats use NidaCore, which is a plastic honeycomb and is an excellent material for this application and has no known problems.

Proper Fillets

A fillet is a built up or reinforced area intended to add strength or distribute concentrated stress loads over a wider area. They are routinely used under bulkhead attachments, stringers and other strength members. They can also be used in way of strut mountings, mooring cleats, tower legs and so on.

A fillet on a cored structure is an area that has no core in way of a hardware attachment. The core can be eliminated and replaced with solid laminate, or material such as wood or aluminum. Numerous builders have built cored bottoms and then drilled holes right through the core to install sea cocks and other hardware. Just about any novice could predict that sooner or later water will find its way into a core. This problem is easily solved by eliminating the core in way of the sea cock installation. The photo and illustration on this page shows what this looks like.

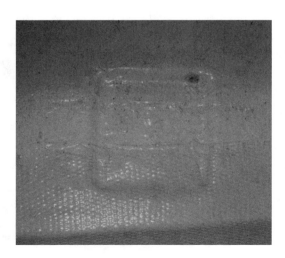

Hardware attachments are equally critical on decks and superstructure, and must be absolutely water tight. The problem of cores crushing under the load of tightened bolts was mentioned earlier, a problem that can be solved either by

Fig.4-31. How the fillet actually looks from inside the boat.

the solid fiberglass fillet method, or by installing a fillet block directly in the laminate. Especially highly stressed hardware such as deck cleats, windlasses, antenna and stanchion bases and so on need not only adequate reinforcement, but a means of keeping water out of the core.

Very often plywood is used under windlasses but this has proved problematical since windlasses are so highly stressed, that it is nearly impossible to keep the bolt holes from leaking, in which case water gets at the plywood and causes it to rot.

Rub Rail Materials

Over the years there have been dozens of varieties of rub rail styles and materials. In the early days of FRP boat building, extruded aluminum with a stainless steel edge banding was one of the most common. Many of us are familiar with that stuff because it is what Bertram had always used. The problem with aluminum, of course, is that the metal is soft and subject to corrosion, especially when stainless is applied on top of it. It's a terrible material to use for this purpose. Then there are the black rubber type with rope inserts that, of course, inevitably got pulled out. This, too, is a soft material that doesn't stand up to the kind of beating rub rails routinely get. Then there are the hard plastics which crack and break.

Finally, in the early 90's, a hard, thick vinyl molding came on the market that did the job we needed a rub rail to do: protect the side of the boat without becoming damaged itself. Typically, these moldings are about one inch wide by 1-1/2" deep and are shaped so as to receive either a solid or cove shaped stainless edge band. This type has the virtue of helping prevent the stainless from denting and bending, making it the near perfect material for the task. Not only that, the stuff comes in different colors, and like vinyl house siding, is very UV resistant. Perfect!

Probably somewhere over 50% of all builders are now using the material, despite its rather high cost, so look for it as a sign of good quality.

Fig.4-32. The best type of rub rail has this unique cross-section that provides support to cove moldings and prevents the stainless molding from denting.

Fig.4-33. It is beyond comprehension why any designer would think that this is an acceptable place to put a window. See photo on facing page.

Windows and Deck Joints

Many boat builders learned the hard way long ago not to place windows close to the deck joint and the rub rail. The reason should be glaringly obvious to anyone with a bit of experience; When the boat hits against a dock piling, the impact load is going to be transferred to the window with predictable results. In the past, we've seen this on a lot of boats where there are no side decks, but the side of the house is attached to the hull side.

In keeping with my earlier statement that we have a new crop of designers in the business who lack experience or training, this sort of foolish design is once again appearing in large numbers of boats. The photo above illustrates this point better than any words I could use. Designs like this produce giggles from the knowledgeable. Might as well put a window on your car bumper too! How could anyone with an ounce of common sense not immediately see what's going to happen here?

A similar situation applies to large windows in hull sides. Since hull sides frequently sustain heavy shock loads, placing windows there is equally foolish.

I should add here that the sensibility of design we are seeing from those builders who are basing their marketing almost exclusively on style is of late diverging so far from practicality as to be breathtaking to any trained designer. There seems to be a trend in hull designs that is convincing the boat owner that he should never allow his boat to touch a dock because if it does, damage will occur. If a boat is so poorly designed that it cannot withstand any contact with a dock, then what the boat buyer is doing is trading off stylishness for a lot of work and a high risk of sustaining damage. To keep a boat off a dock, one has to have a four piling arrangement. Lacking same, this either leaves him

Fig.4-34. The owner was in possession of this 2003 boat for a couple months before the inevitable happened.

to avoid many docks or always have a crew willing to do all this extra work. Sometimes it is simply not possible to avoid hits.

Historically, boats have always been designed so as to be able to withstand fairly hard impacts against docks. Style boats toss this practicality aside. All you have to do is to compare any style boat with that of any sport fisherman to get an understanding of just how far astray from practicality some of these builders are going.

Stress Points

With FRP construction, special care has to be taken with stress points. These are points or areas of a boat hull that are under particularly high stress, points such as where bulkheads and stringers are attached to the hull, as well as struts, rudders and even

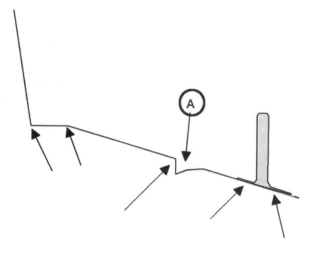

Fig.4-35. The natural hinge points on a boat bottom where stress cracks are likely to develop if the structural design is not adequate.

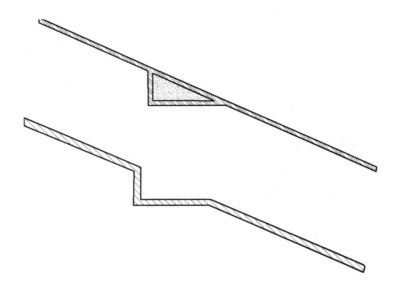

Fig.4-36. The open versus closed bottom strake: The open strake is much weaker and creates a hinge point where cracking is likely to occur whereas the close strake minimizes flexing and hinge points.

bottom strakes, chines and chine flats. Special care has to be taken to distribute high loads on the hull skin by means of incorporating thicker laminates in such a way as to spread a load out to a wider area. You can understand why, when a window is added to the side of the house, there is a need to increase the strength of the structure above the window by adding a header beam. The principle involved here is much the same.

However, stress points occur not only from unusually high loads, but also design elements such as bottom strakes that weaken a flat panel beyond its normal strength. That's why stress cracks are so often found paralleling bottom strakes and bulkheads. Both open and closed bottom strakes are shown in the illustration above. The open strake significantly weakens a bottom panel and increases flexing, causing cracking. The closed strake is filled with some type of material, often foam, and is glassed over on the inside. This creates a mini truss that strengthens the bottom in the same way as adding an inside frame.

Open bottom strakes caused so much trouble in the earlier days of fiberglass boat building that nearly everyone is aware of it. Even so, the problem still turns up occasionally so we have to be alert to it.

Chapter 5

Evaluating Boat Hulls

A man who wouldn't buy a boat because they're too much money, trouble and frustration is like the man who doesn't get married for the same reasons. Both tend to be lonesome and always looking for some foolish thing to do like chasing little white balls around on a large field of grass. Lord, how boring that must be!

In the last chapter we discussed the basics of hull construction. In this one we'll take a look at some of the specific things you can do to evaluate boat hulls yourself. While I don't propose to make a marine surveyor of you, I do wish to be able to arm you sufficiently that you can make intelligent choices about particular boats. I recognize, of course, that some buyers will want to make very thorough inspections of their own, while others would probably prefer to leave all that to a surveyor, but there are advantages to performing at least rudimentary inspections of candidate boats yourself before making an offer and then going to survey with it.

The objective here is to get a better idea of the general construction and condition of the boat before you make an offer on it. This mitigates the potential problem of making an offer, only to find out on survey that the boat was not as good as your first impression suggested. This is a very common problem for most boat buyers, so it pays to make a careful inspection. All too often, boat shoppers concentrate only on the eye candy without taking a close critical look, later to be disappointed by the long list or problems that the surveyor hands them. In most cases, you can avoid a surveyor's fee or two by reining in your enthusiasm and taking a critical look yourself. Even if you are buying a new boat, I recommend that you follow this process as you may very well turn up unexpected findings.

Probably the best way to handle this is to take a second look after you've seen the boat once already. The second time around you'll be in a better state of mind to make critical observations, whereas the first time around your concentration is focused mainly on whether this is the type of boat you want.

It is wise to attempt to obtain as much information as possible about the boat from the builder. This can often be accomplished by calling the builder, but this will work only for boats of fairly late vintage. It's usually easier to get answers from the larger builders than smaller ones. From Hatteras, for example, one can get the low down on virtually any boat since all their records are computerized. That won't be the case for most smaller boat builders.

How to Determine the Presence of Cores

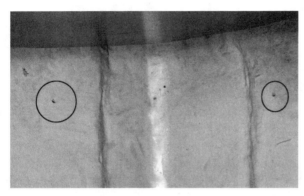

Fig.5-1. Above: This view is looking straight down on the inside keel. The raised parts on either side of the center line indicate that the bottom is cored. The black circles locate where, for unknown reasons, someone drilled two holes in the bottom of this brand new boat.

Fig.5-2. Below: Looking up at hull/deck joint from interior reveals that the hull side is cored and that the deck is bolted through the core. No washers under the nuts.

Since the issue of hull core failures is now doing an encore since its original debut in the 1970's, one of the very first things the used boat buyer will likely want to do is determine whether the hull is cored or not. This is not always an easy thing to do because such information is rarely publicly available. Very often not even the boat owner knows the nature of his hull construction. If you take the time to peruse a number of boat brochures you'll find that, unlike the good ole days, most brochures are totally silent on the subject. Sometimes even the dealer of new boats doesn't know, or won't say.

One sure way of finding out is to look for yourself, and there are three good places to look. The easiest way, and the one which almost always works for older boats, is to go to the rope locker and look inside. Right along the centerline of the hull you may be able to see a dividing line between the two halves of the hall that are cored. Normally, a hull core will not bridge across the keel or stem. If so, this separation will be plain to see.

While you've got your head in there, look up toward the hull joint. The core should terminate just below the point where hull and deck are joined, in which case the raised and thicker area of the cored section will be obvious. This will tell you only that the hull sides are cored, which will be the case on nearly all late model boats. Watch out for some Sea Ray boats which are cored right up to the deck joint, meaning that the joint fasteners go right through the core. This has caused serious deck joint failure and water saturation problems. If that's the case, check for looseness of rub rails. If it's an open cockpit boat, try looking up under the gunwale.

Two other areas one can check for evidence of coring are on the hull bottom, particularly in way of through hull fittings where you should see obvious fillets, as shown in photos of the previous chapter. Evidence of a bottom core may also show up around the stuffing box where the shaft passes through the hull.

While one can fairly easily determine whether part or all of a hull is cored, it is unlikely that you will be able to determine what that hull core material is. However, you may be able to determine what the deck core is, and that is likely to be the same material as the hull. I've never seen anyone use balsa in decks but foam in hulls or vice versa. Normally, the same material is used throughout.

Fig.5-3. Improperly bedded hardware on a transom can cause serious problems, including water into a core. The rust halo around the fitting is a dead giveaway that the installation is not done right. Adding insult to injury, this swim ladder bracket was installed with a lag bolt!

Fig.5-4. Above Right: This photo is a back up plate on a transom platform of a 2002 model boat with severe corrosion setting in after less than one year. It makes one wonder about the competency of a builder who does such things. So what's wrong? The bolts are placed with the nuts on the outside of the hull and the threaded part exposed. This creates the perfect environment for crevice corrosion. As I went around a 2002 boat show I saw a half dozen different boats showing this fault. The bolts should be installed in the opposite direction.

To determine what the deck core is, try looking in the anchor rode hawse pipe hole. Very often the core is exposed at this point. On open cockpit boats, check the underside of the gunwales around cut outs such as hawse holes, rod holder and fuel filler pipes. The core is usually exposed in these places as well. And while you're at it, check to see whether this hardware has been properly bedded, so that water isn't going to get into the core. Very often it isn't.

Banging around with your fist, screwdriver handles or hammers is not a good way to check for presence of cores because sounds are often very misleading. Don't try to rely on this method as even experts have trouble with it.

Examining the Bottom

In most cases the boat shopper will be looking at boats that are afloat, but the following is included in the event that a boat happens to be hauled. You will also find it helpful when attending a hauled survey.

There are several problems that may be encountered that could cost you right away with older boats. The first of these is excessive bottom paint build up that is now loose and flaking. The paint that is flaking away may or may not be exposing the gel coat, but in any case, very rough bottoms can reduce speed considerably and increase fuel consumption. Typically this happens when a boat is 8-10 years old, at which point the bottom needs to have all the old paint stripped off. The cost of doing that is not cheap, so be sure to look closely.

Another common problem results from poor preparation prior to application of the first anti-fouling paint. To get effective adhesion, the bottom should have been sanded. Very often dealers short cut this laborious work by using a product called Liquid Sandpaper, a product that like all miracle solutions in a bottle or can, don't work. If you

Fig.5-5. Sighting down the length of the bottom is very good at revealing defects of all sorts, including blisters and repaired areas. This works best when bottom is wet, as this one is, and much less well when dry. Were this hull dry, none of these blisters would show up in this photo.

see a lot of flaking paint exposing white gel coat, that's a problem that needs to be corrected with a lot of sandpaper and back breaking work, usually at around $35-$55/hr.

Accumulating marine growth means that the anti fouling paint is no longer effective and repainting is in order. Very heavy accumulation of calcareous growth (barnacles, etc.) means even more work. If there are barnacle heads attaching, these will not simply scrape off because barnacle heads are attached with the strongest glue known to mankind; the barnacle will pop off, but the heads won't and will have to be sanded off. Otherwise, the resulting rough surface retards speed and increases fuel consumption.

Bottoms should generally be checked over for stress cracks, damage, repaired damage and, of course, blisters. Sighting down the length of the hull while it is still wet is the best way to discover problems. We should not assume, because the problem of blistering has generally been brought under control, that it can't happen. More on this subject follows later in this chapter.

Examining the Hull Sides

When checking out a used or even new boat, examining the exterior hull above the water line can reveal a lot about the boat. If the boat is sitting at a dock, this can prove to be difficult yet it pays to at least try. It's better one try to locate any problems before the boat goes to survey.

The majority of boats built since 1997 are from molds shaped by computer controlled routers, a method that creates extremely fair surfaces. The significance of this is that such a smooth surface will show up defects and irregularities better than a boat from hand made molds, which constitute nearly all pre 1995 boat hulls. These earlier hulls will always have some degree of imperfection. Higher quality boats will generally have fairer hulls than lower quality boats.

Sighting along the length of the hull is the best way to check for repaired damages. Repairs may become visible either through unfairness of the surface, or by the fact that gel coats are nearly impossible to color match perfectly, very much the same as with auto body repairs. Discoloration or blotchiness is almost always an indication of repairs. The significance here is not merely looking for repairs of scratches and gouges, but more importantly for any evidence of major repairs such as major storm damage.

Chapter Eight is devoted to a complete discussion on the subject of stress cracking.

Fig.**5-6.** If there are any problems with the hull/deck join, sighting down the length of it will likely reveal them. In this photo, the joint is clearly very straight and fair, as is the hull side immediately below it. This is a strong indication that all is well.

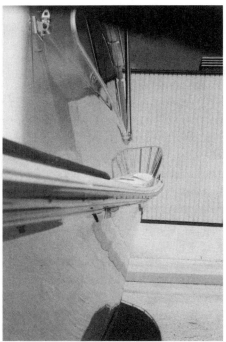

With new boats, you may find gel coat voids, ply separations, repaired molding imperfections and other potential defects. This puts you in the position of either rejecting that builder altogether, or just that specific boat. In the case of a new boat, you may avoid buying a boat that is flawed and possibly having to deal with a warranty issue later.

With used boats, loose and damaged rub rails are often a major issue. Rails can come loose either from damage or as the result of a poorly designed hull join. Often times the later leads to the former, so one should not automatically assume that damage is just damage. A simple test that anyone can perform is by using a screw driver and trying to tighten up any visible screws. When we find that large numbers of screws are standing proud, or will just spin without tightening up, that is almost a sure indication that working between hull and deck has shattered the glass around the screws. When this condition is present, you are facing a serious problem.

Fig.5-7. Stress cracks in hull sides down near the chine are not uncommon, but when they are as extensive as this, it probably means big trouble. An expert is needed to evaluate the seriousness as such cracking is not always catastrophic.

Fig.5-8. A loose rail may be more than just a loose rail. Look closely and note that the deck fasteners are on the very edge of the deck flange. On this "price" boat, the deck is attached with rivets all in one operation with the rub rail. Now that it is falling apart, there is no good way to repair the problem. A seemingly minor problem that is not minor at all.

Deck Join Defects

Yet another but more rare problem is the deck that doesn't fit the hull properly, one that may be over or under sized. This happens for a variety of reasons, usually because the hull distorts after it is pulled out of the mold so that the deck then doesn't fit right because the shape has changed. This always has an effect on the deck joint. It is very much like what happens when putting the lid on a cardboard box that does not fit right – the box buckles when the lid is forced.

The first symptom is typically a loose or damaged rub rail. Upon close examination it may be found that there is a dimple or concavity in the hull side at this location, leaving a large gap that is usually filled with caulking. This defect weakens the deck join so that when it bumps against a piling, the result at best is the rub rail and joint screws breaking loose. Over time cracks will appear and probably ultimately fracture. This dimpling can occur anywhere along the hull sides but most often shows up near the transom.

When loose screws, rails and cracking around the deck joint are present, at this point one needs to do a check for evident leaks from the interior. Try to find out if a cored hull side is cored all the way up through the joint, i.e., the fasteners are run through the cored laminate. If so, someone will be facing an extremely costly problem to attempt to fix as this constitutes a major design flaw that probably cannot be corrected at a reasonable cost.

Seriously loose deck joins are difficult and costly to repair. If it is a simple lap joint and all or most of the fasteners are loose, a proper repair will require removal of the entire rub rail. Depending on how close the screw holes are, it may be necessary to glass over the lap joint so that new pilot holes can be drilled for new fasteners. It should be noted here that there will normally be two sets of fasteners: one for the deck lap join and another for the rub rail. Both sets of screw holes may be elongated and possibly the lap fractured at these points, at which point some tedious fiberglass work will be necessary.

Fig.5-9. A defective deck joint wherein the fasteners are set too close to the edge of the lap, causing the laminate to buckle and crack. Problem was discovered due to severe interior leaks.

Another problem to be alert to is the case of the deck lap that is too short, or in other words there is insufficient lap of the deck lip over the upper hull edge. The net effect of this is shown in the photo above, a forty foot Sea Ray wherein the joint screws are all set on the very edge of the lap. With insufficient material to hold them, the lip fractures and the screws break loose. The net effect is a loose deck and severe leaks into the interior. In this particular case, the problem is economically irreversible.

From this discussion you can see that rub rail/deck join problems, while perhaps appearing to be minor, are often far more complicated and costly to rectify, so it pays to give careful attention to these points. Small problems will only get worse.

Through Hull Fittings

 The nylon or ABS plastic through hull fittings found in the sides of most boat hulls are highly vulnerable to sunlight damage. Though you probably cannot reach them to look closely, one can certainly see whether they are plastic or bronze (chromed or otherwise). For boats five years or older, you can automatically assume that all plastic fittings will need to be replaced. These fittings are very inexpensive but the labor to install them is another matter.

Those cheap plastic or zinc alloy fuel tank vent fittings can cause a world of hurt should the vent line become blocked, or it allows water into the fuel tank. Make sure the vent fittings are in good condition, and pointing down and aftward so that they don't channel water into the fuel tank (s).

Port holes: Check for damage on exterior and leaks on interior. Perhaps it needs new gaskets or possibly they are just cheap ports that have leaks that can't be stopped.

Note whether the boat floats level and along the painted boot stripe. Also note whether the boot stripe is in good condition or not. At yard rates, the cost of repainting these usually runs to more than just a couple hundred dollars, whether it's tape or paint.

What if the boat isn't floating level? Well, you at least have to suspect a potential problem. Of course, it could be low fluids in the tanks, but we also have to recognize that few mid size boats are seriously affected by major changes in tankage status and trim shouldn't change by more than two inches. You should expect that the boat floats level in both planes. If the boat is out of trim, either you or your surveyor will need to find out why, and whether the boat has a chronic trim problem, one that you don't want to buy into.

Interior Hull

One of the hallmarks of entry level boats is often a near-total lack of access to the inner hull. This is not good for a number of reasons: (1) if one should poke a hole in the hull, the area can't be gotten to plug it up with rags or whatever; (2) it's not possible to make inspections to see what's going on in the area. Why is that important? Consider: What if there is water pocketing in some place where it shouldn't be? This can lead to mold, mildew and water damage that occurs in unexpected ways. Also consider that it makes it very difficult to reach plumbing and other systems for periodic inspections and repairs.

Here's an eye-opening case in point. Sea Ray Boats has long engaged a hull construction method that incorporated boxed stringers (See illustration Fig.5-10). In other words, the outboard stringers were decked over and glassed. Engineering-wise, that's fine, but for longevity of the hull, it isn't fine and here's why. For starters, this created a closed compartment with no drainage. The apparent assumption was because this was on the

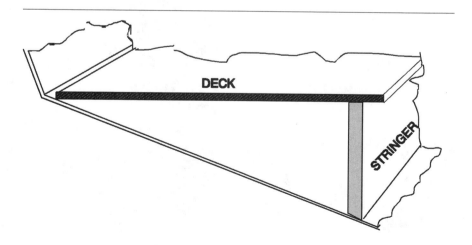

Fig.5-10. Box beam type construction. The area outboard of the stringer is decked over, creating a closed cavity. Should this fill with water, serious problems will result, including rot of wooden structural members.

inside, water getting inside was not an issue. But, of course, being a boat water could and did get inside, most often via a leaking deck join or internal plumbing leaks.

Since both the stringers were plywood cored and decking was plywood, these eventually rotted, compromising the hull integrity. Worst of all, the cost to repair would be so high that it was usually considered economically prohibitive. For the most part, this is an issue for a professional surveyor to evaluate. If a boat has boxed stringers, there should be visible drainage for those enclosed compartments.

However, this also highlights the point that the more internal accesses the builder provides on the interior, the better. If there is an abundance of hatches, that's good, because at least both you and the surveyor can make inspections to see what's going on. Yet all too many, particularly express style boats, have little or no internal hull access in the forward sections. This is particularly true of Sea Ray boats. If there is no access, not even a surveyor is going to be able to inspect the internal hull, and that's not good.

If there is at least some access, it is prudent to at least open up as many of them as possible and have a general look-see. How does the plumbing and other systems look? Are things installed neat and orderly? And what is the general condition of what you can see? Has anything ever been cleaned, or does it have years worth of accumulated sludge?

Are there any suspicious looking high water lines? These are one of the most important teltales that can clue us in to whether the boat has taken on too much water, and whether any systems are likely to be water damaged.

Fig.5-11. This small screw hole in a stringer is a tip-off to a stringer rot problem. The brown water trail plus the brown stains on deck below are evidence as to what is happening.

Fig.5-12. An improperly cut limber hole through a plywood stringer, leaving the wood exposed to water. The second hole is one that was started and not finished and just left that way by builder.

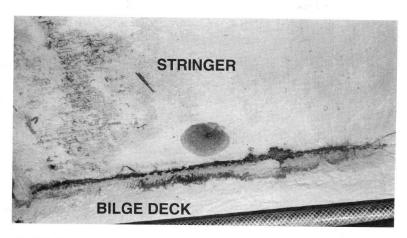

Fig.5-13. By the time stringer rot becomes advance, it usually leaves teltale evidence like these stains which leach through the fiberglass covering. When you see brown stains like this, don't even bother with a survey but go look for another boat.

The engine compartment typically affords the most visibility to the internal hull, as limited as that may be. Your first foray into this area likely reveal a bewildering array of electrical plumbing and machinery. For the time being we want to look past this and concentrate on the hull.

Another difficulty we have in sizing up boat hulls results from the practice of some builders lining the insides of their hulls with some sort of fabric or carpet, usually with contact cement. It is hard to over stress how foolish this is, for (1) the fabric will inevitably get wet and rot, and (2) the contact cement will hold the material in place for a short time until the glue gives out, as it always does. The worst of it is that this practice conceals the hull so that one cannot see what condition it is in. But perhaps that was the builder's original intent.

Some builders use copious amounts of gel coat as paint on the insides of their hulls, painting over wood and fiberglass alike, particularly plywood often making it look like something other than plywood. The problem with this is that gel coat, being so porous, will not seal wood from water which will go right through it and saturate the wood. This makes new boats look really nice inside, but as the years go by, its failure as a coating usually becomes obvious as plywoods swell, shrink and crack and delaminate. These are conditions that the buyer should pay particular attention to on used boats.

When poking around the inside of a hull, take note of the quality of the plywood used in things like bulkheads, decks and any other wood structures that are exposed. Poor quality plywood is distinguishable by having very rough surfaces, usually with cracks, gaps in plies and particularly knots. Also watch out for rough, unsealed edges. The edges of plywood in wet environments need to be sealed so as to avoid absorbing water.

Stringers

While we probably can't tell what the stringers are made of in the forward section, in the aft section we should be able to find out. First, try tapping the sides of them with a hard object, a pocket knife body or screw driver handle works fine. A very hollow or high pitched sound usually means that the stringers are laid up over a foam core or are hollow. We can also check the limber holes that facilitate drainage at the base of the stringers. An exception is on later models where limber holes under engines are prohibited. New Federal rules require the compartment under the engines not drain to the common bilges.

Possibly there is a piece of plastic pipe glued into the limber hole, in which case we can't find out what the material is from this point. Then again, the core material may be exposed. We probably can't see it, but we can stick a knife, pencil or screwdriver up in there, and if it is foam, we can clearly tell by the ease with which the object penetrates.

On the other hand, the core material may be plywood. Plywood cored stringers are distinguishable by the fact that they are usually much thinner in total cross section than foam based stringers. When you tap on them with a coin or other hard object, they should sound very hard and solid. Top hat, or hollow molded fiberglass stringers are almost always distinguishable by being quite wide and will have a notably hollow sound when tapped on. Limber holes normally have no pipe liners so that you can stick your finger in the hole and feel around, determining that it is, indeed, hollow.

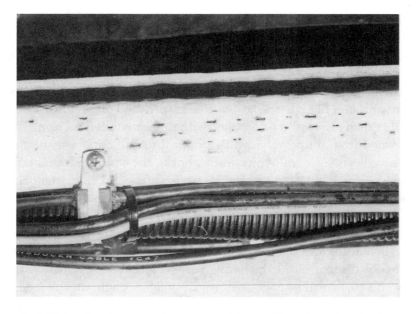

Fig.5-14. Looking down on a glass over wood stringer. The patterned marks along the top look like small staples but is actually brown water weeping through a fiberglass fabric that is incompletely saturated with resin. Rotting wood is the cause of this pattern.

Getting back to plywood stringers, though very strong, this type requires greater care to ensure that the wood has not soaked up water and rotted. That means that limber holes cannot be simply drilled through the stringer. If that's the way it is, then we have to anticipate potential problems, like rot and delamination. By 1998, more and more builders had stopped using wood in stringers, though there is nothing wrong with wood so long as the builder knows how to use it properly. Unfortunately, a lot of them didn't, or didn't care. Therefore, if you're interested in a boat with wooden framing, hiring a good surveyor is highly recommended.

What about using moisture meters on stringers? In theory, this sounds like a great idea, though in reality it poses certain problems. I get more calls than any other type from people saying that their surveyor told them the stringers have high moisture readings, but were unable to say precisely what that means. Thus, the moisture meter ends up raising more questions than it answers.

For example, with a meter an awful lot of boats are going to show up with high readings so that now we're faced with interpreting what those readings mean. Just because wood is damp, it doesn't automatically mean that it is rotten, or will rot. The meaning will be different depending on whether the builder used high or poor quality plywood. High quality plywoods such as Bertram has used have been known to withstand thirty years of being wet without rotting. Conversely, very low quality plywood can rot away in just a few years, so obviously we are faced with a much wider question than merely whether we have high moisture readings.

What high readings can tell us is that we need to investigate further. This should be done by a surveyor in the form of both physical sounding for evidence of delamination or near total deterioration. In some instances, taking test borings will be in order, which can be done with as small as 1/4" drill that will do little damage. Here we find out if the tailings come out wet and/or rotten, and thus we have the clear-cut answer we are looking for. We should not rely on meter readings alone as these can be highly misleading.

Ninety percent of the time, visual evidence will be able to confirm the condition. Rotting wood will usually cause a brown fluid to leach out around any penetration or incomplete bonding of the fiberglass. If you find that there are brown water trails or just water stains, then most assuredly stringer rot is present. Look closely at all attachments to stringers, such as screws holding wire or plumbing clips. Are there stains or signs of corrosion? At this point, you may be able to remove the screw for a better look. If it comes out rusty, then you have your answer and it's time to go look for another boat.

One final point: the use of inferior grade plywood for stringers by Sea Ray Boats and a few others have resulted in problems of severe stringer rot. This mainly occurs in conjunction with box-beam stringer construction. That is where almost always in the forward section, and occasionally in the far aft section of stern drive boats, the stringer is permanently decked over and forming an inaccessible compartment below. These compartments sometimes fill up with water and because it isn't visible, it stays full of water for years and eventually rots the stringers out.

This condition has occurred with hundreds of older Sea Rays and because of the location below the forward cabin areas, the problem cannot be repaired at a reasonable cost. It usually means the end of the boat's useful life. Situations like this are one of the reasons that I make such a big deal out of internal hull areas being accessible.

Limber Holes

Limber holes are holes in bulkheads, stringers or frames for the purpose of drainage. Problems can exist with limber holes in the form of (1) their adequacy and placement, and (2) the type of material they are drilled through.

It should be self evident that the areas outboard of the central stringers need to be drained. Otherwise we'd have to have a separate bilge pump for each compartment. The simple solution is to provide drain holes to allow any accumulated water to drain down. However, if the stringers are fiberglass over wood, this will allow the wood to get wet and usually stay wet, inducing rot. To avoid this condition, the wood on the inside of the hole needs to be sealed. This is often done with epoxy paste. Very often we find that a piece of PVC pipe has been inserted into the hole. This is fine if the PVC itself has been sealed. Unfortunately, neither polyester nor epoxy will bond to PVC and so we usually find that the glue used to seal them does not make a seal, thereby allowing the wood to get and stay wet. If that's the case, the stringers need to be checked more closely for signs of trouble.

Foam cored stringers often have only plain holes drilled through them and that is okay. Yes, the foam will be exposed to water though this is not a problem that causes trouble.

Limber holes in top hat style stringers (premolded and completely hollow) pose a more

Fig.5-15. A typical limber hole in a stringer. Probing with a knife or other sharp instrument will determine whether the core is sealed if it's wood. In this case, the hole has been sealed with epoxy and no wood is exposed.

interesting problem. In fact, this can occur with any kind of stringer and is one that has annoyed, baffled and harassed many a boat owner. A stringer can be like a pipe; put water in one end and it comes out the other. Limber holes provide the means of entry and exit for water. What can happen is that water enters the stringer, travels along a certain distance and comes out in another compartment, leading the boat owner to think he has a leak in that compartment when, in fact, the leak is somewhere else!

Bulkheads

The issue of bulkheads can be a bit difficult for a non expert to evaluate. Unfortunately, there are far too many entry level boats, particularly express types that lack adequate bulkheading because the interior designer wants to create the impression of a cavernous interior. One needs to pay more close attention to this on older boats, as the effect of a lack of bulkheading tends to be cumulative over the years. Express boats in the thirty foot range often have only one full bulkhead at the forward engine room, which is usually not enough. The hull needs additional bulkheading in the forward section between the bottom and the deck to keep the hull from twisting. Bulkheads don't necessarily have to span the entire width, and can have a door in the middle without causing much of a problem.

A lack of bulkheading usually leads to a condition of a hull twisting along its longitudinal axis, or lengthwise. This usually causes clear and obvious signs of the problem on the interior. These usually start with screws backing out of moldings and cabinets, and especially around door frames, doors that are badly misaligned and don't close properly, as well as misalignments in all kinds of joinery. Look for large gaps appearing in partitions or bulkheads, and especially cracks or other irregularities. On smaller boats we often find problems showing up in the galley area with loose counter tops, refrigerators that back out of holes and such.

Fig.5-16. Severe cracks in internal structures, such as around this companionway hatch, are an indicator of tortional stress. In this case, these are not mere gel coat cracks, but go right into the laminate. It likely means that the whole structure is twisting.

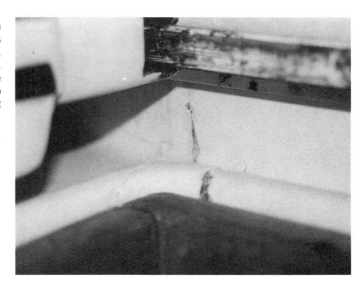

Excessive cracking in lower corners of fiberglass liners, particularly head compartments, is another indicator of potential trouble. Very thin line stress cracks are rather usual, but when the cracks get larger, when they are widespread, and particularly when cracks have jagged edges and with obvious chipping of gel coat, or even complete breakouts, these are signs of trouble.

Also look for disturbances around cabin entrance doors and sills similar to that shown in photo Fig.5-16. Large numbers of gel coat cracks around doorways and hatches are usually a signal that all is not well. Combinations of the above signs along with loose and damaged rub rails is usually a sure sign of an overly flexible hull.

Checking For Cabin Leaks

Excessive water leakage into the cabin often means more than a mere leakage problem, and may be signaling a larger structural problem. Express cruisers that have long, low profile windows between the low cabin top/foredeck, often have a problem with inadequate support for the deck along this expanse of windows. As a result, the window frame is stressed and constantly leaks. There is usually no reasonable costing repair for this condition.

Flybridge sedans and similar types which have nothing to support the flying bridge deck but a bunch of window frames are often plagued with chronic window leakage. Check closely to see what is holding the bridge deck up. If it's just the window frames, consider the leakage problem as uncorrectable.

As mentioned previously, poorly designed hull/deck joints can result in chronic leakage at these points. Check for signs of leakage entirely around the perimeter of the cabin in way of the deck join area. Also check for water damage down on the cabin sole. Very often leakage from the deck join runs down the inside of the hull and out onto the

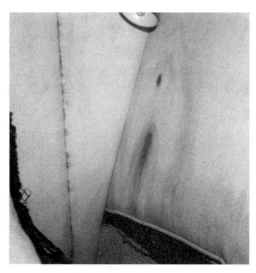

Fig.5-17. Few people would miss this obvious evidence of serious leakage but for the fact that it was cleverly hidden by a pillow. This photo is of a padded liner on the hull side in a stateroom. When checking for leaks, it is necessary to look behind things that could be covering up water damage. This is often the case.

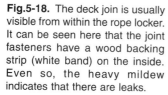

Fig.5-18. The deck join is usually visible from within the rope locker. It can be seen here that the joint fasteners have a wood backing strip (white band) on the inside. Even so, the heavy mildew indicates that there are leaks.

cabin sole, often the only place it will become visible. Damaged or wet carpeting and water stained wooden soles will signal a problem of some sort. So do water stains on the inside of storage cabinets or under seating. You may see that the inner hull sides are covered with mildew and that there are obvious water trails running downward, particularly in the forward section. This usually indicates a leaking deck join.

It very often occurs that leaks come into the boat, but between the cabin spaces and the hull sides, without any obvious signs. This is yet another reason why we need access to the internal hull in boats. Chronic interior mildew problems are often the result of these invisible leaks. Heavy mildew is not normal in a boat that doesn't leak and develop high humidity inside, and for that reason excessive mildew may signal a greater problem than just mildew.

If there is any access at all behind cabinets and paneling, or inside lockers, open it up if possible. Water trails down the inner hull sides will be signaling that there are deck join leaks. Another place to look is the rope locker, if there is one. Are there water trails coming from the deck join?

While you're at it, check the overhead. Water stains around hatches usually mean that the hatches are leaking. Or there may be leaks around hardware attachments, particularly windshields. To repair any kind of overhead leak usually means that the headliner has to be dropped, always an expensive proposition.

While you're down there poking around in the bilge, make it a point to look for high water marks. Because bilges get dirty, whenever a boat takes on water, the level to which the water rose will usually be clearly indicated by a high water mark. This is similar to the proverbial ring around the bathtub. It may reveal a lot about the history of the boat. For example, no high water marks tend to indicate that all is well. A high water mark eighteen inches above the bottom of the bilge tends to suggest that the boat came darn close to sinking; that bilge pumps failed, batteries went dead, and very likely that the boat has been neglected.

Also note that a boat can have high water at only one end, or on one side as the boat settles to one end or one side. Just because you don't see a high water mark in one area – say the forward half– doesn't mean that there isn't one at the other end, so check both ends and both sides.

Fuel Tanks

Aluminum Fuel Tanks

The vast majority of boats today have aluminum fuel tanks which work out well so long as they are properly installed. In order to understand what proper installation means, we need to understand something about how aluminum corrodes. Aluminum is not a corrosion resistant metal as one might think. At least not initially. Actually, it is rather like Corten steel in that aluminum is capable of protecting itself with a corrosive oxide that is so thin that it actually is invisible to the eye. So long as nothing interferes with that invisible layer of oxide, the aluminum will not continue to corrode.

For example, we could take an aluminum tank, set it on wood blocks out in a field somewhere and rig a pump to pour saltwater over the tank for years and years. That tank would not seriously corrode except in an unexpected place; that would be directly under the blocks that it is sitting on. Here's why.

When aluminum does corrode it actually involves a chemical process that increases the Ph of water (increasing the number of hydrogen ions) causing it to become acidic and

Fig.5-19 & 5-20. Placing fuel tanks directly on flat decks causes corrosion problems. Tank at left should have shims under bottom so it won't trap water underneath. Tank at right is two inches above the bottom of boat and will at times be sitting in water - this tank is guaranteed to fail sooner rather than later.

thus it is an acid that actually causes the corrosion, not merely water. Ph neutral sea water won't do it. But, when you remove the free flow of oxygen, as from the air, such as when a tank is set down on those wood blocks, thereby allowing water to become trapped under the tank, this, in conjunction with the cut off of an oxygen supply is what will cause damage to the tank. This is a very similar situation as with swamps that become stagnant and create methane gas that is in large part hydrogen. Metallurgically, the basic corrosion mechanism is known as crevice corrosion which is a widespread problems for metals of all types on boats, including stainless steel.

Thus, the problem for aluminum tanks is how they're mounted, or what they're sitting on. The very worst way is to sit an aluminum tank onto a wooden deck that frequently gets wet and is slow to dry out, allowing water to be in contact with the metal for long periods of time with no oxygen supply like the one shown in Fig.5-19.

Aluminum tanks are best mounted on fiberglassed wood decks with plastic shims under them so that water doesn't get trapped under the tank. Rubber can be and is often used. That is okay so long as it is not *carbon rubber*. Carbon is cathodic to aluminum and ordinary carbon rubber will cause galvanic corrosion big-time. Unfortunately, there is no easy way to find out what kind of rubber it is, so we're all left hanging with this one!

In mid sized boats tanks are usually either mounted in the wings of the engine room (outboard sides) or across the hull stringers in the aft section and both types of installations rarely cause problems. Both Tiara and Pursuit boats had a large recall due to corroded and leaking tanks. Most of this was due, not to improper mounting, but

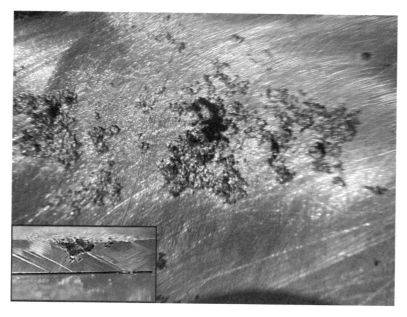

Fig.5-21. Corrosion of aluminum tanks is usually more serious than it initially appears. This macro view is taken after cleaning all the oxidation off. Appearing only as a small spot, the pit goes 3/4ths the way through the plate. This demonstrates the real meaning of crevice corrosion.

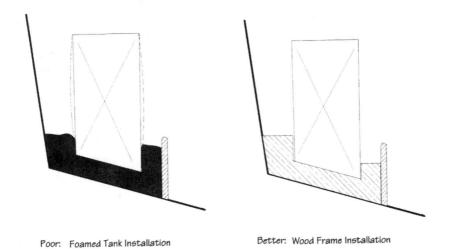

Poor: Foamed Tank Installation

Better: Wood Frame Installation

Best: Tank Installed Above Stringer With Transverse Frame Support

Fig.5-22

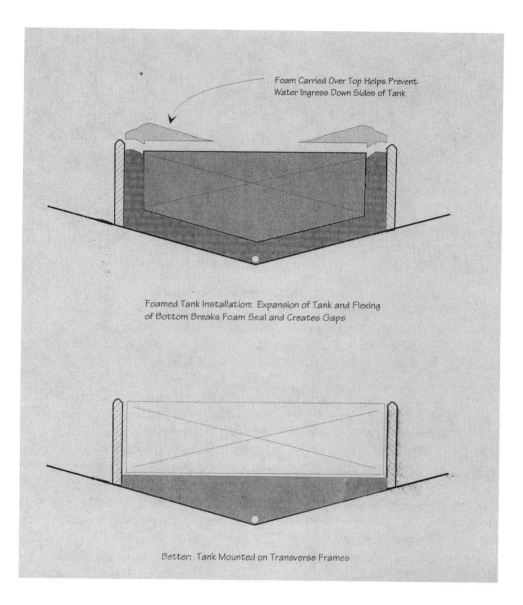

Foam Carried Over Top Helps Prevent
Water Ingress Down Sides of Tank

Foamed Tank Installation: Expansion of Tank and Flexing
of Bottom Breaks Foam Seal and Creates Gaps

Better: Tank Mounted on Transverse Frames

Fig.5-23. Small boats, particularly stern drive boats, are likely to have fuel tanks installed similar to that shown above. These are very often foamed in place, which presents potential corrosion problems. This illustration shows why and how a tank should be installed to avoid such problems.

Fig.5-24. Two effective types of fuel vent fittings, both are stainless steel. The type on the right must be pointing down and aft. Many boats have chromed zinc fittings that corrode and become plugged with corrosion. Plastic deteriorates from the sun. For the lack of good fitting, water may get into the fuel tanks, causing engine failure and damage.

Fig.5-25. This fitting is chromed zinc and has corroded so badly that the vent is blocked, causing a fuel suction problem. Identical looking fittings are also made of solid stainless. The presence of white oxides will tell which it is.

because the tanks were in contact with bare wood at some point.

Corrosion problems can also occur when tanks are installed adjacent to leaking stuffing boxes and when batteries are installed close to the tanks. In the later case, hydrogen gas generated by battery charging is responsible for attacking the aluminum.

Aluminum tanks holding diesel fuel can also develop corrosion problems from the inside when significant amounts (meaning a couple ounces) of water contaminate the fuel. Since the water is surrounded by oil, there is no oxygen supply and crevice corrosion results. Thus, aluminum tanks can fail from the inside-out, though this is quite rare because water in the tank will usually cause engine problems that lead to tank flushing.

If there are tank corrosion issues, a key question for older boats is whether fuel tanks can easily be replaced without cutting the boat up to get tanks out. Otherwise, fuel tank replacements are not terribly expensive. The vast majority of post 1990 open cockpit boats are designed with removable deck sections so that this is not a big problem.

Black Iron Tanks

The use of black iron for fuel tanks in domestically built boats ceased well over thirty years ago owing to the huge number of tank failures with this material. Boats built in the Orient with iron tanks continue to be exported in to the U.S. to this day. Iron tanks can corrode and fail even after minimal contact with water and by the time a boat with these tanks is five years old the tanks should be considered guilty until proven innocent. To find out if a tank is made of black iron, all that is needed is a magnet.

Stainless Steel Tanks

After thirty years of prohibiting them, ABYC in 1999 has now approved the use of stainless steel for fuel tanks, no doubt having done so under pressure from the industry as nothing has changed since it was banned. As with aluminum, stainless is highly vulnerable to crevice corrosion. A stainless tank cannot be mounted on flat surface without risk of crevice corrosion. And because stainless is much stronger than aluminum, the tanks can be much thinner, thereby rendering them more highly susceptible to failure than aluminum.

My personal view is that I would not buy a boat with either stainless water or fuel tanks. So far as I know, no domestic builder uses stainless tanks and it's mainly the Europeans who use it.

Yet another problem with stainless is that because the metal used will be much thinner gauge material, it becomes much harder to make reliable welds. Weld failures have been a constant problem of stainless tanks of any kind.

For all its weaknesses, aluminum remains the best material for fuel tanks. Okay, so what about fiberglass tanks? They are EXPENSIVE! that's what. Actually, there are only three production boat builders that build their own fiberglass tanks, either now or in the past, Bertram, Cabo and Hatteras. Incredibly, I've never heard of any tanks ever built by these three companies having ever failed.

Aluminum Water Tanks

Aluminum water tanks have been in use for decades. The only serious problem stems from the same improper installation problem as fuel tanks. A more minor problem is that fresh water in a sealed aluminum tank does cause considerable corrosion. However, the tanks typically last 20 years or more with the main problem being the buildup of large amounts of aluminum oxide scale inside. If the water being used is heavily chlorinated, the oxide resulting is aluminum chlorhydrate, that can build up in very large quantities. I've seen tanks where this stuff was an inch deep on the bottom. It typically takes the form of small flakes that are deadly to water pumps and water heaters, mandating that fresh water pumps be equipped with proper filters to protect them.

Water tanks are rather easily cleaned by circulation flushing.

Fig.5-26. Blisters aren't always as obvious as these are, particularly on boats that have been out of the water for a while. Here we've hosed the bottom down to make it wet so the blisters stand out. The bottom also needs to be clean.

Mr. Blister

No discussion of boat hulls would be complete without addressing the issue of bottom blisters. This subject can either be very simple or terribly complex, depending on how one wishes to address it, and there are two ways of doing so. The first approach is to recognize that any boat hull that has blisters constitutes a defective product. Period. There are those who would argue with this, saying that blisters are just the "nature of the beast" and "something we all have to deal with," as though there weren't much we can do about it. This is the view point proffered by those in the sales end of the business.

On the consumer side, we should reject this notion, rightly arguing that it is possible to build boats that don't blister without greatly increasing costs. Indeed, we can go all the way back to the 1960's and find forty year-old boats that aren't blistered. Moreover, most of those companies that did build boats that blistered, no longer do so. Somehow, they found it within themselves to find a way to eliminate the problem. Therefore, if one can do it, they all can do it, and that some boats continue to blister can only mean one thing: It is made with inferior materials and process. It is by definition, defective, because the proper materials and methods to prevent blistering are well known.

Of course, we could get into a long, drawn out discussion of how and why blisters occur, and how to repair them, but repairing defects is not the subject of this book; how to avoid buying into the problem in the first place, is.

By 1995 nearly all builders of mid size boats have eliminated the problem of blistering by introducing the necessary changes in their materials and methods needed to prevent blistering. That builders have managed to put an end to blistering without resorting to costly epoxy and vinylester resins is about the best confirmation that my conclusions about the cause of blistering is correct.

Every time I am in a boat yard (which is nearly every day) I do a quick look at all the boats that are hauled, noting whether they have blisters or not, and what brand they are. That means that over the course of decades I have seen uncountable thousands of boats, and I can safely say that it is extremely rare to see a U.S. built boat, post 1995 that has blisters. This pretty much proves my point, does it not?

Therefore, with late model used boats, there really isn't any cause to be greatly concerned about any boat that doesn't already have blisters. It is those boats that do have any degree of blistering that will pose a problem, for the presence of even one blister means that more are likely to appear.

The blistering problem has never been confined to merely low price boats, but has affected even some of the most revered names in boat building. Hatteras, for example, earned the reputation as the king of blisters. Yet it is the Taiwanese boats generally that take the award for having the largest and most damaging blisters. This is due to two factors: The use of general purpose resins (orthopthalic) and excessive application of the chopper gun, the machine that gives us chopped strand mat (CMS) which, combined with GP resin almost guarantees severe blistering problems.

Fig.5-27. A "peeled" hull. Using a carbide rotary planer, part of the mat (CSM) was peeled off. This reveals that virtually all of the blisters formed within the mat, not the structural laminates. The round white spots are remnants of blisters which are voids. As can be seen here, efforts at prior repairs had failed. All of this CSM needs to be peeled off before a fully effective repair can be made.

The Real Cause of Blisters

Fiberglass blistering, whether it occurs on the topsides or bottom, ninety nine percent of the time is a surface phenomenon. Blistering almost never occurs deep within a laminate, so that right there we have a clue as to the nature of the problem. Nearly all builders utilize CSM whether laid in by hand or blown out of a chopper gun; it is a necessary component of creating strong laminate. Being made up of random directional short fibers, the material is very soft and pliable making it useful to mate against the coarse texture of heavier fabric layers. If one placed two heavy fabrics like roving against each other, the coarse texture would leave hollows between the high spots. This would result in pockets of plastic resin – or worse yet, air voids. This would cause serious weakness along with making ply separation highly likely.

The use of the softer, flatter texture of mat prevents this and is thus used between all layers of coarse fabric of any kind. But CSM is also needed to prevent the texture of coarse fabrics from showing through the finish surface. We often see boats, particularly when they have a dark colored gel coat, wherein the pattern of the fabrics do show through. This is because as the resin cures, it shrinks very slightly, but enough to make a finish surface look like a tweed coat. That is why CSM always appears under the gel coat.

Unfortunately, CSM placed next to the gel coat surface can cause water absorption problems. Gel coat, due to its high content of pigment, is highly porous. CSM, unlike woven fabrics has very short fibers. When fabrics are wetted out with plastic resin, what happens is that the resin covers the fiber bundles but does not always work it's way into those tiny bundles of fibers. Thus, a fiber bundle that contains, say 50 strands of glass, is not saturated with resin in toward the center of the bundle. Fiber bundles can act just like drinking straws due to the capillary effect. This means that any fiber bundle

Fig.5-28. This photo reveals the incredible porosity of CSM and why attempts to prevent blisters are doomed to fail. See photo on next page.

Fig.5-29. Anatomy of a price leader; a Taiwan built boat where the builder used his chopper gun to build up hull thickness. The outer white layer is CSM about 1/4" thick and about as strong as carboard. Here, for whatever reason, the bond to inner laminate failed (or never existed) and we are peeling it off with a screw driver. The owner thought he got a heck of good deal on this boat. Two years later he had changed his mind about that.

that intersects the gel coat surface is likely to draw water into the laminate. And because there are thousands of fiber bundle strands that intersect the surface, CSM is capable of pulling a lot of water into the outer skin. Thus the number and density of blisters is related to the number of voids in the CSM.

The water is communicated by the fiber bundles until it reaches a void where the water collects in larger volume, probably less than one cubic centimeter. The mechanism that next takes place is crevice corrosion. Lacking a free oxygen source, that tiny pocket of water turns acidic and begins to break down the polyester plastic which enlarges the pocket, and creates gas or fluid pressure. Because all this is taking place between the thin gel coat and the first layer of CSM, a blister is pushed out by the pressure.

Blistering can be prevented by several means. The most effective is to use a higher quality resin that is less subject to corrosion. Unfortunately, because a hull is already built with lower grade resin, the idea of repairing or preventing further blistering by various means isn't very likely to work because of the extreme difficulty of completely sealing off the old from the new. Stripping the CSM from the outer surface of the bottom has worked out quite well because now the basis for blisters forming has been removed.

Fig.5-30. On older boats one never knows what lies under the bottom paint until one looks. The bottom of this boat was stripped to repair blisters only to find a number of old repairs that were improperly made and a bottom that is a hodge-podge of fillers and putties. Be wary of any bottom that shows surface irregularities. What looks like blister repair could be a lot more than that.

Note here that blisters forming within a laminate of heavy fabric almost never occurs. That is because with very long fibers, there are few, if any, fiber bundle ends exposed to a water source, and are thus far less likely to be transmitting water into the laminate. Secondly, being far stronger than CSM, heavy fabrics are less like likely to allow gas pressure to push out a blister, even if the pocket of fluid does exist within the laminate. However, it is a well documented fact that blisters almost never occur within a structural laminate. When they do, it is always associated with a larger defect.

One of the problems of CSM is that the nature of this material makes it difficult to fully wet out with resin. That means that, compared to other fabrics, it tends to leave millions of minute voids or air bubbles that contribute to the blistering problem. People have long been perplexed as to why there is no consistency to the size and frequency of blisters. In large part, this is due to the extent of invisible voids within the CSM laminate. The fewer and smaller there are, the less blistering will occur.

It is also interesting to note that there is a direct correlation between the thickness of CSM on the outer hull and the propensity and severity of blistering. Taiwanese boats are well known for having the most severe blistering but usually have very thick layers of CSM, often over a 1/4" or more. Likewise Hatteras Yachts that had the second worst blistering problems (after Uniflite) also usually had very thick layers of mat on the outer surface. There is virtually no evidence that CSM used between structural plies contributes in any way, nor layers on the inside of the hull.

Barrier Coating

Somewhere along the line someone came up with the notion of barrier coating hulls. The idea seems to have been that if you could coat the bottom with some sort of water-proof coating, that would prevent a hull from absorbing water and thus prevent blistering. On the face of it, this seems reasonable, but when we examine the idea in depth we find that the notion proves completely false.

First of all, there is no correlation between potential sources of water entry into a laminate and the location where blisters occur. By this concept, if a boat bottom has a deep gouge in it, one should expect that blisters will develop somewhere near the gouge because the gel coat has been breached and is letting water into the laminate. However, on inspecting thousands of boats, I've never seen one single case where blisters occur near gouges, through hull openings, fastener holes or anywhere else where water has a chance to enter the laminate. There simply is no relationship to areas of water entry and the locations where blisters occur.

We can also ask another probing question: What about water on the inside of the hull? Would we not also have to provide a barrier coating to the inside of the hull where water lays in the bilge? But, no one has ever associated blisters with bilge water. This factor fully discredits the notion that barrier coating could (a) prevent water absorption into a laminate and, (b) that it would prevent blisters.

Because boat bottoms are completely immersed, it is not possible to prevent water absorption into the laminate to the extent that a laminate is capable of absorbing water. Fiberglass hulls can't be prevented from absorbing water any more than a wood hull could. The truth is that the factor that determines whether it will blister or not is the quality of the laminate, including the quality of the plastic resin involved. The best quality plastics — epoxy and vinylester — do not blister even when laminates involve poor workmanship. Moderate quality laminates — isopthalic resins — won't blister when good workmanship is employed, but sometimes will when excessive CSM is used. Even low grade GP polyester (orthopthalic) resin is known not to blister when superior laminate design and workmanship is employed.

From these demonstrable facts we can see an obvious correlation that quality of material, laminate design and workmanship are all factors in the blistering phenomenon; that mere water absorption is not the primary factor, so that attempting to keep water out isn't going to have any effect on preventing blistering because keeping water out isn't possible.

Pre 1996 Boats

Almost no U.S. power boat builders that I am aware of engaged in the excessive use of the chopper gun in the hull to build up hull thickness, so that very severe blistering problems are rare, although numerous older boats do have blisters, and it is here that we have to decide whether these are something we can live with when considering a used boat, or do we continue looking for a boat that is not blistered.

The sad truth is that we have no way of ever knowing what kind of plastic a boat hull is made with. Nor is it any guarantee that because it is not blistered now, it won't ever. It is true that the olds of an unblistered older boat developing blisters are very low, though it has been known to happen.

But what about boats that do have blisters? Should they automatically be rejected? My answer is that there are wider issues to consider:

- Blisters are indeed mainly a cosmetic defect. The problem comes about from people's opinions about blisters. There are a lot of myths that disguise the truth about them.

- The presence of blisters occasionally affects the resale value of boats. Generally, blisters are less accepted on newer boats and more accepted on older boats.

- The manner in which blisters affect the strength of the hull first depends on hull thickness, as well as the age of the boat. Blisters, even in the long term will have little effect on a hull that is at least ½" thick, but it's not hard to see why blisters could have a significant effect on a bottom that is only 1/4" thick or so.

- In the last twenty years I have seen only a handful of later model boat sales that were compromised by blisters. In several cases, boats 2-5 years old were flat out rejected because of it.

- In most cases of ten year old or older boats where a buyer demands a price reduction for blister repair, the seller usually rejects the amended offer and successfully sells the boat to someone else. This points up the degree to which blistered bottoms are acceptable to buyers of older boats.

Repaired Blisters

Blister repair jobs often fail, a point which leaves us with something of a dilemma. When the repair job fails, the question arises whether this has left the boat in better or worse condition. Very often with older boats, spot repairs of blisters are found, which means that only individual blisters were ground out and filled. This poses less of a problem because in that case, we know exactly what was done and spot repaired blisters almost never fail so long as epoxy was used to fill the depression. If new blisters appear, that only means that the hull is continuing to develop blisters, so that one must judge as to whether the continued blistering is excessive or not.

In the case where a bottom has been completely stripped of gel coat and then recoated, but this repair has failed to prevent the continued blistering, we are faced with the issue of whether the repair job is faulty and has only made the situation worse. In that case, it would be wise to have second thoughts about the purchase, as it becomes extremely difficult for even an expert to know what he's getting into. However, repair jobs wherein complete stripping of the mat was done are not known to fail, so if a repair has failed, it is unlikely that the bottom was stripped, or possibly was incompletely stripped, thus allowing blisters to reform.

Repairs can also fail due to a failure to eliminate pockets of water in a laminate. This is hard to do because the fluid is no longer pure water, but a much lower viscosity fluid made up of dissolved solids, including salt, that does not evaporate readily. And being hydroscopic, it will reabsorb water very readily.

The bottom line is that repair jobs are usually either completely successful or complete failures. Partial success is really only a less than fully developed failure.

Blisters on Used Boats

You won't find out whether a boat has blisters until it is hauled for survey. If it does, you have a decision to make. Should you buy a used boat that has blisters? I have some very definite opinions about that, but you are likely to hear many opinions that are contrary to mine. I would point out, however, that my view is based on 35 years of looking at boats on a daily basis, including many years of dedicated research on this problem of blistering.

First, I would recommend against buying a boat that is only 1-3 years old that is developing blister problems, since the only expectation that you can reasonably have is that the blistering will get worse. And because you will be paying much higher prices for a late model boat, it really doesn't make good sense to buy a boat that demonstrates the potential for a widespread problem.

Second, if the boat is 5 years or older, and it only reveals a few blisters, then the odds of ending up with a severe blistering problem decreases dramatically the older the boat is. Many boats develop blisters only in some limited areas, which suggests that the cause is due to isolated workmanship deficiencies, in which case on an older boat it is not likely, or at least less likely, to blossom into widespread blisters all over the bottom.

Third, hull blistering in larger boats (above 30') rarely causes significant structural weakening of the hull. The main reason is that blistering is primarily a phenomenon involving gel coat and CSM (chopped strand mat). I have yet to ever see a blister under a layer of woven roving. Larger hulls are sufficiently thick that the damage caused by the blister doesn't affect the strength very much. This is less true the thinner the hull skin is. And since small boat hulls are naturally thinner, the potential for causing serious weakening is greater. While the number of boats that have actually experienced blister-related weakening is quite small, you still should be aware of this possibility.

A few larger blisters cause more damage and weaken the hull laminate far more than hundreds of small pimples. Consider dime-sized or smaller pimples as being more acceptable that quarter-sized blisters or larger. Very small blisters have little effect on hull laminate strength. Having inspected thousands of boat hulls, I have never seen or heard of one single case of extensive pimple rash (our term for a hull with hundreds or thousands of pimple-sized blisters) that resulted in a hull failure. In fact, I only know of three cases where even large blisters resulted in catastrophic hull damage, but there are probably quite a few more. On the other hand, a few larger blisters are rather easy to repair.

Forth, there are no absolute rules. One of the most common and frequent factors involved in the sudden appearance of blisters, or a sudden increase in the number of blisters, is the moving of a boat from colder waters to warmer waters. This occasionally happens when, say, boat owner in Michigan moves to Florida. A year later his boat, which only had a few blisters, now has hundreds of them. Higher water temperatures are known to have an effect on blister development.

Fifth, for older boats, say seven years plus, consider blistering as being relatively less important, if only because the value of the boat is so much lower, and is neither going to affect resale value as much, nor the integrity of the hull. By the time a hull has reached this age, the laminate has pretty much stabilized and has done whatever it's going to do. If it's only developed a few blisters, it is likely only to develop a few more. It is very unlikely to suddenly develop a bad case of acne if it presently hasn't any. But, as I said, there are no absolute rules and all bets are off if you move it to warmer waters.

Repairing Blisters

I am continually being bombarded with the question of whether blisters on small boats have to be "fixed" or something done to prevent them. Let's start with the fact that there are no known guaranteed fixes. A very high percentage of all attempts to repair the problem have failed. Add to that the relative high cost versus the boat's value and it may become economically impractical.

Over the years I've had lengthy discussion with engineers in the aerospace industry which makes extensive use of exotic composites. Most recently I have been told that epoxy/honeycomb sandwich construction of fighter jet wings and tails are showing up with water inside the hollow honeycomb. So much as for the notion that epoxy is impervious to water. Let's start with the fact that no fiber reinforced laminate is impervious to water. It's ability to resist water penetration is directly related to the nature of the fabric being used and the thoroughness of saturation with resin.

I could go on and on with all the "ifs," "ands" or "buts" about the causation of blistering. The fact is that there are so many variables to the issue that is not possible to obtain definitive answers at a reasonable cost. The very same applies to the issue of repairing and preventing blisters. It all depends on the nature of the individual hull laminate that we are dealing with. But it will cost a great deal of money just to find out.

Should you do it yourself? I suggest not for several reasons. Unless you are versed in the proper techniques and materials, and have the skills and tools to do the job properly, you are likely to end up with a boat bottom that looks worse than the original problem. And you will have wasted all that time and effort for nothing. Unless you are particularly skilled at this sort of thing, you'd probably best leave it alone.

So what does it cost to repair a heavily blister bottom? As of this writing, to use a fully qualified professional, the rate is about $200/ft.

Summary

It will take a person about an hour to check out a boat hull as I've outlined below, but it's well worth the effort. While we don't always get good access to check these points, I recommend that you make a reasonable effort to personally look for yourself as much as possible. If you're looking at a used boat, don't be shy about opening things up for a look-see; you have a right to do that before you make an offer. If a seller displays misgivings about your poking around, perhaps you should begin to have misgivings about his boat, which would be an incentive to look even closer.

1   Find out what part of the hull, if any, is cored and with what.

2.   Inspect inner hull in forward sections as best possible.

3.   Check out the manner in which bulkheads and stringers are tabbed into the hull. Beware if all you see is chopped strand mat. Look for looseness and cracks.

4.   Examine wooden structures, paying particular attention to the use of plywood. Don't be fooled by gel coat coated plywood; look for ply separation, heavy grain checking and discoloration that may denote rot.

5.   Check deck joint and rub rail for looseness and damage.

6.   Check in anchor locker, looking upward to see deck joint and underside of deck for evidence of water in core (mold, fungus).

7.   Inspect port holes and hatches for leaks.

8.   Examine headliner for water stains.

9.   Examine cabin sole for water damage, dark areas on wood or carpet.

10.   Examine interior paneling for water staining and darkening.

11.   Check all doors that they are properly aligned. Look for unusual gaps or looseness in moldings.

12.   Note whether there is an excessive amount of mildew in interior. No mildew at all is a good sign.

13.   In after sections, check for excessive mildew, water pocketing and high water marks. Generally note the corrosion levels of metals.

14.   Check present water levels in forward bilge and observe high water marks.

15.   For boats with framed windows, check the frames inside and out. Look behind all fixed curtains to check for corrosion and damaged paneling.

Chapter 6

Performance and Sea Keeping

In this chapter I'll discuss some of the critical reasons why it's not a good idea to just go out and buy whatever looks good to you stylishly, or simply fits your needs in terms of that wonderful cabin layout that Mrs. Boat Buyer dearly loves. In fact, you may want her to read this chapter, too.

The two big reasons why so many boat builders can get away with creating such terribly performing boats results from (1) a majority of new boat buyers are inexperienced, and (2) no matter how much boating you do, few people ever get the opportunity to actually operate, under adverse conditions, more than a few boats throughout their entire boating careers. Thus, the "average" boater never really learns the difference between good and poor handling boats, particularly since most of the really good performing boats are in the sport fishing category.

My purpose in this chapter is to get you to think a bit more carefully about the performance characteristics of the type of boat you propose to buy through a discussion of what accounts for both good and bad performance. Moreover, if you have any notions that the boat you buy will only be used on nice days when conditions are favorable (that's a rationalization I hear at least once a week), I'm suggesting that you rethink that idea carefully. The truth is that reality rarely cooperates with that notion, leaving the boat owner, more often than not, disappointed with his very expensive choice.

If you've ever walked through a boat yard, you've probably noticed that boat hulls come in an almost infinite variety of shapes and sizes. Hull shape is responsible for a wide

Fig. 6-1. As more and more people take to boating, waterways become increasingly crowded. Thus, the notion, "I don't plan to go out in rough water." is often an exercise in wishful thinking.

variety of performance characteristics, and there is no one hull type that does everything equally well. Therefore, we don't want to end up paying a lot of money for something that does not meet our expectations.

Since there are numerous factors that combine to make for either good or poor performance, it's best to avoid drawing simplistic conclusions. Indeed, when we use the term "good performance," we are referring to many factors including things like good fuel economy, the ability to handle a rough chop without pounding, rolling motion, pitching and dynamic trim among others.

We should also understand that perceptions of sea keeping ability will vary depending on operator skill. A highly skilled pilot can make good with the worst of boats, whereas the unskilled pilot is likely to have great difficulty. Thus, when considering sea keeping, bear in mind that much depends on boating skills. For example, in one of my published boat reviews, I stated that a particular boat had fairly good sea keeping abilities. An individual went out and purchased that boat based on my review. Shortly afterward, I received an e-mail from the person taking exception to my evaluation of the boat. The new owner stated that he found the boat almost impossible to control in a following sea.

Not understanding why his opinion and mine were at great odds, I called the man and discussed it with him. It turned out that this was the first boat he had ever owned, and that he had never taken a piloting or seamanship course. He had a problem with broaching in following seas because he was operating the boat too fast for the conditions. Broaching is the situation wherein when you bury the bow into the backside of a wave, it forces the boat to veer off, often uncontrollably. I had to explain to him that virtually

Fig. 6-2, 6-3 & 6-4. Boats that look top-heavy usually are.

any boat will broach in high following seas if you try to run too fast. His problem was one of a lack of experience, not poor hull design. Almost all boats will behave this way under such conditions.

The Meaning of Sea Keeping

Sea keeping, defined for our purposes, is the ability of a vessel to handle adverse or less than ideal conditions. That is to say, less than ideal conditions in which wave height adversely affects the comfort levels of the passengers aboard. Sea keeping should be important to us despite the fact that we may never intend to go out when conditions are unfavorable. Unfortunately, good conditions have a way of turning bad fast, or there will be times when we find it necessary to brave the adversities of weather.

The most common scenario is when a boater travels somewhere and, a few days later is met with bad weather for the return trip home. He'll then be faced with a choice, either leave the boat and find another way home, or brave the poor sea conditions. For reasons such as this, it is advisable to select a boat that has better sea keeping abilities than one might intend to make use of. Ultimately, you have to be the judge as to whether a boat with greater sea keeping ability is worth the extra cost, or the various compromises that have to be made. I can only tell you that one of the primary reasons people sell their old boats to buy new ones is to acquire a boat with better sea keeping abilities. Therefore, you may find it worthwhile to consider whether you expect to become an avid boater, and whether it will be advantageous for you to buy the right boat from the start, rather than go through the buying and selling process several times.

People have a tendency to grossly over estimate wave heights. Waves have a way of looking bigger than they really are. For this reason I'll talk a bit about how boats handle various conditions. Boat size, of course, is relevant to how it handles sea conditions, at least up to a point. Even more relevant is the distance between waves. The distance between waves is the wave frequency which is affected by water depth as well as currents. Both shallow water and waves heading in the opposite direction of current causes waves to become steeper and therefore more frequent. Deeper water and current running with the wind direction results in less steep waves with a greater distance between crests.

The worst sea conditions for any boat are those where wave frequency is 150% or less than the boat's length. This leads to the difficulty to comprehend situation in which larger waves can be more comfortable and less dangerous than smaller waves. That is because when wave frequency is greater (less distance between crests), the boat is constantly being affected by the waves. Whereas when the wave spacing is much greater,

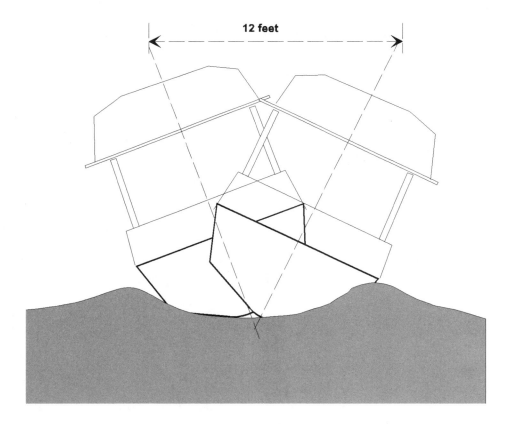

Fig. 6-5. This high profile motor yacht illustration shows it rollling through an arc of about 40 degrees. More important is the actual distance the passenger is traveling, in this case about 12 feet.

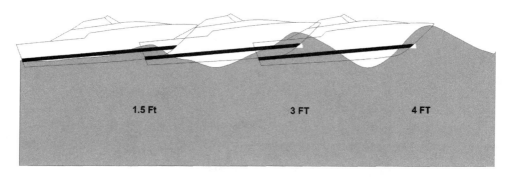

Fig. 6-6. The effect of wave size on a 35 foot boat. Note the significance of wave frequency, or the distance between crests. The going gets tougher, the closer waves are.

the boat spends more time in the troughs and less time falling off wave crests.

From this it should be clear that the vast majority of sea conditions between calm and very rough will greatly affect most boats. A boat that is 30-40 feet long is right at the frequency of the most common conditions, the two to four foot waves. Most family-type cruisers are greatly affected by two foot seas; at three feet it becomes very uncomfortable, and at four feet the boat can only make idle speed up wind. How often are seas two to four? Well, most of the time on open water such as oceans and The Great Lakes.

Even the deepest vee hulled cruiser, say a Bertram or Hatteras, will not provide a comfortable ride at cruise speed heading upwind in four foot seas. Even at three feet, it's going to be uncomfortable. At two feet, these boats will provide a smooth ride, whereas the shallower hulls will not. Keep in mind we're not talking about long, rolling three foot swells here, but short, steep chops. To give you a direct comparison, not long ago I sea trialed a 40' Hatteras during a severe thunderstorm where winds were blowing a good 50 mph and kicking up a very steep 3-4' chop in shallow water. Visibility was so bad it was hard to tell how steep the waves were, but we tested this boat at a full 29 knots head into the seas. Though the ride wasn't pleasant, it was tolerable but at the very limits of tolerance for both boat and passengers. A sea trial performed during similar conditions in a 50' Sea Ray we could make little more than fast idle speed because the pounding was so bad with this very shallow hulled cruiser. So here we had one boat that was ten feet longer than the other, but could not handle similar conditions. I can think of no better illustration than this of what differences in hull design can make.

Juggling a Host of Factors

As with nearly everything in life, it's almost impossible to combine all the positive factors, while excluding all the negatives, into one perfect little package. This stems from the fact that certain positive factors are mutually exclusive of each other. For

Fig. 6-7, 6-8 & 6-9. Deadrise angle measured at the transom is only a small factor in determining performance. The beam at the bow and depth of entry is far more important. Shown above are three boats that represent the three most common shapes. TOP: this Sea Ray has a very broad, flat entry that will perform poorly in waves. MIDDLE: The Tiara hull is a moderately deep entry still with considerable beam forward. BOTTOM: A 38' Hatteras hull shows why it is the superior performer. Its depth is enhanced by the much narrower beam in the forward section at the water line. Note the amount of flare in the bows.

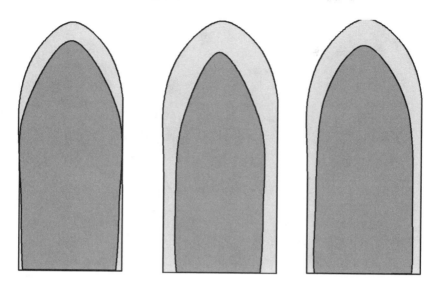

Fig. 6-10. Three basic boat hull types shown upside down revealing the "foot print" or wetted surface area of the beam at the water line. Far right is the typical express, at center a sport fisherman, and left a motor yacht. Note how the center boat presents a much finer entry as well as having a lower wetted surface area. The interior space, of course, will not be as large.

example, very deep vee hulls draw more water and create more resistance. Therefore, the best rough water boats are not going to be the most fuel efficient. Additionally, heavier boats will ride better, often *much* better, than lighter boats, but they cost more to buy and operate.

Then there is the issue of interior volume. Hull designs that afford the most commodious interior spaces have hull shapes that are contrary to the principles of hull design that make for the best sea keeping hulls. So it is that the vast majority of boats that have the broadest appeal to the widest segment of people are generally not the best sea boats. These days, boat buyers are usually more interested in style and accommodations than how well a boat handles rough water. That is the reason why the majority of boats on the market tend to be poor performers.

For our purposes it is useful to divide boats into two categories; sport fishermen and everything else. The reason being that for any sport fisherman, sea keeping must rank at or near the top of his list of virtues since the sport fisherman is not a boater who can pick and choose his weather. Therefore, amongst the sportfishing class of boats, the best sea keeping boats are usually to be found and we can use these as a yardstick by which to gauge all others.

The deep, heavy Hatterases and Bertrams have a well-earned reputation for being amongst the best rough water boats. They also have a reputation for being fuel hogs and chewing up engines as though money were never an issue. The reason: They are heavy and deep.

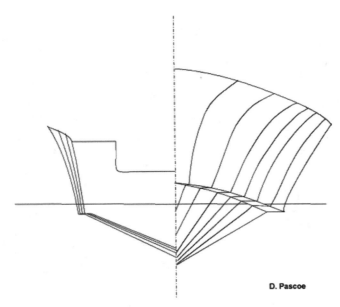

D. Pascoe

Fig. 6-11. With a constant deadrise angle vee, the bottom angle is the same right up
to the bow section where it becomes steeper because the hull gets narrower.

About Speed

How fast will she go? is the question almost no boat buyer fails to ask. Except for the
economy freaks it seems just about everyone wants to go fast just for the sake of going
fast. The fisherman wants to get 80 miles offshore as fast as possible; for the cruising
yachtsman, a few extra knots can shave many hours off of a long voyage. And, of course,
there are those who are concerned about bragging rights when it comes time to belly up
to the bar.

The problem is, speed always comes with a substantial penalty of some sorts. The most
obvious of these is the cost; going faster always costs more both in terms of extra fuel
burned and the higher cost of more powerful engines. Boat buyers often look at the
difference in price between, say, a boat with 300 hp engines and one with 350 hp engines
and wonder why that measly 100 hp difference costs thousands of dollars more. The
builder is just gouging, they're apt to think. But what they haven't considered is that
higher horsepowers require that certain aspects of the boat be built stronger in order to
handle that increased power.

Things like engine mounts, shafts, and struts all have to be bigger and stronger. But by
far the biggest item is the hull itself. Not only are more powerful engines heavier, but
the boat will be going faster, and that means it will be subject to higher stresses and
therefore have to be built stronger. That's why we often see a ten to twenty thousand
dollar spread in prices between boats with different horse power.

Yet speed can have even more costly effects than these, effects that include rapid engine wear and damage to the boat itself. I'll talk more about the penalty of reduced engine life in the Power Options chapter, but suffice it to say here that high performance engines have substantially lower service lives than engines of more normal power ratings. My rule of thumb for diesel engines is a 1:1 ratio of horse power to displacement (in cubic inches). For gas engines it's a bit lower, 0.75:1. These ratios have proven to be very accurate at predicting engine longevity.

Perhaps the worst penalty of high speed is that one pays a very high premium for, but rarely ever gets to use that power. The average boat, that is, production boats that are designed for more or less average boaters, are almost never designed for exceptional performance at high speeds. That's because high speed hulls are not particularly efficient, and since the "average" boater cares more about fuel economy than he does about high speeds, that's the way most builders build them. Of course you can always go out and buy a Cigarette, Fountain, or Magnum, pay a huge amount of money for it, and not get all the space and accommodations you want because that high performance hull is very deep and narrow.

Yet another problem with high speed is that while the boat owner may love going fast, most of his passengers won't. At least not for any length of time. The fact is that 30 mph is plenty fast when traveling over water, and under the median conditions that prevail, will produce a rather uncomfortable ride in most boats. Bear in mind that it is always more uncomfortable for passengers than the pilot because he's holding onto the wheel while the passengers are being bounced around while looking for something to hold onto.

If high speed is hard on passengers, it's even harder on a boat, especially one that's all decked out like a house. Imagine giving a house a bashing like most boats receive! Even the most well built boats can easily be damaged by careless operation but, as one might

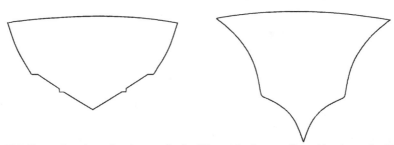

Fig. 6-12. This illustration shows just how radically different the bow profiles of boats can be. The one on the left is representative of a typical express cruiser while the one on the right is similar to an Ocean Yachts or Hatteras convertible. Section area is 1/4 LOA aft of bow.

well imagine, the effects of high speed over rough water are cumulative over a period of years. The constant banging of the hull year after year even under "normal" conditions naturally takes its toll. Not only are basic structures affected, but also machinery and electronics.

But shallow bottomed boats, when pushed to or beyond limits, can suffer even worse damages of the sort that can have very serious affects on resale value. Such damages often go unnoticed by owners but are easily picked up by marine surveyors who then report such findings to the prospective buyer.

Hull Types and Efficiency

If we were to go around with an angle finder measuring deadrise at the stern of all boats we looked at, we would be likely to walk away with many false conclusions about some boat hulls. To properly evaluate boat hulls by merely looking at them, we need to look at the whole bottom shape. It is not enough that we classify hulls as deep vee or shallow, for there are many variations on the theme.

There are two types of vee bottoms, constant deadrise and modified vee. A constant deadrise, as its name implies, maintains a constant angle throughout most of its length. As the vee moves toward the bow, it necessarily tapers into a greater angle because the beam narrows to a point. But, for the most part, it will be the same throughout about 2/3rds of the length.

A variation of the vee bottom is the warped plane hull. A warped plane hull changes the deadrise angle at certain points. The bottom panels are essentially flat, but resemble a board that is twisted in opposite directions at the ends. Take a piece of cardboard and hold one end in each hand. Now, twist each end in opposite directions. When applied to hull bottoms, here you can see that we end up with a bow section which can be very deep, and a stern section that is almost flat, yet it is still a vee shaped hull. Thus, simply referring to the deadrise angle as measured at the transom does not tell the whole story about hull depth unless we are talking only about constant deadrise vee hulls. In fact, we can have a warped plane vee that is nearly flat at the transom, and yet has a moderately deep vee section amidships and a very deep vee up forward that makes for a boat with a fairly good rough water ride.

Now, let's focus our attention on a boat hull planing along the surface of the water. It is not riding along at the same level angle as it was when resting at the dock. No, our boat is riding along at an angle with the bow raised. Typically, a good trim angle, or angle of attack, is about seven degrees. The faster the speed, the higher the hull is going to rise out of the water; this is a function of the engine power driving the hull up, onto the surface of the water. Therefore, the faster the boat goes, the more efficient it becomes.

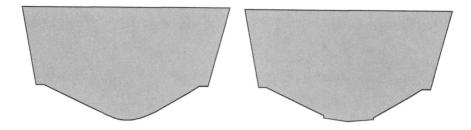

Fig. 6-13. Modified vee hulls with the main modification being to the apex of the vee. This appears to defeat the purpose of the deep vee and has the same effect of making the hull a few degrees shallower. Bertram, among others, has used the form on left, while Viking uses the one on the right. The only real advantage is that the engines can be gotten down a bit deeper for better ballasting.

Why? Because, with less hull in contact with the water, the less resistance there is. But, of course, it takes a lot of power (and fuel) to get to that point.

Depending on speed, we may have anywhere from only fifty to seventy-five percent of the hull length in contact with the water surface. Due to the trim angle with the bow raised, the part of the hull in contact with the water's surface shifts aft. In this case, having a knife-edged bow helps to part the seas, but it is the mid section of the hull bottom that is really hitting the waves. Obviously, the flatter that area is, the more the hull is going to pound. This is the reason why very high speed boats usually have constant deadrise vee hulls.

The constant deadrise vee hull is very inefficient at lower speeds and, while accelerating, will drive the bow high into the air until a sufficient amount of power is applied to fully drive the hull up onto the surface. At that point it will level out and become more efficient. The modified vee, because of its flatter, shallower stern section, will get up on plane much faster without pointing its bow toward the sky. But once it is up on plane, the part of the bottom meeting the waves is flatter and will, therefore, pound more.

Both the warped plane and constant deadrise vee hulls have the characteristic that the bottom sections are made up of straight lines. Cut the boat in half, and you will not find any curved lines on the bottom. Not so for the modified vee, which modifies the vee sections by introducing curves into the sections. The bottom section profiles can be either concave or convex, either transversely or longitudinally. And in most cases of the modified vee it is both.

As shown in Fig.6-13, we can try to achieve the best of both worlds by taking our vee sections and curving them. Instead of having very flat sections in the stern, we can bend them downward and make them deep in an effort to reduce pounding. The hull in cross-section view has concave-shaped bottom panels. This greatly increases sea keeping

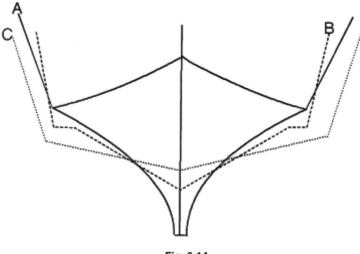

Fig. 6-14

but also it greatly reduces efficiency because no longer do we have the nice, wide flat surface to drive the hull up onto the surface. Instead, our modified vee hull is going to behave somewhat like a displacement hull. Most of the early Hargrave designed Hatteras hulls were of this form (hull section A in Fig.6-14).

The opposite of the concave bottom section is the convex curved section. This modification is found on many Bertram hulls and others. In some cases, we find bottom panels that have very slight convex curve to them. More often we find that the bottom, instead of coming to a point at the apex of the vee, is heavily rounded off. This limits the effect of deep vee, providing a flatter surface that creates more lift. It also causes more pounding. Alternately, in recent years many designers have taken to squaring off the point of the vee (Viking, for instance) so that there is a wide flat section where the apex of the vee would have been. This really increases both efficiency and speed while also increasing pounding, thus producing a net advantage of about zero.

Whether the keel section is rounded over or squared off, the net effect is no different than increasing or lowering vee angle. Another feature that does have an effect are bottom strakes which create long, narrow flat sections. Obviously strakes create lift by creating flat sections that, in turn, increase pounding.

So it is that while all sorts of ways have been devised to attempt to achieve the best of both worlds (sea keeping and efficiency), in the final analysis you'll either get one or the other and never both. If you want the most in fuel economy, buy a flat bottomed boat and confine yourself to the several days per year when the water is flat. Or take up sailing: The wind is free! No matter how you slice it, power boating is expensive at even its most efficient. The bottom line here is that you can evaluate efficiency by the weight of the vessel and evaluating bottom shape. The lightest, fastest, more fuel efficient boats will be the ones with the flattest bottoms. Conversely, if you need good sea keeping ability, be prepared to pay for it.

Pitching

This term refers to the motion represented by the rise and fall of the bow of a boat, particularly as it is headed directly into waves. It stands to reason that a very light boat with relatively little weight in the bow section, will rise very rapidly as it begins to nose into a wave. This can cause the bow to be literally thrown upward with a very violent motion.

Virtually all boats are subject to pitching to some degree. The problem here is that someone standing in the cabin can be either thrown upward or crushed downward into the deck, depending on the rapidity of the motion as the bow rises and falls. In the typical express cruiser, it is often impossible to go forward into the cabin under even rather moderate sea conditions because the motion is too violent.

The factors that determine this are bow shape and weight. Obviously, a boat with a very pointy snoot is going to be less affected as its narrow bow slices through a wave, than the typical express cruiser that has a spoon-bill bow. As that wide, full bow meets the oncoming wave, it is forced to rise very rapidly, followed by a sudden drop.

This is a particular problem with rear engine express boats wherein all the major weights (engines and fuel tanks) are positioned aft. This makes the bow very light, the stern very heavy, and thus induces extreme pitching. If this is of particular concern to you, pay close attention to this factor if you're interested in an express style boat with a vee drive engine installation. Many of these make good day boats, but lousy cruisers. Boats with engines closer to amidships will demonstrate far less violent motion, even when bows are very full.

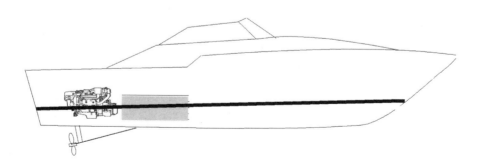

Fig. 6-15. With the major weights located aft in rear engine boats, the bow is lighter and pitches more easily thereby increasing pounding, vertical motion and discomfort.

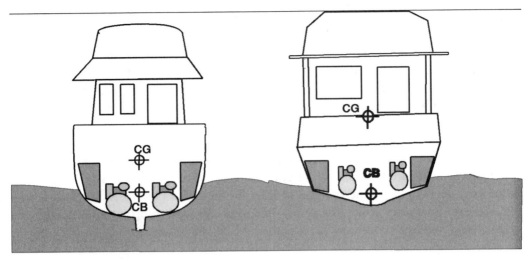

Fig. 6-16. An old style displacement hull can carry a greater height owing to a deeper hull and better ballasting. Note how in the modern motor yacht (right) the major weights are mostly above the water line, whereas in the trawler they are lower. The greater the distance between center of buoyancy and center of gravity, the less stable a yacht will be.

Vertical Center of Gravity

The vertical center of gravity on a vessel (known as VCG) plays a major role in what most boaters refer to as the stability of a boat. Technically, stability does not mean the ability of a vessel to remain level, for virtually all vessels will roll and pitch when subjected to waves. Stability means the ability of a vessel to return to the upright position *after* it has been thrown out of the level position. What we don't want is a boat that rolls over and stays over. Ballasting, or the placement of more weight down low, combined with the shape of the hull, are the factors that determine whether or how quickly a boat will right itself.

In this discussion we have to disregard the oft-repeated statement by some boaters that, "I'm never going to take my boat out in rough weather." Consideration of what it can be like in a crowded inlet or waterway on Sunday afternoon when there is no wind at all, but numerous large boats are throwing three and four foot wakes will sink any notions one may have about avoiding rough water conditions.

In fact, it is usually the encountering of big wakes that causes many boat owners to realize that the boats they own are top heavy, or have high centers of gravity. This happens when they get caught in wakes and discover that their boats are nearly uncontrollable. They're sitting there up on the flying bridge having a good time when, suddenly, the boat rolls precariously to one side and everything that is loose goes flying; drinks, seat cushions and everything that isn't bolted down. Then, as the owner struggles to gain control of the boat, it rolls heavily back to the other side, and all loose things along with it. Anyone unfortunate enough to have been standing up has been thrown about. Even seated passsengers suddenly find that they are nearly thrown out of their seats.

Fig.6-17. Bertram 31

Make no mistake about it, all boats are affected by these conditions, some more than others, mostly based on hull form and the VCG. The higher the CG and the wider and more squarish the hull shape, the more uncontrollable the boat becomes. How hull shape affects what we perceive as stability is a subject that is much too complex for us to consider. However, centers of gravity are not because we all more or less understand the basic principle here. It's the pendulum effect that we learned back in seventh grade science class.

Of course, it would be useless for me to discuss this issue unless you, the reader, have some way of putting this information to use when selecting a boat. Therefore, be aware that we're not going to escape from the fact that boats will roll in adverse conditions, sometimes even precariously. In seeking out the best designs, our primary interest should be on controlability, and here we have some identifiable factors to go on. Shown above is the classic Bertram 31, designed in 1960 by Ray Hunt. It is, hands down, the most popular boat ever built, and was in production for 23 years with over 2,000 having been built.

What makes this such a great boat is performance. It is a very deep, continuous vee hull that is low and lean with a center of gravity that is little more than a foot above the water line. This boat has little trouble plowing through big wakes in the most crowded inlets and with barely a hit of losing control. With her deep vee hull, she is more rolly-polly when sitting at rest than many others of her class, but while underway few others come close to her superb performance.

We contrast this with two other radically different boats, the obviously top-heavy 45' Silverton and the Sea Ray 450 Express, both circa 1998, that doesn't not appear top heavy at all. During a sea trial, the operator of the Silverton, when running at cruise speed and caught in a nasty confluence of boat wakes in a crowded inlet, completely lost control of the vessel when she rolled over to one side, stayed there and started to surf-board along the wake. The operator could not steer out of it and had to chop the throttles to dramatically reduce speed to get out of the wake, which was causing the boat to veer into oncoming traffic. This was like slamming on the brakes on an expressway because there was another boat barreling along right behind us, too close for comfort. Fortunately, it was able to veer away to avoid running us down.

The Sea Ray had a similar problem in that it also got caught in the wakes with the operator losing control because the wakes were steering the boat. But each of these boats lost control for differing reasons. For the Silverton, it was a grossly high center of gravity, but for the Sea Ray it was hull shape. Its extremely wide bow and flat entry simply would not track in the direction the rudders wanted her to because this boat lacks directional stability. That means that water pressure against one side of her bow would cause her to veer off in the opposite direction. The end result was that in both cases, the waves were steering the boat, not the operator.

Our little Bertram, much smaller than the other two, has no such trouble with these terrible conditions. Of course, we got a lot wetter than the folks did on the big boats, but the operator did not have to reduce speed to maintain control; the boat basically steered where the rudders told it to go. That's not to say that the waves didn't have any influence, for they surely did, but the difference was between maintaining and losing control.

Passenger Height Above the Water

On of the most important factors that affects our perception of stability, and therefore comfort level, is their physical distance above the water. That's because a boat can only roll about its center of buoyancy, and since all boats in this size range have drafts of around two to four feet, this factor is more or less the same for all size boats. This demonstrates the pendulum effect as the higher one is above the center of motion (the water line), the greater the length of arc the passenger will travel as the boat rolls.

Yet this is not the only factor that affects comfort for, when we think about it, it is not merely the distance we travel but how rapidly the boat rolls through that arc. Clearly, passengers will be more comfortable on a boat that rolls more slowly than one that rolls faster.

So how do we apply these principles? Simply stated, boats with wider beams and flater bottoms may roll with fewer total degrees of arc, but they will roll faster than a deep vee hull with a narrower beam at water line and where the ballasting engines are a bit deeper in the hull. This generally accounts for yet one more reason why those big, boxy modern motor yachts with huge interiors make for really lousy sea boats.

The Effects of Trim

The trim of a boat is an issue of balance as well as that of hull design. Clearly, one cannot locate all the major weights toward the stern of a vessel and expect it to perform well. When we talk about trim, we need to understand that there several types of trim, static and dynamic. Static trim is the trim of the vessel as she sits at the dock, while dynamic trim is the trim while underway. These two are related but not exactly the same.

Obviously, we want a boat that sits level when at rest; otherwise it is uncomfortable and water starts piling up in places it shouldn't be. Yet to get a boat to run at just the right trim angle so that it is most efficient becomes quite a juggling act for the designer when he also has to consider the optimal interior layout in conjunction with the placement of major weights. This is why great performing boats don't always have the most convenient layout. Conversely, it's also why the greatest layouts are to be found in boats that don't perform all that well.

Hull shape and overall design affects both types of trim and involve factors of floatation and placement of weights within the boat. These are referred to as centers of buoyancy and centers of gravity. In a perfectly balanced boat, the center of gravity would be directly over the center of buoyancy and, all other things being equal, the boat while underway would be expected to ride perfectly level.

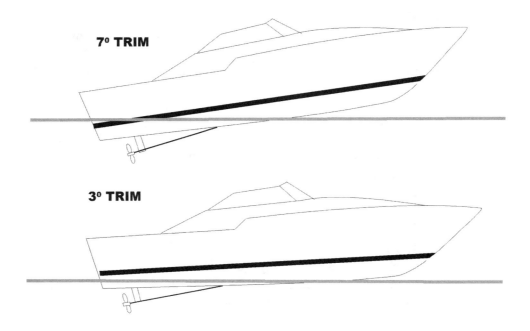

Fig. 6-18.

We don't want a hull to ride perfectly level because that would present certain problems, such as making the boat very hard to steer, plus it would have a tendency to bury its bow in waves rather than to ride up over them. Therefore, the center of gravity is almost always placed aft of the center of buoyancy. That assures the boat will ride with a slightly bow-up angle. The ideal is usually considered to be about 5-7 degrees. This has another advantage, in that it allows for the use of trim tabs to adjust the trim angle when needed. The illustration on previous page shows two boats, one at 7 degree trim angle and the other at 3 degrees. In this case the 7 degree trim is excessive and causing the hull to squat, lose efficiency and increase fuel consumption. Note the extreme angle of the propeller shaft. It is pushing up almost as much as forward, thus resulting in a loss of efficiency. At 3 degrees this hull is riding a bit too level for all but very calm conditions; in significant waves the bow would be submarining. In this case a 5 degree angle of trim would be just right for most sea conditions.

Note here that trim tabs only allow for the adjustment of bow-up/bow-down changes in trim. Trim tabs can never compensate for too much weight in the bow; tabs only help for a stern-heavy condition.

Dynamic trim is extremely important to fuel economy as every boat will have an ideal trim angle that will allow for both the greatest speed and fuel efficiency. Unfortunately, the ideal trim often does not come about naturally. That's why nearly all boats are equipped with trim tabs. In the past, before their use was widely understood, trim tabs were mainly installed for the purpose of correcting trim problems. Today it is recognized that tabs are a necessary means of achieving optimum trim angle and speed.

However, in order to be most effective, a boat needs to be properly designed and trimmed in the first place. Unfortunately, there are many boats that aren't. Most performance-related trim problems result from poor hull design and/or balance of weights. Squatting, or too much of a bow-high/stern down angle, is the most common problem. Not only does it become difficult to see over the bow, but trim angles like this are usually extremely inefficient.

Boat hulls that are poorly designed and balanced so that they squat and don't trim out properly are usually referred to as "dogs" and fuel hogs. They result in excessive fuel consumption that ends up giving them a bad reputation once it becomes widely known. Boats like this are best avoided by performing careful trial runs and observation of it's trim characteristics.

Occasionally we find boats that also have problems with static trim. Typically, the problem becomes noticeable as fuel tanks approach empty and the stern starts to float very high. This can cause water to puddle in places it shouldn't, sometimes resulting in leakage and water damage, as when water piles up on the forward end of a bridge deck when tanks get empty.

Fig. 6-19. Propeller pockets can reduce draft substantially, but this usually comes with a penalty of decreased performance. In the case of this 45 footer, the combination of the props being very close together and the pockets make for very poor slow speed maneuvering. It will not pivot on its axis as most twin engine boats will. Because the rudder are recessed, they provide little directional control except at low speed. Thus, at idle speeds the boat wanders and refuses to track straight. Amazing for a boat costing well over a half million dollars.

Shaft Angle, Propeller Pockets and Vee Drives

Earlier I mentioned that shaft angle has a considerable effect on performance. If the shaft angle is too high (steep), much of the drive energy is directed upward rather than pushing the boat forward and thus the engine's power is not being used effectively. Normally, the angle of the propeller shaft is totally dependent on the placement of engines. If a designer decides that he wants to squeeze the maximum cabin space from a hull, he can move the engines back more, albeit with a performance penalty because the shaft angle is going to be steeper.

One thing the designer can do to reduce that penalty is to create propeller pockets in the hull in way of the propellers. This allows him to reduce the shaft angle. Unfortunately, there is also a penalty for adding propeller pockets, which is that pockets disturb the planing surface of the hull bottom at a critical point. While maintaining a better shaft angle, the hull will not trim out as readily or as well, so it becomes a toss up as to whether anything is gained other than a tad more cabin space at the expense of some degree of performance penalty which in some cases is extreme.

The propeller pocket penalty comes in the form of causing increased trim angle, as well as reduced low speed steerage. A common feature of propeller pocket boats is extremely high trim angles during accelleration (while getting up on plane) where the operator finds it hard to see over the bow. But that's just the obvious effect. Less obvious is the poor efficiency that results from this increased drag. During the trial run of a pocket boat one should pay extra close attention to acceleration performance and trim angle.

The other penalty is poor slow speed steering. I've sea trialed numerous Sea Ray expresses that exhibited both very bad tracking and maneuvering. For instance, during a long treck down the Intracoastal Waterway at idle speeds, the boat would wander, causing me to constantly oversteer; the boat simply would not track straight for more than 30 seconds at a time. This is extremely annoying when one has to travel for any length of time.

Another handling problem was poor steering response, both from the rudders and from using engine control while docking. The rudders, not only being burried in pockets, were found to be much too small. In addition, putting one engine in forward and the other in reverse to rotate the boat on its axis is the common method of control while docking. This is because rudders don't offer much steerage when the boat is at rest. But when the props are burried in pockets, much of this shifting control is lost, yielding a boat that has greatly reduced maneuvering as compared to any boat without propeller pockets. Indeed, propeller pocket boats are often the main attraction at the Saturday afternoon circuses at the marina as the proud owner of one of these boats draws lots attention as he attempts to dock his boat without creating an insurance claim.

Yet another method of achieving more cabin space is with the vee drive engine installation. This allows the designer to move the engines very far aft, increasing cabin space by more than merely a bit. He's moving the engines back by a matter of four or five feet which, of course, greatly alters the balance of the boat. Most vee drive installations end up suffering from both a high shaft angle and excessive trim aft. To counter this, the hull needs to be redesigned so as to provide more buoyancy aft, a feat that generally creates more surface area aft, increasing drag, lowering the amount of deadrise possible, and overall reducing sea keeping to a considerable degree. To counter these negatives, the designer makes the boat as light as possible to keep speed up. Now we end up with a vicious circle of corrections that cause yet more negative conditions.

So it is that the vee drive system is almost exclusively found in the so called family cruiser class of express boats, a class of boat that is largely dominated by novice boaters. And since these require more power to push them at comparable speeds, fuel efficiency usually suffers, as does sea keeping ability. With so much of the major weights concentrated aft, the bows tend to be unusually light, and so they tend to bounce or hobby-horse too much which, of course, increases slamming.

The Effects of Beam

Boats with very wide beams make for very commodious interior spaces. A wider beam also presents more hull surface to the water, creating greater drag. They also result in shallower vees and increased tendency toward pounding. A simple rule of thumb is that the wider the beam, the less sea kindly a hull is likely to be. Why is that? A vee bottomed boat is basically the shape of a triangle with the base of the triangle at the water line. The wider the base (beam), the shallower the vee will be if you want to maintain a reasonable draft. If you had a 12 foot beam at water line and wanted a 24 degree deadrise, you'd end up with a boat that has an eight foot draft and would have to weigh sixty thousand pounds (to design any boat to float right, the design weight must equal the weight of water displaced by the hull).

It is also an erroneous notion that wider beam boats are more stable and roll less than narrower beam boats. The reality is that wider beam boats become more unwieldy in rough water conditions, and will rock and roll more violently. The reason, of course, is that the wider beam has a greater offset distance. It is similar to the way a rotating disk is going the same RPM at any point on the disk; but the outside is traveling at a much faster rate than the inside.

The Effects of Weight

Boat weight plays a very important role in determining how sea kindly a boat is. Many people do not seem to understand that the lighter a boat is, the more violent its motion will be. This is the result of a simple law of physics that we are all familiar with: lighter things can be moved more easily than heavy things. That applies to the power required to power the boat, as well as the effect of waves against the boat. Very light boats literally bob like corks when at sea. Though they may be very efficient to power, they will tend to have very violent motion. That includes very rapid pitching motions while underway and rapid rolling motion while at rest or at low speed.

Light boats with wide beams, because they tend toward very rapid motion, are harder to stand up on while at sea. There are two criteria to consider, *period of roll* and *degree of roll*, which is something that concerns all designers of larger yachts but, apparently, rarely of smaller ones. Period of roll is the time it takes the hull to swing through the arc of roll. Degree of roll is the total number of degrees off of upright.

I have heard many boat owners make the statement that deep vee hulls are less stable because they roll more. What they are referring to is the *degree of roll*. It is true that deep vee hulls tend to have a higher *degree of roll*. It is also true that their *period of roll* is longer. What this means is that while it may roll farther from side to side, the time it takes to complete a roll cycle is longer.

All boats are in one way or another ballasted: By their engines, tanks and various equipment and accommodations on board. How high or low, and how far off the center of buoyancy these major weights are located generally determine how a boat will roll. A single engine boat with its one engine on center will have a faster period of roll than a twin engine boat, owing to the two engines being located off center, that tend to reduce period of roll because they act as counter weights. Will this make one or the other more or less stable? No, it only means that the degree and rate of roll will be somewhat different.

At this point, it should become readily apparent which is the more desirable characteristic, a boat with a lesser degree of, but more rapid period of roll, or its opposite. Why? Well, because the boat that rolls more rapidly is harder to stand up in. Flatter bottomed, wide beamed boats tend to rock with a whip-snap motion that throws occupants off their feet. Conversely, a boat that rolls further but more slowly gives passengers more time to adjust to the motion.

The longer, deeper and heavier the hull, the better and more comfortably it will perform in rough water. The reason why we can't build ultra light boats that get really great fuel economy is that ultra light boats are also ultra uncomfortable. To understand this, consider how much a wave might weigh. Since water weighs 64 lbs. per cubic foot, a four foot wave might easily weigh a hundred tons. A boat that is heading directly into waves is undergoing frequent collisions with those waves; it's a situation of force against force: the forward motion and mass of the boat against that of the wave. The more a boat weighs, the more it's going to win its battle against the waves. If it has the ability to slice through waves, so much the better.

This also means that the heavier boat will require more horsepower from bigger engines and a much greater fuel consumption to push it. Were cost not an issue for most boat buyers, there would be little doubt about what type of boat to choose. Therefore, in our desire to achieve the best of both worlds (economy and comfort), we usually seek a compromise between weight and economy. The type of boating you expect to do should determine how much emphasis one should give to one or the other.

And while we're at it, we might also consider that mid engine boats generally perform considerably better than rear engine boats. The reason for this should be obvious when you think about it. With much of the weight centered in the stern, the rear engine boat is going to oscillate about the center of gravity. Thus, the forward part of the vessel is going to be a very unpleasant place to be. Indeed, with most all of the rear engine express boats that I have sea trialed, going up forward into the cabin areas is a real challenge in any kind of weather conditions.

Beginning in the late 1990's I began writing and speaking, as others did, about the serious downside of building very light boats so that builders eventually began to realize that this is not the way to go. Mercifully, the emphasis on ultra light boats has since been dropped and boats have gotten a bit heavier. Moreover, because of this truth, there is no longer any good reason to create ultra light machinery, as in using aluminum castings for engines that has been the trend in recent years. See chapter Power Options for more on lightweight engines.

Stability

When we refer to the stability of a boat, this means the ability to remain upright. Yet to the average boater it is likely to mean how much a boat rocks and rolls. I've known boaters who expect that boats shouldn't roll at all under any conditions. I've heard boaters with little experience say that a boat which has good stability would roll dangerously and was hard to control. That's because they don't understand hydrodynamics.

The truth is that *all boats roll*, and that certain sea conditions can lay virtually any boat over on its side, or roll it over. The fact that it can happen doesn't mean the boat is unstable; it means that conditions *overcame* the boat's inherent stability. In marine parlance, stability means the ability of a boat to right itself after it has been knocked off its normal trim. It's also equally true that some few power boats have dangerously high centers of gravity. Those that do are usually flying bridge cruisers wherein the profile is so high that they just look top heavy.

I strongly recommend avoiding any boat that looks top heavy. If it looks top heavy, it probably is. Unfortunately, there's no way to get a positive handle on gauging the stability of a boat short of guesswork by judging how it looks. Actual stability testing is performed by means inclining the vessel with weights and levers. If you're lucky enough to get a sea trial in any kind of sea conditions, you'll easily be able to determine whether the boat rolls too much. The most important thing is that motion of the boat be reasonably comfortable.

While just about everyone understands ballast keels in sailboats, rarely do boaters ever consider ballasting in a power boat. Yet power boats are ballasted by their engines, tanks, batteries and other particularly heavy objects which the designer needs to place as low in the hull as possible. Thus, when you see those builders like Carver, Silverton, et. al. creating those three story motor yachts with very high aspect ratios, one need realize that a lot of weight is being placed up very high. And that this weight is bound to reduce stability. One of the worst cases of low stability I've ever seen was in a Viking 55' motor yacht (1987-91). This boat looks top heavy and it is. Beware that even top name builders can make big mistakes.

Fig. 6-20. Boats that are too light and don't float on their designed water line can end up with transverse trim problems, commonly known as chine riding wherein the boat leans to one side or the other. This is often erroneously thought to be a propeller torque situation. A boat that floats with its chines exposed is usually an indication of this problem.

Dynamic Instability - Chine Riding

It might seem odd that a boat could be stable while it's not moving but unstable while it is. This is referred to as dynamic instability because the unstableness is caused by movement. The condition known as chine riding was first very common to single engine outboards, mainly due to propeller torque that caused a hull to list to one side. However, as boats became increasingly lighter chine riding started occurring in twin engine boats where propeller torque could not be blamed for the phenomenom.

Chine riding occurs when a hull rises so far out of the water at higher speeds that the major part of the hull is no loner immersed. As it does so, the boat begins to balance on the apex of the vee as shown in the illustration on the opposite page. At this point, all it takes is a steering input in one direction or the other and the hull will flop over on one side and stay there until something forces a change.

I've had many brokers try to explain away the problem by saying that it's caused by the trim tabs not being adjusted right. The point can be proven by retracting the tabs fully. If the boat still flops over, it's got a case of dynamic instability. Boats that perform this way are extremely aggravating and tiring to operate for any length of time, plus they can also be dangerous as the condition often causes a loss of control. Any boat that performs this way should be avoided.

Extreme Cases

Now that shameless pandering to style and luxury marketing has taken hold in so many segments of the boating industry, it is happening with increasing frequency that builders

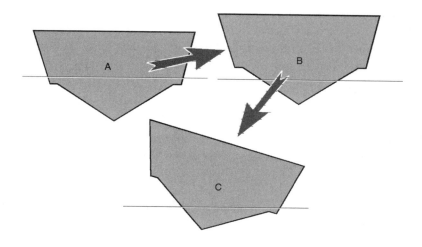

Fig.6-21. The progression toward chine riding.

enamored of their glamorous creations seem to have the idea that the vessel might never go to sea on anything but a dead flat, calm day. Increasingly large numbers of boats in the so called luxury class are becoming boat show beauties whose virtues begin and end at the dock. In other words, you take one of these gleaming sculptures to sea at your own risk.

Beware that if style is your primary attraction, that is mostly what you will get, style with little practicality. This sort of extremism predominates most in the larger boat market, yet still is found in mid size boats. The worst of these are those boats that begin to look like hi-rise condominiums. Carver is one U.S. builder in particular that seems to have a predilection for building upward to almost bizarre heights, with Silverton and a few others beginning to follow suit.

Summary

In the past, most boats were designed for a particular geographic local of operation. The vast majority of boats today are designed for nationwide and even international markets with little or no regard for regional conditions or sea keeping abilities. For most of the big builders, it's a one-size- fits-all approach. This has resulted in the unfortunate situation drastically reducing range of choices in sea keeping abilities with new and late model boats. The lone exception, of course, is with the sport fishing category.

Even so, there are still sufficient differences amongst a line-up of more or less cookie cutter look- alikes that it will pay to give careful consideration of these. For older used boats there remains a wide array of choices and performance capabilities, but over time these differences will slowly disappear unless there is some drastic change in the market. Perhaps this era of instant corporate empire building will pass and real boat builders will once again reemerge on the scene. But I'm not holding my breath.

As I stated at the opening of this chapter, builders get away with producing such poorly handling boats because the average boater never has the opportunity to experience the amazing differences between a good and poorly handling boat. The person who owns a Sea Ray or Carver is unlikely to ever find himself at the controls of a Bertram or Blackfin, so chances are he'll never know. The remedy for this, of course, is obvious.

While most boat reviews published in magazines don't offer much in the way of honest critique, a useful thumbnail hint at hull efficiency can be had from those that contain speed, RPM and fuel consumption charts. Note and compare the engine RPM at which the boat attains a 20 knot speed and use this as a comparison. The lower the engine speed at which a boat attains 20 knots is a good indicator of hull efficiency. You'll find some diesel boats hit 20 knots at 1600 RPM while others don't get there until 2600 RPM. That one thousand RPM difference burns a lot of additional fuel.

However, when making such comparisons be sure that you're comparing apples to apples and not apples to oranges, with the various boat styles. A very deep vee boat like a Blackfin will in no way compare to a flat bottomed Sea Ray or similar.

Chapter 7

Decks & Superstructure

In the chapter on hull construction we learned that decks aren't just for walking on and to keep the water out, but are an integral part of the hull structure, or at least should be. Decks are the horizontal bulkheads of the boat. The significance of this is that decks are usually subjected to a lot of stress, and unless well designed and constructed, may end up showing the effects of that stress, often in unexpected ways.

Deck Cores

While it may be hard to imagine why anything should ever go wrong with a fiberglass deck, the truth is that things often go wrong with decks. Most frequently the problem involves the core, for virtually all decks in modern boats are cored by necessity. For over forty years balsa was the standard material for deck coring that has served us well, except . . . .

Except when the laminate is breached in one way or another and water gets into the core. Being wood, balsa can rot over time. When balsa rots, it essentially disappears or is reduced to mush so that the end result is two thin fiberglass skins with nothing between them. When you walk on it, the deck is apt to feel soft and spongy. It defects or gives way. If this progresses far enough, pretty soon hardware starts pulling off and massive leaks occur into the interior. But long before it reaches this stage, telltale signs begin to appear. Surveyors rarely miss this sort of problem on a pre purchase survey since it is so easy to locate.

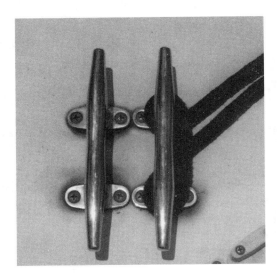 

Fig.7-1 & 7-2. LEFT: Rusty halos around hardware usually means a lack of bedding or that hardware is fastened into a core, as was the case in photo above. RIGHT, the heavy rust is caused by crevice corrosion from water trapped in a screw holes for this vent cover.

Trouble with deck cores almost never presents a problem that has to be fixed to a boat owner. In most cases he doesn't even know the problem exists, or chooses to ignore it. The reason all this is important to boat buyers comes at resale time when the problem is discovered by the buyer's surveyor. *Then*, it becomes a big expensive problem for the owner just at the very time he thought he was done with the boat and whatever problems it had would be passed on to someone else. Deck core problems usually kill boat sales so you don't want to end up buying into a problem like this.

So far, foam cored decks have proved fairly trouble-free, though while foam stands up to water intrusion better than balsa, the long term effects of water intrusion are largely unknown. Fortunately, we don't have the problem of hydraulic erosion of deck cores that we do with bottoms.

Incomplete bonding occasionally turns up in cored decks. Incomplete bonding is distinguished from voids by virtue of size. Often called *neverbonds*, these are voids, albeit very large ones that result from very sloppy work. Since very few production boats are vacuum bagged when cored, especially when foam is used, decks are apt to contain a number of voids. Depending on how well the lay up crew does its job, there may be only a few voids or many of them. This is one reason why I recommend that new boats should be surveyed. This is one of those cases where hull #125 may be defect free, while hull #126 is riddled with voids. Surveyors have various techniques for finding voids.

Virtually all boats – unless vacuum bagged – will contain at least a few small voids. Either the skin never makes contact with the core, or the laminate pulls away while it is curing. The end result is an air filled void between core and outer skin which is akin to a blister without water in it. Over time, that incomplete bond is prone to expanding due to internal stresses and being walked on. That is not to say that it will, only that it may. Nobody can really say whether or why it will or will not.

In any case, a few voids usually do not create any problem and are an acceptable condition. But, when there are numerous voids, the risk for much larger area delamination occurring poses a serious threat. For example, in a moderate sized foredeck area, as many as 10 small voids (1" and smaller) may be considered acceptable. At fifteen we start having our doubts and at 20 voids we know we have a badly laid up deck on our hands. Consider up to three small voids per 10 square feet acceptable. More than that not. Incomplete bonding or ply separation, when it covers an area of a few square inches or more, usually has the distinguishing characteristic of a crackling sound when you walk on it.

Voids also occur between the gel coat and the laminate. Most often they occur on inside corners. These are the type that often becomes visible as the thin gel coat cracks or breaks open when any kind of pressure is applied. A few of these are usually considered acceptible and can easily be surface repaired. However, large numbers of these voids will seriously degrade the appearance of the boat whether repaired or not.

Deck Designs

Few people would give much thought to deck design; most are simply flat surfaces. Back in the days of wooden boats, decks were designed with crowns in them so that there was no chance of any small amount of sagging causing puddles of water. Because we don't have to worry about wood rot with a fiberglass deck, most designers no longer feel the need for the extra time and expense that is entailed with creating a crowned deck.

Fig.7-3. Bubble decks, or decks that have rounded contours are downright dangerous. This one doesn't even have a non-skid surface.

Fig.7-4. The odds are very high that had it not been for a rainstorm, I would not have discovered this problem.The water is flooding off the foredeck, running down the side deck and thence into this opening formed by a fold-out step. The water then goes straight into the engine room, flooding a compartment without pumps. The side deck simply lacked any means to divert the water overboard.

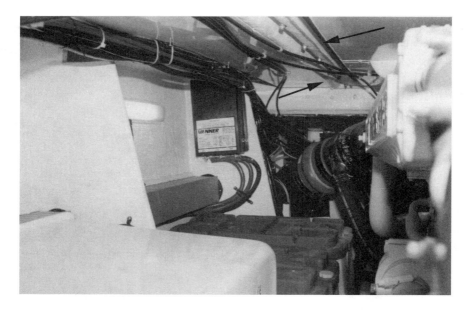

Fig.7-5. On this new boat there are profuse water leaks in the removable deck sections above the engines. The photo doesn't quite show it, but water is cascading into the engine room and about to cause serious damage. This is a fairly common problem with express or open boats. With new boats one can avoid this sort of thing by water testing with a hose before you buy. For used boats, the resultant water damage usually tells the tale.

Crowned decks are much stronger than flat decks in the same way that egg shells are strong. Plus, there is almost no chance of sagging, and even if it does occur, it would not be noticeable or cause water puddling. So why is water puddling a problem? As with sagging side decks, water in puddles dries up, leaving big stains that are hard to remove. More than a few boats have depressions so deep that they end up with stagnant ponds of slime-green water baking in the sun.

The fore decks of most boats will be found to be crowned, but cockpit decks most often are flat and water will not drain off them as well as might be expected. You know you're looking at good design when you see a crown in a cockpit deck. Cockpit decks should at least have a gutter around the perimeter. This facilitates better drainage, and in conjunction with a crown, serves to keep more water out of the hatch gutters. On some of the better designs, the hatch gutters are tied into the perimeter gutter with a series of recessed channels. This eliminates the need for any kind of drain hoses being attached on the underside to drain the gutters. This works very well with a crowned deck, but if there is any sagging of a flat deck, this can create pockets of standing water in the gutters that collects debris and becomes an ugly mess.

Of course when it rains very hard on a flat deck, even though hatches may have gutters, unless these have superior drainage capabilities, the gutters are likely to overflow. Only the highest quality boats are to be found with good gaskets, hatch dogs and/or oversize

Fig.7-6. Since the early 1990's the better boat builders have incorporated molded-in hatch gutters. Toward the end of the decade, the use of pipes and hoses to drain gutters ended when decks were designed to include channels that drain the gutters to cockpit margins, thus eliminating all extraneous plumbing. On this boat, all three hatch gutters drain directly to the scuppers, plus the hatches are gasketed and have lock-down latches.

Fig.7-7. The effects of bad hatch design has been known to sink boats and cause severe damage. In this case, the shallow hatch gutter edge is bisected by an aluminum channel (top of photo) that defeats the purpose of the gutter. It causes water to run directly onto the circuit breaker panel seen immediately below it. The use of aluminum channels like this is common and the results are never satisfactory.

gutters. None of this would appear to be of much significance until years later when all the damage done by leaking hatches starts to make an impression on your wallet in the form of corroded pumps, motors, steering systems and any other components that may be located in the drip line of that overflowing gutter.

Gimmicks and Weird Stuff

Sometimes designers get carried away, as they did with the Tiara 40 Express wherein someone got the bright idea to create a recessed hydraulic table into the cockpit deck. This was done without any thought to the consequences of such a brain storm. Of course the recess for the table became a trap for so much dirt and debris that after a year or so was more akin to a sewer as few people ever bothered to use this silly thing.

It's the better part of wisdom to be skeptical about fancy gadgets like this. Often they are more of a problem than a convenience. Another example was the trunk fashioned into the what was once a transom for the purpose of stowing away a jet ski. In this instance, the arrangement had a hydraulic trunk door and a stowaway crane for lifting the jst ski aboard. Unfortunately, the davit collided with the hydraulic trunk cylinders, they failed to provide any drainage for the compartment, and the weight of the jet ski caused the boat to squat severely, hindering performance and increasing fuel consumption dramatically.

Yet another such faux pas was the hydraulic jet ski platform that Sea Ray was selling with their larger express models. A mostly aluminum affair, these platforms were cantilevered off the stern of the boat. Not only did they have huge corrosion and maintenance problems with these things, but the transoms were never designed to carry this kind of leverage load and the brackets began crushing through the transoms. Adding insult to injury, these gimmicks also severely impeded vessel trim and performance.

The point here is that such features are usually marketing gimmicks that are usually ill-conceived and executed.

Making Inspections

One should inspect the exterior surfaces generally for signs of cracking, gel coat voids and break outs. Look for open holes or signs of poorly filled holes, as these could be leaking water into the core. On late model boats, the outer surface should be free of defects and cracks. Older boats are likely to have a number of holes from old hardware that was removed and holes never filled. If so, the condition of the core needs to be carefully evaluated.

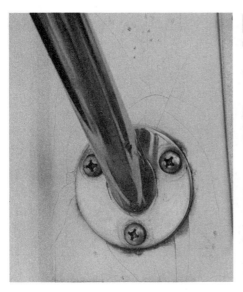 

Fig.7-8. This railing stanchion is screwed to a cored deck. The rust halo and stress cracks are evidence of the problem.

Fig.7-9. While cleats can't be too large, we think this fellow is a bit extreme.

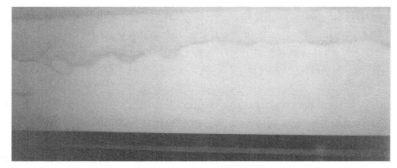

Fig.7-10. Discoloration of gel coat finish such as this may indicate a damage repair, or it could have been the repair of a molding defect by the builder. Checking from the back side may reveal whether it's a damage repair, but molding defects are impossible to prove.

Stress cracking is a common occurrence in older boats, normally in tight corners and around hatches and so on. If cracks appear in the center of a deck, this is usually an indication of a greater problem, such as deteriorating or separated core.

One can make an initial check simply by walking around on the decks stomping a bit. This works well with thin soled shoes like boat shoes but not soft, spongy athletic shoes.

Hardware Attachments

Cored structures pose certain problems for hardware attachments, namely the prevention of water intrusion and core crushing. Nothing should ever be screwed directly into a cored structure. Not only does it offer little holding ability due to the thin skins, but

Fig.7-12. Pop-up cleats are OK for attaching fenders but never as mooring cleats.

Fig.7-11. Tempted to buy a cheap automatic windlass? More often than not, this is how they perform.

Fig.7-13. Proper method of attachment of a cleat or any load bearing hardware to a cored deck. The fillet where there is no core is plainly evident. Cleat is backed up with 1/4" aluminum plate.

also poses the risk of leaks. For bolt-on items it is necessary that a fillet be designed into the laminate before it was molded, otherwise we have the problem of bolt tension crushing the core. Washers won't do, but in some cases wide area doubler plates can be used.

For high stress items like mooring cleats, windlasses and arches, it is necessary that the laminate be pre engineered to accept these items. Beware of any boat with major after market add-ons as these items may not have been adequately supported when installed. This is particularly true of windlasses, jet ski and tender cradles and after market towers. Most, but probably not all, post 1995 boats will have a fillet installed in the foredeck for a windlass: Whether there is one installed or not, still it is necessary to check if you intend to add a windlass. Without such reinforcement the strain on the windlass will loosen it and cause all sorts of problems.

Improperly installed hardware on boats more than two years old will usually show symptoms such as cracking around the base of the mounting, leaks on the interior and rust stains around stainless steel. Unless poor quality stainless is involved (rare on all but oriental boats), rust stains usually signify that water is getting underneath the piece of hardware, or down into screw holes causing crevice corrosion. For high stress items such as cleats, rail stanchion bases and so on, rust stains may be a precursor of a yet more serious problem, particularly when gel coat cracks are present. Complete and proper bedding of all hardware is necessary to prevent corrosion and rust stains.

Improper mounting of tuna towers and pipe frame tops pretty much stopped being a common problem by 1995, but before this date it will be important to carefully check the foundations of such structures. All four of the support legs should be individually inspected. Another important question: Are metal framed tops and towers properly grounded for lightning protection? In my experience, most are not.

On a flying bridge, Bimini top and pedestal seat mounts should be checked for loose fasteners and insecure bases. Pedestal seat mounts in particular pose a serious potential for water ingress into a deck core if for any reason the fasteners loosen. Because the pedestal creates a tremendous lever arm that stresses the fasteners, this is a common problem. To prevent this, the designer has to create a very solid foundation for these seats. Unfortunately, that doesn't always happen, so if you see a loose pedestal, this could end up as a very costly problem.

To this end, one should very carefully inspect the overhead in the salon for signs of leaks. Water staining and corrosion around overhead lights and other hardware is usually an indication of leakage, but it's not just the leakage we're concerned about but the potential damage to deck cores.

Windlasses

Most boat owners don't realize that these powerful winches are often capable of causing damage to itself and the deck to which it is attached. This is particularly true of windlasses that have a taller capstan that is capable of creating more leverage. Windlasses often put so much stress on the mounting bolts that they begin to loosen and leak. Since the drive motor is immediately below, that means that leaks almost always go onto the electric motor and cause damage. The only way to stop a leaky windlass is to pull it off and rebed the base and bolts.

Where Does the Water Go?

It is a sorry commentary on the boating industry that all too often, builders and/or designers fail to consider the issue of water drainage. Go figure! for just about everyone knows that the water running off the roof of your house is capable of causing great damage if it is not safely gotten rid of. Could that be any less true for a boat? Of course, not, so in the next few paragraphs I'll cover some of the more common faults that are encountered with boats.

Rope or Chain Locker

This area is sort of like the old troll living under the bridge. Bad things often hide in this forgotten space. The lack of a gutter around the hatch is the most common problem. This allows water into the compartment not only to rot out anchor rodes and rust up chains and anchors, but very often the electric windlass motor and electrical controls are directly in the drip line of the leaky hatch. The windlass drive and motor should be located so that these are not affected by water entry and be free of all but minor corrosion.

Fig.7-14. There are still quite a few boats to be found that lack gutters on the rope locker hatch as shown here. This may seem unimportant untill your anchor and chain become a rusty mess from sitting in an eternally wet locker.

Therefore, it pays to open the hatch and stick your head in there to see what's going on. See also bow pulpit section below.

Since the rope locker usually has a plywood bulkhead, and immediately aft of it is an owners stateroom berth, it is imperative that the locker bottom have good drainage lest standing water rots the bulkhead out and thence get into bed with you! The photo below shows what can happen when not properly designed.

Fig.7-15. Deck leaks, in this case the hull/deck joint, can cause major interior damage as it has here. It can also be hidden. In this instance, moving the forward berth mattress revealed the problem. Be alert to musty odors and the presence of dehumidifiers.

Guttering

Proper guttering on a boat is just as important as on a house. Though a boat doesn't have a roof, per se, it does have lots of recessed hatches that need to be designed to keep water out. In the modern fiberglass boat, a good design incorporates a hatch drain gutter into the deck molding, the purpose of which is to catch the water and not allow it to flow through the gap around the perimeter of the hatch. Designing a good guttering system adds a lot to the cost of a boat, and so we see many builders who don't waste much time or money on this important design aspect. Because of the tendency of flat decks to hold water longer, flat decks need deeper gutters and better drains.

Gutters have been a sore spot right from the beginning of fiberglass boats when they either had no gutters at all, or they were made of wood. Then molded gutters appeared, but these usually had a morass of hoses and other plumbing in order to drain them. And, of course, these were constantly getting plugged up and overflowing.

Not only do flat deck hatches need drain gutters, but so do many types of doors and types of storage lockers. Under seat storage lockers are good example of a storage area that often does not have gutters to keep water out. If not, this can render the storage space useless for anything that is damaged when wetted.

Recent improvements in design are capable of eliminating most of the problems. The integral channel design is a design that looks at drainage and guttering as a whole system. Whereas in the past hatches and decks utilized a series of scuppers and drainage pipes and hoses, resulting in a bit of a maintenance nightmare, the integral channel design use a series of linked channels in an overall scheme of deck drainage. Obviously, it takes quite a bit more forethought and extra detail in a mold design, but when carried out properly results in a most excellent product by keeping water out of places it shouldn't

Fig.7-16. This beautifully designed engine room hatch (Tiara) is made in two parts with the insulation panel sandwiched between so that it will not fall down and can be easily replaced.

go. This goes a long way toward eliminating damage and reducing maintenance. The quality and efficacy of drainage is almost always linked to the cost of the boat.

Pre 1990 express and stern drive boats, and even some later models, often have very serious problems with leakage around engine hatches where leaks are capable of causing the most costly damage. These usually involve removable hatch supports that are tied into the gutters that are impossible to seal. The only solution for these is to use a cockpit cover; which won't help with sea spray while at sea.

Deck Hatches

This section refers primarily to molded fiberglass hatches which are often a problem in boats in two ways. First, since hatches are almost always cored, it is extremely important that the hardware, including the lift handle, not be attached with fasteners running through the core. Next, all hardware such as hinges should be bolted, not attached with screws because screws won't hold. Once they pull loose, you've got a real problem trying to figure out how to reattach them. In most cases to use bolts, it had to be designed for bolts in the first place.

The last and most serious problem is with hatches sagging as a result of not being stiff enough. You can easily test this for yourself by standing on the hatch and then bouncing slightly. A well designed hatch cover should have very little detectable give. Large hatches with widths of two feet or more should be checked closely. There should be some framing

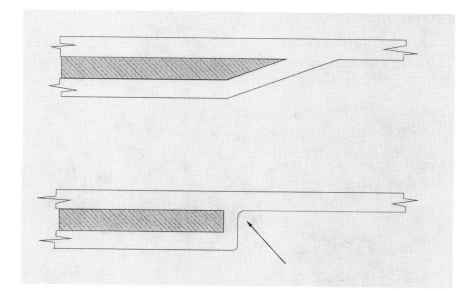

Fig.7-17. While it is necessary to core deck hatches to keep them from sagging, unless the core is properly designed, it will likely fail. Hatches are particularly prone to this problem. This illustration shows how and why cored hatches tend to crack due to the hard angle formed by the core. The edges of the core should be beveled as shown at top.

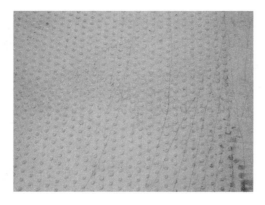

Fig.7-18. Numerous stress cracks in a deck or hatch cover are usually associated with a sagging or flexing problem. Check the underside if possible.

on the bottom of the hatch; if there isn't, give the ole bounce test and if it bends too much, you can expect problems in the future. Check the underside for signs of cracking. Excessive bending will eventually lead to cracking, water entry into the core and eventual demise of the hatch cover.

Pay particular attention to hatches in older boats. Check for delaminations and rot of the core. Look at the under side closely. Are there many spots of fungus showing? Fungus spots around a small hole usually indicate that the core is rotting. Often I find that the laminating on the under side of the hatch cover is very poorly done with only a single layer of roving fabric that has small holes in it. Do the hatches sit flush, or are they warped with one or more corners sticking up? Weak and damaged hatches can be repaired, but it's a time consuming process that gets expensive if you're paying a professional to do it.

Deck Problems With Express Cruisers

The express style boat includes the largest number of low-priced or entry level boats. This style really became popular in the 1980's and marks an era when we find the most structural problems. Recently I surveyed several mid and late 1980's mid size express boats where major deck problems were present, all of which resulted from poor design and improper attachment of hardware. As pointed out earlier, all decks require a core of some kind, and all kinds are subject to water damage resulting from improper hardware

Fig.7-19. This unsecured, unsealed hatch in a catamaran hull only 14" above the water line renders the boat unseaworthy.

Fig.7-20. Somebody wasn't thining. This deck scupper has no screen over it, causing it to clog with debris. In turn, this caused the deck to flood, the fuel filler to go underwater and the fuel tank became contaminated with water. Fuel contamination had been a long-term problem, the cause of which wasn't discovered for years.

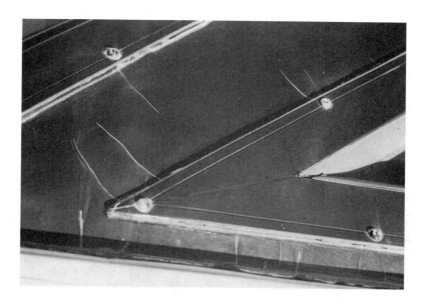

Fig.7-21. Painted black accents on a superstructure has long caused serious heat distortion problems, but builders still do it. Here, not only have severe cracks occurred but also actual buckling of the laminate (visible at bottom).

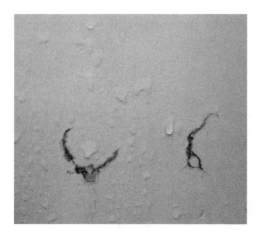

Fig.7-22. Improperly repaired fastener holes in cored structure. The dark gunk highlighting the cracks is fluid coming out of the core and signals potentially serious trouble.

attachments.

Many boats are found with a built-in recesses in the deck for sunbathing cushions. Although they may have large drain gutters, the main problem is that the cushion will trap and hold large amounts of water which often causes severe blistering.

These cushions have to be secured in some way lest they blow away, so what they do is foolishly screw dozens of snap fasteners into the deck. A few years later, many of these fasteners have pulled out of the deck, leaving open holes that funnel water into the core. And since most of these decks are not flat, but crowned, the water in the core does not remain on the high side, like under or around the cushions. No, gravity pulls that water to the lowest area. Thus, core degradation and interior leaks are likely to appear at points other than near the actual source of entry. In one case, the side deck core was completely rotted out all the way back to the cockpit, and the major part of the leaks were actually in the engine compartment! Imagine, a nice little sunbathing pad ends up destroying the value of a $250,000 boat in less than ten years.

Bow Pulpits

Prior to the 1980's bow pulpits were usually bolt-on teak affairs, after which time pulpits molded into the deck became the standard. Many of these earlier molded pulpits

Fig.7-23. This pulpit is seriously damaged as a result of being stuffed into a large wave. In this case, not only is it cracked, but the fasteners at the deck join have been pulled out. All cracks appearing around a pulpit should be taken seriously.

developed problems for more reasons that you'd care to hear about. Suffice to say, look at any pulpit for signs of cracking which is among the first indicators of trouble.

Pulpits become highly stressed when the bow is stuffed into a wave. This can lead to actual breakage, as well as lifting the deck from the hull. Any rub rail or deck join damage is likely to be part of a general pulpit problem. In addition, most pulpits have cores of solid wood for strength. Because of all the fasteners – a typical pulpit can have as many as three dozen fastener holes – core rot

Fig.7-24. The problem of anchor stowage is solved by the permanent pulput. Be sure sure the anchor will fit firmly and can drop without hitting the hull.

over time is common. A simple crack that looks like minor damage may actually be the result of weakness caused by a rotting core. The cost of rebuilding one is very high.

Windows & Frames

Windows have long been a trouble spot on boats and continue to be to this day. Some builders try to solve the problem by not making any opening windows, instead giving you a piece of plastic glued to the side of the boat. As it turns out, frameless windows can be a bigger problem than framed windows. First, you end up with no ventilation. Ah, you say, but the boat is air conditioned. Of course, there are never any problems with dock power, generators and air conditioners, right? It's a strange thing that on at least half the boats I survey, the air conditioning doesn't work.

Secondly, frameless windows don't solve leaking problems because plexiglass or Lexan heats up under the sun and then buckles, not only causing leaks, but a very peculiar appearance to the boat as well. Luhrs tried putting dark plexiglass frameless windows in their boats with almost laughable results, but not so funny for owners who ended up with windows that looked like washboards due to heat expansion of the plastic that was firmly fixed with glue.

Most boats have aluminum window frames which can be good or bad depending on the quality of the aluminum and anodizing. When it comes to aluminum, there is a very wide range of alloys, the vast majority of which are unsuitable for marine applications. Most "price" boats will have low grade aluminum that tends to corrode badly over time. Many are painted and the quality of painting varies with price. Again, many low price boats will have frames that are painted without even being properly primed – just painted right over bare aluminum. This is why we find so many boats with blistering, peeling paint on the window frames.

Once an aluminum window frame begins to corrode, there is little one can do about it as it cannot be properly repainted at a reasonable cost. To do it right, the frame has to be pulled out and stripped bare, followed application of the correct coating system. I don't think I've ever seen anyone do that, so if you're looking at a boat with corroded frames and you think you can solve that problem quickly and easily, think again. Just slapping some paint over it only makes the situation worse.

Replacing window frames is rarely an option. The reason is that builders do not stock these as replacement parts for boats out of production. Replacements will have to be custom fabricated.

Good quality frames easily last twenty years and longer. You can gauge the quality by the age of the boat and how far corrosion has progressed. If you're looking at an eight year old boat with very little corrosion, chances are these are quality frames. But when you're looking at a price boat only a few years old with considerable corrosion developing, you can be certain that in a few more years time those frames will be an unsightly mess.

Aluminum frames are as prone to corrosion and leakage on the inside as out, so be sure to check inside. Water stains on wood work and accumulations of salt crystals are an usual telltale of leakage problems.

The most obvious telltale sign that windows are leaking is that the exterior frames are smeared with caulking. Applying caulking to the outside of a window frame will not stop leaks. To be properly sealed, the frames must be pulled and bedded with sealant under the frame. If you see smeared caulking on the exterior, be sure to check the interior closely, behind all those curtains that are covering things up.

Many builders have lately gone to using frameless windows. In some cases these are just a hinged piece of glass set against the fiberglass house side. In others, the glass is fixed and bedded into the opening with a black glazing that relies primarily on suction to hold it in place. Very dark, tinted windows can heat up to very high temperatures in the sun causing expansion, buckling and loosening of the glass.

Heavy pounding can result in distortions of the cabin structure that can cause window glass to blow out. A number of such instances have been reported. Check frameless window glazing closely for cracks and gaps for reglazing this type can often be quite costly.

Port Holes

Port holes often have as many leakage problems as windows do, particularly on older boats. Gone are the days when port holes were cast bronze or solid stainless. Today, most are either plastic or stamped stainless. Plastic, of course, is a poor material to use for a component that should be strong. Breakage and distortions are what normally cause problems with these. Stamped stainless usually suffers from crevice corrosion because so few ports are properly bedded when they are installed.

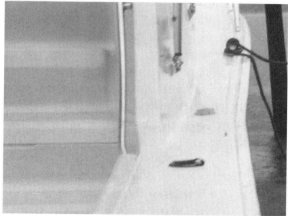

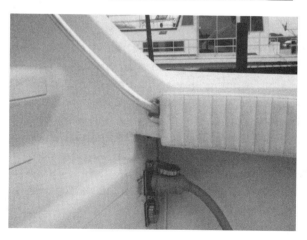

Fig.7-25, 7-26 & 7-27. Structural weakness and failure with a deck/house molding with a Luhrs 360. In the center photo it can clearly be seen that the side deck is sagging inboard, which causes water running off the foredeck into the cockpit. Bottom photo shows the degree of distortion. Discolored area around hand railing is a prior attempt to repair a large crack just ahead of the padding. This sagging occurred due to a lack of support that resulted in the whole staircase sagging and becoming full of stress cracks. This points up the fact that there may be more to stress cracking than meets the eye.

Port holes located in the bow area are often subject to considerable water pressure when the bow plows into a wave. If the port is not well made, it's going to leak and there's probably nothing you can do about that won't cost a small fortune. Check port holes for broken parts, leakage and water damage, bearing in mind that the cost of solving these problems, along with repairing any water damage is likely to be quite high. Rust stains around stainless steel ports usually indicates, not poor stainless, but water trapped under the metal.

Sagging Decks

This is a problem that was very prevalent in the past with older boats, mostly involving side decks that sag inward, commonly on boats with raised superstructures such as fly bridge sedans sport fishermen and motor yachts. Photos and illustration on previous and next pages illustrates how and why side decks can sag and the problems this causes.

The biggest problem with a sagging side deck is what it does to the structure immediately above the sagging deck. Normally there is a window frame at this point and the sagging deck pulls the window frame apart. Another problem it occasionally causes is with fuel filler plates and pipes working loose because the deck pulled away, thereby allowing water to drain on top of the fuel tank.

Checking for this is easy, simply sight along the side decks and make sure that they don't slope inward. Another clue is window frames that are all smeared with caulking or silicone sealer. Also look for signs of water puddling indicated by standing water stains and marks.

A similar and possibly related problem is the side deck that channels water into the cockpit. Side decks need to be designed so as to channel water away from the cockpit before it reaches this point, otherwise the entire watershed of the foredeck could be channeling massive amounts of water into the cockpit where it enters lockers and down through hatches because the volume is so large that ordinary gutters cannot carry it away fast enough. Look for a stop water and channel that takes the water overboard.

Whenever there is evidence of leaking windows, I usually do the hose test on them. At the same time I'll note any areas where water puddles excessively. I do this after the sea trial, pretending I'm being Mr. Helpful by washing the boat down. What I'm really doing is looking for leaks and drainage problems.

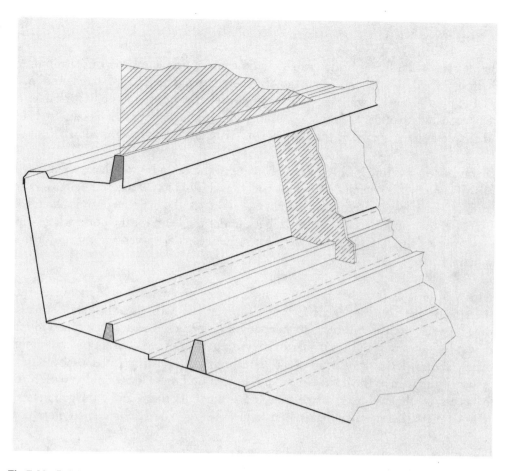

Fig.7-28. Builders often fail to provide adequate support for side decks. This cross section of a hull and deck reveals why this becomes a serious problem.

Interior Headliners

Headliners are attached to the under sides of decks; therefore leaky decks usually show up as damage to headliners. Water stains are the most common clue, but buckling, warping and wrinkling in fabrics and other materials can be another clue.

A number of late model boats are turning up with thin, molded fiberglass salon headliners. This is a nice idea for these are not easily damaged, and make for easy cleaning. I have found a few that have not been adequately supported, so that while underway, the overhead bounced, rattled and sometimes sagged. One can check by banging on it with a fist; if it flops around too much, imagine what it's going to do while at sea.

Flying Bridges

The design of the flying bridge can sometimes have problems, the most common of which is poor drainage. Poor drainage can cause damage by causing large amounts of water to puddle, overflowing hatch lips and flowing down through holes for cables and the like located up under the bridge coaming. This often happens when boats are hauled and shored at an angle other than the normal trim angle, usually bow-down.

For this reason it is imperative that any hatches to the cabin interior have what is called a raised *carlin* that is several inches above deck level. This acts as a coffer dam to prevent puddling water from entering the hatch. Conduits for the engine controls should also have coffer dams for the same reason. Check under the helm for the point where cables and so on pass through the bridge deck for some means of preventing this unfortunate happening.

Water puddling is usually made obvious and easy to identify by dark water stains appearing on the deck, under the forward coaming, and within seat lockers. Under-seat storage is very often a poor place to store anything because the designer failed to make the seat lockers water tight. Or that once water gets in, it won't drain out. Sometimes drainage holes down at deck level let water into the space, but it doesn't drain out because of the trim of the boat. On surveys I often find these lockers filled with rotting life jackets, cardboard boxes, rusted cans and all sorts of other water damaged materials and equipment. Later model boats tend to have better locker designs than older boats.

Older boats are also more likely to have wood used in bridge components than later models. Seat hatches, interior partitions, compartment decks and the like could all be

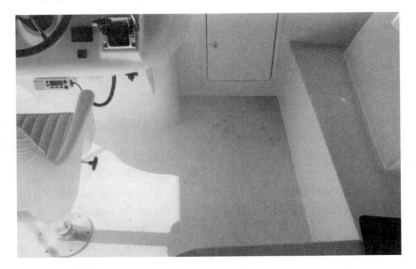

Fig.7-29. The designer of this boat completely forgot about drainage on the flying bridge which slopes forward and outboard. After a light rain, the water puddled three inches deep and had no place to go. Then, when the boat got underway, it all ran aft and cascaded into the cockpit.

plywood, and because the bridge area is so exposed, the potential for rotting plywood always need be considered. On larger boats, pay attention to seating and bar-like modules made of plastic laminate over plywood. These items need to be inspected from the inside as well as out.

Summary of potential problems on bridges:

- Poor drainage, under seating and within forward coaming.
- Storage compartments under seating that is not water tight
- Substandard upholstery
- Weak pedestal seating mounts
- Leaky hatches
- Insufficient space around helm seating
- Controls poorly positioned
- Lack of handholds
- Exposed instrumentation and other electrical apparatus.
- Unsupported plastic windscreens that are likely to be used as a hand-hold and broken off.
- Instrument panels that trap water. Many smaller size boats with racy styling often have helm panels that are more suited to a car than a boat. I've seen gauges set down in depressions that fill up with water.
- Radar arches that are poorly attached that may be wobbly and threaten the structures to which they are attached.
- Hardware on arches is often found to be attached without bedding, resulting in interior leaks and frequently electrical equipment damage such as lighting and wire connections.

Helm Stations Generally

The pilot station of a boat is referred to as the helm, a term in the days of sailing ships meant the steering wheel or tiller. Of course, ancient sailing ships didn't have instrument panels, but still today we call the entire pilot station "the helm." It is also technically correct to call it the "binnacle," which name is derived from the pedestal upon which the ship's compass was mounted.

The helm stations on far too many boats suffer from a lack of experienced design. Far too often it looks like these things were designed by an automotive designer or marketing committee with no regard for the fact that this is a boat, and all that electrical apparatus is exposed to weather and heavy salt water spray. Looking in the drawers of an older boat, more likely than not I'll find a drawer full of dead gauges and switches, all of which met their demise as a result of getting wet. I've yet to see a gauge that is water proof, but they all get mounted as though they were.

Fig.7-30. Cool styling looks great, but a little reflection will reveal that the windshield offers almost no protection from spray. Most of these electronics will be in the trash within a couple years, never mind what the panel will look like after being doused with saltwater numerous times. Would you really want a 13" wheel like this?

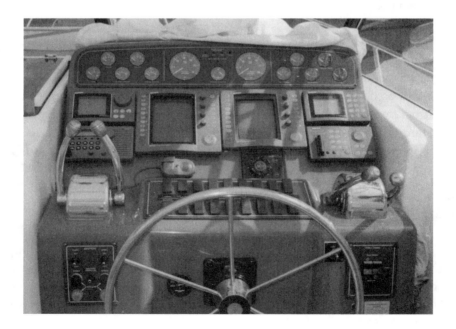

Fig.7-31. This superb design is based on the philosophy that function is more important than form, which is not to say that the two can't go together. A twin engine boat, the panel follows that theme with the engine instruments where it is no problem figuring which group belongs to which engine. Note that they are placed up high, in line of sight, with the navigation instruments between. Unlike an auto, it is important to monitor gauges on a boat. The 24" destroyer wheel greatly reduces steering stress.

Fig.7-32. To all appearances, this autopilot looks like it's water-proof, but when it stopped working I took it apart to see how it was constructed. I wasn't surprised when several ounces of water ran out. Then I checked manufacturer literature and found it makes no representations as to water-proofing.

A few boats will be found that have gauges mounted under some kind of plastic cover, but more often they are completely exposed. Condensation under the glass is usually the first sign of trouble and if it exists, they will soon fail. At the very least, an exterior helm station should have a water proof cover; otherwise expect problems either now or in the future.

Gauges that are horizontally mounted suffer the worst, for these create pockets of standing water that eventually works its way inside. Yet more or less vertically mounted gauges can do the same thing when water collects on the lower lip. Though panels may have fabric covers, often times I find that that water goes right through them. Originally Scotch Guarded, sunshine eats it away and the fabric does little more than strain the water. Even when dry, the patterns of dust and dirt, if any, under the cover will tell whether it is water proof or not, unless it has been recently cleaned. If dirt is going through it, so is water.

Costly electronics are often assumed to be water proof. But are they really? The high failure rate of electronics seems to indicate they are not. I have dismantled numerous pieces of electronics to see how they are put together. Believe me, all those numerical push button pads are not water proof, but have flimsy rubber seals that do no usually fit well. That includes all those great looking Raytheon electronics on which the gasket seals are visible. Again, owners usually assume that their fabric covers keep water out. It does when the fabric is new, but not after it's been baking in the sun for a few years. Therefore, it's wise that electronics not be mounted in locations where these things get wet.

I recently saw a very ingenious helm cover. It consisted of a clear plastic (such as eisenglass) sewn into a standard dacron or plasticized fabric in such a way that one can not only see all the gauges and switches, but work them as well without removing the cover. This is a superbly great idea for express and other boats where salt spray on the panel is a problem and I highly recommend that you have one made.

Take a look at the overall helm layout. There are designs wherein a large expanse of deck up under a windshield will channel water directly onto the helm. We see this sort of thing most often on racy looking entry level boats, but rarely ever on higher quality boats. The older Sea Ray 36 & 39 expresses are notorious for this, where badly leaking windshields channel water back into the helm panel and thence down through the electrical system and into the galley where it rots out a bulkhead, the cabin sole and wrecks the refrigerator, all before the owner ever figures out what is happening.

Windshield leakage problems cannot be prevented, but can easily be contained by creating a channel on the inside around the base of the windshield. Thus, any water leaks are safely channeled away. The later model the boat, the more likely this design is incorporated into the deck mold. The 1980's vintage Wellcrafts and Sea Rays, among others, were notorious for these leakage problems. If there isn't a channel, expect water to be streaming all over the deck and going to places where it will cause damage.

Another problem that appears fairly frequently are panels designed in such a way as that they have pockets that will trap water like the three-tiered panel shown in Fig.7-33 below below. People tend to assume that because a boat has a soft top, that the top is going to keep water out. Of course it doesn't and those pockets on the panel can fill up with water. Not only will this damage instruments, but the water will leak behind the

Fig.7-33

panel damaging electrical wiring and other apparatus. Be sure to check behind the panel for evidence of leaks and corrosion damage.

Helm panels, because they are either directly exposed, or exposed to sunlight and extreme heat up under windshields, are subject to severe UV damage. The best solution for this is an exterior windshield cover, and an separate panel cover. Granted, it is inconvenient to use them, but this is the price of boating. Use these or not, either way you pay. Lacking same, painted and stenciled aluminum panels, as well as plastic panels suffer greatly. These things never get replaced because the cost is so high, yet their degradation greatly detracts from resale value. The stenciled aluminum panels of the older Tiaras and Pursuits are particularly troublesome in this regard despite their overall outstanding helm designs. Gauges popped into holes cut in plain old fiberglass isn't nearly as fancy, but it's a whole lot more durable.

Chapter 8

Stress Cracks, Finishes and Surface Defects

Boat Finishes

Rather than being painted, nearly all FRP boats have a finish called a gel coat. A gel coat is simply a highly pigmented plastic resin that is first sprayed into the mold, after which fiberglass fabric wetted with plastic resin is laid directly on top of the gel coat. Thus the finish and the molded part become one. Many people ask why they don't paint boats instead of using gel coat which, as anyone with a little boating experience knows, is a rather poor finish.

The primary reason is that the gel coat ensures a proper mold release so a gel coat has to be used in any case. Without it, a hull or deck would probably end up permanently stuck to the mold. And for that reason, we are stuck with gel coat. Hatteras Yachts paints all their boats, but they don't make small boats anymore because no one can or wants to pay the price of that kind of quality.

Secondly, as we all know, paint finishes can chip. Gel coat can chip too, but not nearly as easily, and because it is bonded to the surface, it does not flake off like paint can. Gel coat is thick, and it will tolerate a lot of abuse, without scratches going through the surface to reveal the darker surface beneath. So while gel coat doesn't hold a shine well, it does have other advantages that painted surfaces do not have.

If you are familiar with boats at all, you are probably aware that gel coat does not hold that bright, shiny new finish for very long. The material is highly vulnerable to sunlight, despite the best efforts to create a gel coat that is durable. It will oxidize and become chalky. If you're also wondering why boats are almost always white, it is for the same reason why the finish on dark color cars, particularly dark blue or black, fade more rapidly than other colors. Basically, gel coats do what all plastics do in the sun: deteriorate, albeit at a much slower rate due to the high concentration of pigments. Thus, gel coat also serves to protect the structural substrate from U.V. damage.

When the gel coat does become chalky, that's because the plastic on the surface, after being bombarded by ultraviolet rays from the sun, has disappeared, leaving only the pigment. Fortunately, this is only the surface layer, and if one polishes it away, at least some of the original shine can be restored. How much is a function of the quality of the gel coat.

Many folks want boats with colors other than white, but experience over the years shows that colored gel coats are a mistake. They will fade and discolor very rapidly, and once it does, that finish cannot be restored. The boat will forever after have a faded, chalky finish that can only be remedied by painting with a costly urethane finish. So, as much as you might detest a white boat that looks like every other white boat, there is a very high price to be paid for color. Only if you plan to keep the boat in inside storage should you consider any other color.

Claims to UV Resistance

Numerous builders lay claim to using highly UV resistant gel coats that won't chalk and become dull. Over the last ten years, I haven't seen one that has lived up to that claim. Generally speaking, the quality of gel coat seems to be in proportion to the price of the boat. Higher priced boats usually seem to have more durable finishes.

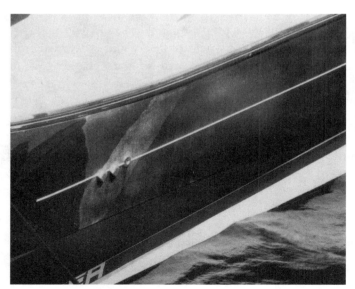

Fig.8-1. After only three years in the sun, this navy blue gel coat on a million dollar boat is a mess with four different levels of discoloration. The diagonal stripe of discoloration was a repair done by the builder that aged differently. The darker area at left was a more recent repair to the transom corner which points out the fact that dark colors can't be repaired. This boat is four year old.

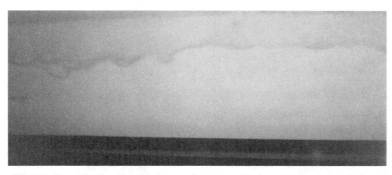

Fig.8-2. Discoloration like this is usually the result of an old repair that fades at a different rate.

Stress Cracks

Stress cracks are often upsetting to boat owners, particularly to owners of new boats. While that is understandable, in the majority of cases stress cracks are unsightly, they are also usually harmless. However, when they become too numerous and too large, they can also serve as indicators that all is not well. Stress cracks are a problem that has been with us from day one and every boater will encounter them sooner or later, so it's important that we have an understanding of them. This is particularly true when it comes to looking at used boats, which are likely to have at least a few of these pesky critters.

Because gel coat is a hard, fairly brittle material, it has little or no elasticity and is subject to cracking. Cracks can appear on the exterior surface of a boat for a variety of reasons. You probably know that painted wood cracks because the wood absorbs water and swells; then it dries out and shrinks. Thus, the foundation to which the paint is

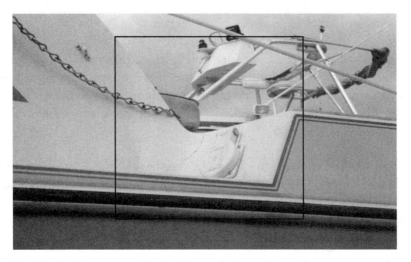

Fig.8-3. Hard corners combined with poor design and/or weak structures usually end with serious cracking as shown here. Discoloration of gel coat in such areas usually means failed attempts to repair the cracks.

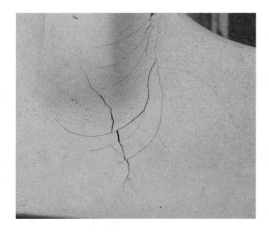

Fig.8-4. This type of cracking is the result of age and gel coat that is too thick.

Fig.8-5. This cracking is due to an improper repair using an unstable filler.

attached is changing shape, which is mostly what causes the cracking. The situation is much the same with gel coat, except the cause is usually the result of the laminate bending or receiving shock loads, since fiberglass does not absorb water and swell.

The cause of the cracking is closely related to the area where they appear. Stress cracking in gel coat may or may not indicate a serious underlying problem, so you need to know where they occur and why.

Gel coat cracks most often appear on the gunwale just above the guard rail, or in the toe rail, as a result of the stress caused by hitting up against dock pilings. How many and how severe they are is usually an indication of the weakness of the hull/deck joint. Better built boats can withstand more abuse, while lower quality boats won't hold up as well to this kind of use. The lack of stress cracks on an older boat is pretty good evidence of adequate design and strength.

Unlike a painted surface, gel coat is fairly thick, about 1/16" or 30 mils. A mill is one thousandth of an inch. And because it is brittle, it is not very tolerant of bending. In fact, the underlying fiberglass laminate can bend far more than gel coat without cracking. Thus, when fiberglass bends, the gel coat finish can crack *without meaning that the underlying laminate is also cracked or damaged.*

Stress cracks can also be related to shrinkage, shrinkage of the gel coat, or shrinkage of the underlying substrate. That's because gel coat and the fiberglass laminate to which it is attached is not the same material and may result in dimensional temperature changes . This is a fairly rare problem that has shown up on boats in the northeast and Canada where very cold temperatures occur.

Common stress cracking appears more frequently on boats built throughout the 1980's that utilized a plastic called dicyclopentadiene resin, or DCDP for short. One unfortunate

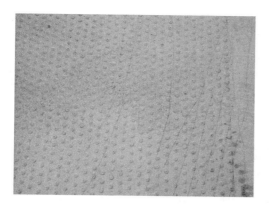

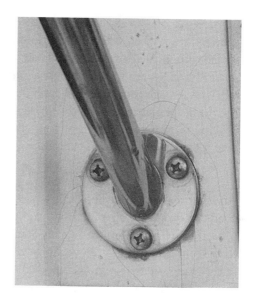

Fig.8-6. LEFT: The parallel cracks on this deck indicate a likely core problem.

Fig.8-7. RIGHT: The cracks around this stanchion are an indicator that the underlying structure is weak.

thing that happens when resin cures is that it shrinks a little. When that happens, the fabric pattern of the fiberglass may show through the surface, which is cosmetically unpleasant looking. A new resin was developed called DCPD doesn't shrink. Here's yet another example of a material rushed onto the market without testing. DCDP based gel coats turned out to be so hard and brittle that excessive stress cracking always occurred with its use.

How do we know if a boat is made with DCDP? We don't; there is no way to tell at all, although we can speculate that a boat which has an excessive number of stress cracks all over which appears unexplainable, may have been made with this resin. After around 1989, we don't find any boats made with DCDP at all; builders returned to the use of softer gel coats that fade faster.

Stress cracks frequently appear on decks and around cabin structures for no apparent reason. For example, cracks that appear on inside corners are usually the result of a corner that wasn't designed right. It is a principle of fiberglass construction that corners should have a fairly large radius, say about one inch. Cracking is apt to occur at any point where there is a sharp, 90 degree inside corner. If you go around and look at a number of used boats, the pattern of this cracking— that is, the locations in which it occurs— will rather quickly become obvious.

Very well designed and well made boats are capable of remaining free of stress cracking. The average boat is likely to have some small degree of cracking, while poorly made boats tend to have an excessive amount of cracking. How much cracking exists on a boat is a measure of the quality of construction. There are, however, other reasons why stress cracks can occur. Here are some tips and clues what to look for.

Most stress cracks appear as very fine lines. In new boats, or boats kept under cover, they can be very hard to see. The fineness of a crack generally indicates how much the surface is bending. The wider the crack, the more cause for concern there should be. On newer boats where there is an indication of many cracks that are hard to see, I simply wet a finger, rub it in some dirt, and then rub the dirt into the affected area. Or you can rub some pencil lead over the surface, and then smear it around with a wet finger. Obviously, this means dirty cracks show up much better than clean ones, so you can take it from here that old boats show cracks better than new ones because the cracks get dirty.

Another reason cracks appear is when the gel coat is either sprayed on too thick, or it is over-catalyzed, causing it to over cure and become excessively brittle. This is often indicated by cracks appearing on open spaces or flat surfaces, such as the middle of a deck. This occasionally shows up as crinkled or wavy surface, especially in corners. It is fairly common that textured, nonskid surfaces sometimes have a gel coat that is too thick and ends up with large numbers of random cracks for no apparent reason. The cracks will often appear in odd patterns. Gel coat should be about 30-40 mils thick, or slightly over 1/16" thick. When it's more than that, the finish will tend to crack in high stress areas.

Star burst patterned cracks appearing in decks, cracks that radiate out from a common center, typically indicate that there is a hard spot under the deck that causes the deck to dimple upward slightly. You can tap around and locate the hard spot just like locating a stud in a wall. When there is a hard spot, it will quite logically sound harder than the surrounding area. Sometimes star burst cracks are caused by dropping a heavy object on the deck like an anchor, although this is fairly rare.

Sets of closely spaced, parallel cracks anywhere indicate that a hinging or bending action is occurring, such as what you would find on the gunwale, toe rail or at the point where the deck meets the side liner of a cockpit. This is rarely a serious problem on decks, but is always cause for concern on the bottom of a hull.

Stress cracks often occur at the points where hardware is screwed to the deck. The cracking pattern usually radiates outward from the piece of hardware or fastener point. If there are a lot of cracks around hardware attachments, it's usually because the gel coat is too thick, or that the pilot hole for the screw was drilled too small. It does not usually indicate a structural weakness at this point.

One exception may be railings. Push against a stanchion and see if the deck to which it is attached moves. If the cracks radiate outward from the center, then such cracks are merely stress related. But, if the cracks are circular, this is an indication that the laminate is dimpling under the strain of hardware and may be an indicator of a more serious problem.

To summarize, surface cracking at these locations are cause for concern:

> Severe cracking around deck hatches
> Severe gunwale cracking without evident impact damage
> Unexplained large cracks in decks
> Circular cracks around railing stanchions.
> Around bow pulpits
> Hull sides and chines
> Bottoms

Common areas of cracking that are usually considered as "normal":

> Inside corners of cockpit liners
> Inside corners at base of trunk cabin or any raised extremity.
> Along gunwales at impact points
> Light cracks at hatch corners, though cracks may be moderately thick
> Radial cracking at hardware attachments

When evaluating gel coat cracks, keep in mind boats routinely go flying off of waves at high speed, that boats are subject to vibration and severe jarring and shaking. With that kind of stress, any boat is bound to develop at least a few cracks. The trick here is to learn to discern when a boat has more than what might be considered as "normal" amount of stress cracking and not end up with one that looks like a piece of crazed ceramic.

Repaired Areas

Cracks appear fairly commonly around repaired areas. This is usually the result of gel coat being applied over a polyester filler that is porous and water absorbant. After absorbing water, the material swell, causing the gel coat to crack, almost always in irregular patterns and never in regular patterns.

Fig.8-8, 8-9 & 8-10. Stress cracking on hull sides may be barely visible or pronounced but in this location almost always indicates a serious weakness, usually a structural design fault. The bottom two photos are leading up to a laminate failure.

Stress Cracks on Hull Bottoms

Anytime stress cracks appear on the bottom of a hull, the structural integrity of the hull should be considered as suspect until proven innocent. There should not be any cracks on the bottom or sides of a hull. The appearance of the cracks is telling you that something may be wrong.

Most often stress cracks indicate that the bottom laminate is flexing or "oil canning" between the frames. Longitudinal cracks, usually appearing in parallel rows, indicate that the panel is hinging off the stringers or a bottom strake.

Stress cracks that appear in a more or less circular pattern over a fairly large area indicate dimpling or oil canning. Such cracks are an indicator of probable serious trouble.

Fig.8-12. A circular cracking pattern indicates oil canning or panel deflection between structurals. Paint often flakes off around cracks.

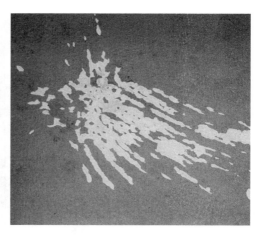

Fig.8-13. Severe cracking across a bottom strake such as this is an indicator of a serious problem that needs expert evaluation and immediate repair.

Fig.8-14. Starburst patters are indicative of hard spots. Here the paint has flaked away to clearly reveal the situation. The hard spot can be relieved before it causes any serious damage.

Cracks appearing transversely to the length of the hull are the most serious of all, indicating flexing off of a bulkhead or frame, and are the type most likely to result in a bottom failure, i.e. the bottom laminate actually beginning to fracture. Anytime you see pieces of gel coat flaking off around the cracks, the problem is particularly severe. If you find multiple cracks appearing across, or perpendicular to a bottom strake, as in figure above left, this may indicate a serious structural defect.

When there are single line cracks appearing in radius of a bottom strake (if the boat has any), you should have a professional evaluate the situation to determine if the cracking is serious or benign. Much depends on how the boat is built as to whether this type of

Fig.8-15. This degree of cracking is severe and is signaling an immanent catastrophic failure in progress. Note how the internal structurals are outlined by the cracks. In this case, the hull laminate was simply too thin.

Fig.8-16. Even on dirty bottoms, stress cracks can show up prominently.

cracking indicates a structural problem or not. When there are multiple cracks appearing in the radius of the strake, there is a likely structural defect. Star burst cracks usually indicate a hard spot caused by something on the interior. In most cases, the hard spot can be eliminated, but in any case the source of the condition should be corrected.

Gel Coat Voids

Gel coat voids often scare people, particularly when they are fairly large. The common size for voids is about 3/4". At one inch, that is fairly large. Fortunately, gel coat voids are actually pretty harmless and are easily repaired. Anything more than just a couple of them, however, is an indication of poor workmanship. Voids occur when there is an air bubble between the gel coat and the first layer of reinforcement. You'll recall that I described the lay up process as one of laying in sheets of fiberglass fabric wetted with resin, and then rolling out the entrapped air bubbles. Working on a lay up crew is about as pleasant as working a garbage collection crew, so it's not hard to understand why there are problems with workmanship. It's an ugly job.

Depending on the thickness of the gel coat, these voids may go on unnoticed for years. Then suddenly pressure is applied to exactly the point of the void and it breaks open, exposing the void that had long been hidden. Very often, voids begin to show up as crescent shaped, circular ot semi circular cracks. If you press on them with a sharp instrument, they will usually break open. Older boats will seem to have more voids than newer boats. It's not that old boats have more, but that more voids have broken and become exposed over time.

Aside from flawing the appearance, voids are relatively harmless and can easily be fixed without making a mess of things. Since so many people do make a mess trying to repair them, I will tell you how to do it right a little further on.

A Common Question

People often question whether stress cracks and voids are allowing water to enter the laminate and cause blisters. The answer is that, yes, these things are allowing water to enter the laminate, but there is no evidence that this causes blisters. Water enters the laminate through the gel coat anyway simply because it is naturally porous, but there's no evidence that either water entering gel coat voids or stress cracks is associated with blistering.

Laminates do absorb water, but it's important to understand how. Only an exceedingly low grade polyester plastic will absorb water. Laminates absorb water, not into the plastic itself, but along unsaturated glass fiber bundles via the capillary effect. It is "normal" that fiber bundles do not get 100% saturated. Any time there are unsaturated fibers near the surface (or in contact with porous gel coat) it is likely that some small amount of water will be absorbed. This does not cause swelling or any significant degree of degradation.

The lone exception is when wet seat cushions or deck carpeting keeps the laminate wet for a long time, then blisters can and usually will form. Taiwanese boats are the worst offenders.

Should Stress Cracks be Repaired?

My answer to that is no. First, most attempts to repair the cracks fail, with the cracks just reappearing again because the root cause of the problem was not corrected. If the problem is a weak or flexing laminate, the laminate would need to be strengthened, and of course this is not worth the cost to do so. Second, attempts to repair cracks usually end up creating an unsightly mess because restoring the original contours and the exact shade of finish is very difficult, not to mention costly.

It is possible to repair stress cracks with the proper materials and methods, but the main problem is with restoring the gel coat finish. Over time, the original finish fades and changes color, and to attempt to match the changed color is nearly impossible. Even repairs made early in the boat's life usually end up blotchy looking. Therefore, it is usually better to leave them be.

Damage Repair

When damage occurs, it is the unfortunate nature of all finishes that they are very difficult to repair without complete refinishing. You know about this through experience with auto body damage. A large scratch in a nearly new finish can be touched up more successfully, while one on an old, faded finish cannot. That's why when auto body damage is repaired, they will often paint the whole fender, but then the different coloration will stand out because the rest of the car is faded. We have the very same problem with boats, only it is a bit worse.

When it comes to scratches and abrasions, the repair can be worse than the damage. People who understand this usually opt not to attempt to repair scratches and dings, particularly if they cover a larger area. If the scratch does not penetrate into the laminate, it's often best just to leave it alone.

Gel Coat Crazing

Sometimes we find boats where the gel coat — usually on the bottom — is best described as "crazed" rather than merely stress cracked. What we're dealing with here are not normal stress cracks, but cracks appearing for a different reason than stress to certain points in the laminate. Crazing means an irregular cracking pattern which is usually the result of a defect in the application of the gel coat, or an unstable substrate. It can be

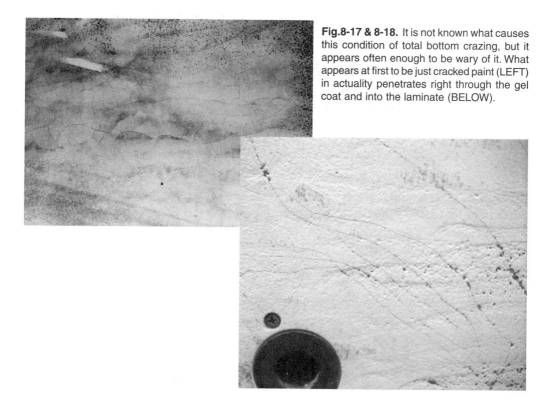

Fig.8-17 & 8-18. It is not known what causes this condition of total bottom crazing, but it appears often enough to be wary of it. What appears at first to be just cracked paint (LEFT) in actuality penetrates right through the gel coat and into the laminate (BELOW).

Fig.8-19. Deformations caused to laminate by painting hull side black, causing the texture of the underlying fabric to telegraph through to the surface. This is caused by shrinkage from high temperatures created by intense sunlight.

that the gel coat is either too thick, or that it was improperly handled or catalyzed; the cause is largely unknown. Fortunately, this condition appears very infrequently, and usually does not begin to appear until a boat is five years or older. In either case, there is probably nothing you can do about it except not to buy a used boat in that condition. Or be prepared to live with it. If a boat is plagued with this type of defect, it is best to walk away from it, not because of any potential danger but because of what the condition does to resale value.

Dark Colored Boats

Another reason why boats should not be made with dark colors, aside from the fading problem, is what happens when the dark finish absorbs heat from the sun. I've measured temperatures of black gel coat at close to 200°. Heating up, the plastic, which was once a liquid, will often continue to cure. And as it cures, it may continue to shrink. The end result may be that the lovely red or dark blue boat that had such a flawless finish on the day you bought it, a year or two later may end up suffering from post-cure shrinkage. What happens is that as the plastic continues to cure as a result of heat, it shrinks and begins to take on the coarse pattern of the reinforcing fiberglass cloth beneath the surface. An even worse condition is that when it shrinks so much that it cracks and begins to curl up.

Blistering and cracking is a common problem with very dark surfaces, such as black and navy blue that is often used for trim features. As a general rule, these colors should never be used because the sun can heat them up beyond the deformation point of the plastic. Boats with hulls painted these colors are often found with very large blisters on their hull sides which are the result of heat-induced ply separation.

In recent years high deformation temperature plastics have been developed with a few on the market. Though these are not widely used at this point, they may come into more widespread use in the future. If you're looking at a new boat with large black painted areas, you need to find out if high heat deformation temperature resin was used. For used boats, its age and existing U.V. damage will probably tell the story.

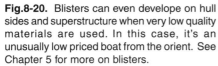

Fig.8-20. Blisters can even develope on hull sides and superstructure when very low quality materials are used. In this case, it's an unusually low priced boat from the orient. See Chapter 5 for more on blisters.

Blotchy, Discolored Finishes

As I mentioned at the beginning of this chapter, sometimes parts stick in the mold. When that happens, pieces of gel coat will tear off the part and remain stuck to the mold. This can happen for a variety of reasons, most often the result of a worn out mold. Molds are only good for making so many parts, after which they develop serious problems.

It is fairly common that parts get damaged during mold release. Because of the size and cost of the part, such as a hull or deck, damaged parts are not rejected and discarded, but repaired. The repair is fairly successful because the builder is using the same exact batch of gel coat to make the repair, and the finish isn't aged, so there isn't much of a color matching problem here. At least not initially. After the boat leaves the builder it's another matter entirely.

There is a problem with uneven aging and fading of the repaired part. After a period of a year or two, perhaps even longer, the repaired spots are going to start to show up as discolored areas. While there is no structural problem involved with this, it can be a bit unsightly and there is nothing you can do about it unless you want to paint the whole boat. Taiwan boats are notorious for this. Those of you who are interested in Taiwan trawlers will see a lot of this if you look closely. This sort of thing is far less prominent in U.S. built boats.

Gel coat repairs made by the builder can present problems with used boats from the stand point that this can look just like damage repairs years later. I've seen numerous Taiwan boats that have so many discolored spots on them that they look as if maybe they've been through a hurricane. If you can look at the area from the inside, this may tell you whether it's a gel coat problem or a damage repair. Uneven fairing or lumpiness, perhaps even grinder marks, are other indicators of damage repair.

Longevity of Finish

The highest quality gel coats that are most resistant to losing their luster and chalking are very expensive, and few builders, even of large yachts, use them. My review of numerous boat brochures shows that while many of them trumpet high quality gel coats for "long lasting finish," experience shows that few live up to this promise, and that they end up just as faded and chalky as all the others.

I get many questions from people asking what they can do to preserve the finish. It is, of course, easier to keep a finish up than to try to bring a faded one back. If the finish will not hold wax, and turns dull and chalky very quickly, then you have a poor quality finish that cannot be preserved. If it fades without heavy chalking (run your hand over it to see how much comes off), then frequent waxing and occasional compounding with a buffer will probably keep it up fairly well. There's really no way to tell except by experience.

What about some of these preparations being sold that offer miracle solutions? I have seen a few of these and the result was not exactly encouraging. At first, it can make the finish really shine, but when that miracle goo begins to fade itself, the result can be a finish that looks worse than ever, becoming streaked and blotchy. Then you can't get the stuff off easily without using a very abrasive compound or solvent. I haven't seen any that I'd recommend.

Repairing Chips and Dings

More often than not, minor chips and dings are better left alone, mainly for the same reasons I described about repairing stress cracks. The cure is often worse than the disease, just as it is with auto finishes. Unless you are skilled at this kind of thing, I would recommend that you either hire a professional to do it (minor chips and scrapes aren't all that expensive to repair) or just leave it alone.

What about chips or gouges that penetrate into the laminate? Won't water get into the laminate and cause damage? Usually not, but if the area is unsightly, it's a good idea to repair it. Deep gouges or chips that make a deep hole (also gel coat molding voids) should be filled with two part epoxy first, before applying the gel coat finish. Merely filling the void with gel coat will usually result in cracking and an unsightly appearance later on.

What about damage on the hull bottom? Won't that cause blisters by letting water in? In all my years of surveying, I have not seen blisters appearing around bottom scrapes, so my presumption is that breaches in gel coat will not cause blisters. Conversely, so called "barrier coating" will not prevent blisters by keeping water out. It is next to impossible to avoid breaches in the finish. It's like trying to keep your car tires clean. For trailer boats and dry stored boats, dinged up bottoms from handling are considered as normal wear and tear.

To fill a void or deep gouge, use a marine two-part epoxy. Do not use the kind for use around the home. You will probably have to buy a quantity 100 times more than you'll need. While you're at it, pick up a pint of acetone. Dig out all loose material in the area to be repaired, and make sure that it is completely dry. Use a flat plastic or rubbery applicator of the type commonly found in auto parts stores. If it's too big, use scissors or a knife and cut it down to the right size for the job. Before filling, apply masking tape to the borders of the area to be filled. Apply the mixed epoxy to the hole, pushing it down to make sure of good adhesion. They use the applicator to scrape away all excess material so that there is epoxy only in the cavity. Use the acetone and a rag to clean away all the excess on the surrounding surface. If you don't do this, you will end up with an ugly spot, so be sure to get it all off.

Now, you want the surface of the epoxy-filled hole to be slightly lower than the surrounding surface. The reason being that you are going to apply a thick layer of gel coat after the epoxy has cured. Use the corner of the applicator to remove the excess so that the fill is about 1/32" or so lower. You will have either purchased a standard white gel coat repair kit, or the builder supplied some with the boat. Following the instructions on how to catalyze it, you will pile the gel coat into the repaired area which still has a slight depression. You pile it on until it stands just slightly above the surrounding surface, because you are going to sand the excess off with nothing less than 300 grit paper, and finishing off with 600 grit. Be sure to use a very small sanding block if on a flat surface.

Finally, allow at least a week, preferably more, for the gel coat to completely cure. Then you can use some fiberglass compound and polish the sanded surface by hand. And that's it. On an older boat, the area where you sanded and polished is going to show a blotch for a while, but it will age back to the surrounding color, while the new gel coat you put in the hole will not.

Cleaning

Many people use abrasive boat cleaners or just plain scouring powder. You know what would happen if you used these materials on your car, so why would you use them on your boat? It's one thing to use abrasives on hard-to-remove dirt on nonskid deck surfaces, but you certainly don't want to use it on any other parts of the boat. Remember that any cleanser is going to remove the wax, if any. If simple brushing won't remove those dark water stains, try a little petroleum based detergent such as Fantastic or 409. If that doesn't do it, you'll have to use the abrasive such as Bon Ami, but remember that the abrasive is scratching the surface, which now will get dirtier, faster. Do not use petroleum based products, or products that contain bleach on large areas as these are very damaging to anodized aluminum, plastics and other material.

Should Old Boats be Painted?

A professionally applied linear urethane spray finish can make an old boat look darn near like new. It is, of course, expensive, but expense should be considered relative to the cost of a new boat.

Ninety percent of the cost of a paint job is in the preparation. The only way to get professional results is by using a professional who knows what he's doing. The preparation and use of this costly coating is not for amateur use. While expensive — usually figured at around $125 per foot — having a boat painted is a very viable option in buying an older boat and making it look new, especially if you are capable of doing much of the prep work yourself.

Many people consider the cost and decide that it is too expensive. If you are in the market for an older boat, consider including the cost of painting in the financing. Tell your lender what it is that you intend to do, and that you want to work out an arrangement to finance the boat and have it painted with the financing. Painting substantially increases the value of the boat and some lenders will be open to this option, particularly the ones that specialize in boat loans.

Maintaining the Finish

Gel coat oxidizes rapidly because it has a very high ratio of pigments to plastic. Restoring the dulled finish is mostly a matter of removing the surface oxidation, but also a matter of burnishing the plastic, which is where the shine comes from. Therefore, just hand waxing a faded, chalky finish rarely produces the desired results.

To fully restore the finish, you need to perform a two-part process, compounding and waxing. And for this a serious buffing machine is the right tool to use. Please note that the inexpensive ones made for cars isn't going to fit the bill very well, for these are not designed to work in all the nooks and crannies of a boat, nor do they operate at high enough speeds. A light duty angle grinder with buffing pads is the most versatile.

Depending on the degree of oxidation, use a light to medium grit buffing compound. It does not matter if it is specially formulated for fiberglass, but it does matter what color the compound is. DO NOT use anything but WHITE as colored compound will discolor the gel coat.

When compounding, you must be very careful not to burn the finish by pushing too hard, or leaving the buffer in one place too long. Get a feel for the right amount of pressure by working on a few test spots, buffing first, then applying a coat of wax to see how it looks. The trick here is to avoid a blotchy looking finish as the result of over and under buffing from area to area. This will be less of a problem on the top sides than on the hull sides where you want to use a smooth, sweeping movement of the machine to achieve a consistent degree of luster.

Work on a test area about 4 - 5 feet long. Buff it out, then apply the wax. If it looks blotchy or you see too much swirling pattern, go over it again, this time more lightly, until it looks right. Use a very light pressure on the machine to minimize swirls, and move it quickly and evenly across the surface. Eventually you'll get the feel for how much pressure to apply, and how long to buff. When working with the machine, be very careful to not work with the edges of the pad. You want to tilt the machine about 2 degrees so that the pad is contacting the hull at a point about midway between the center and edge of the pad. If you hold it perfectly flat, you're going to end up with a pronounced swirling pattern and the buffer will bounce around.

On the hull sides, work from top to bottom, side to side, in long rows, as if you were working on a series of rectangles. Because gel coat is so very porous, generally two coats of wax are needed.

If there are stains that won't come out, you can try dabbing on a little chlorine or oxygen bleach. This may or may not work depending on the nature of the stain. Bleach will not work for grease or oil stains. For the bleach to work, you must wash off all polishing compound and oil. It's best to apply the bleach to the stain before compounding. For rust stains, try a rust stain remover, but be sure to use both these products very judiciously, a little bit at a time. It's best to try a test spot in and out of the way location, just in case things go wrong.

Chapter 9

Power Options

In this power options section, we take a look at not only engine types such as gas and diesel, but also the various types of drive systems. In this chapter you will find gas and diesel engine issues discussed concurrently. The reason for this is to provide a simpler means of comparison between the two types. For many buyers, the choice of gas versus diesel simply boils down to a matter of price: A diesel engine with the comparable horsepower of a gas engine is about three times the cost of a gas engine.

Note: In this chapter I use American measures, cubic inches rather than liters, because most of us have a better feel for the system we are most familiar with, and to maintain consistency. Not many people can judge the difference between a seven and eight litre engine because the numbers are so small. One litre equals about 61 cubic inches.

So why are diesels so much more expensive just because they burn a slightly different type of fuel? The main reason is due to higher internal pressures and stresses, followed by a more complex fuel system. Gas engines are pretty simple engines and do not require the very high tolerances that a diesel does. For example, combustion chamber pressures in a gas engine normally run around 150 psi while in the diesel they are 500 psi. Gas engines also have fewer moving parts and the fuel systems are far cheaper.

Because of these high internal pressures, diesels develop more internal heat, heat that has to be removed by means of extra cooling devices. Still another is that in order to achieve the kinds of horsepower that people want, diesels have to be turbo charged.

Turbo charging uses the high flow of exhaust gasses to power a turbine that, in turn, is used to force air into the cylinders to improve aspiration. Exhaust gasses, of course, are hot, so the air has to be cooled by means of what is called an intercooler. This, alone, adds considerable cost to the engine.

There are still more factors that drive up costs, such as requiring a stronger drive train, meaning that things like propeller shafts and struts have to be bigger and stronger, and transmissions as well; engine foundations also have to be stronger with larger engine mounts.

Diesel Myths

Over the years a lot of myths have developed about the virtues of diesel engines. The most persistent of these is that diesel engines will run for many thousands of hours without requiring major servicing. This is certainly true of engines in commercial and industrial operation, but it has not proved true in pleasure craft usage. But, then, commercial and pleasure craft engines are not the same thing; since commercial engines are not high performance engines but designed for commercial duty. The comparison therefore creates an erroneous concept.

The virtue of the diesel engine was once the fact that it burned a much lower cost fuel, and a lot less of it. All you have to do is look at the pump prices at your local fuel dock, and talk to a few boat owners to find out that this is no longer true. But there is more to it than the type and cost of fuel.

The reason why most modern diesel engines are not significantly more economical to own and operate over gas engines can be explained by two words: *high performance*. The real virtue of the diesel engine comes about as the result of turning at lower RPM's and putting out considerably higher torque with less horsepower and a bit less fuel than comparably sized gas engines. However, with high performance diesels most of its virtues are canceled out by souping them up to run very fast. They're not stingy on fuel consumption anymore, but often ram in as much or more fuel than gas engines.

We find that the engines used in commercial applications, such as trucks, ships and power generating plant achieve those thousands of hours of operating time between overhauls due to the following factors:

  Slower turning, usually 2000 RPM and less
  Continuous operation
  Operating at more constant loads
  Operating at constant speeds
  Lower horse powers
  Rigid and professional maintenance schedules

To make a very long story short, we can't have our cake and eat it, too, when we expect to have high performance, low operating cost and long engine life. When we use the horse power-to-displacement ratio as a bench mark, engine hours along with age in years, we can get a much better idea of what to expect from a particular engine.

The most successful diesel engine ever built was the Detroit Diesel 6-71, six cylinder engine. This is a two-cycle diesel that operates similar to an outboard engine. Two cycle engines have been wiped out of our lexicon by our good friends at the EPA, so I'll not discuss their virtues or evils beyond stating that two-cycle engines are capable of developing more power at lower RPM's. Just a useful tidbit in case you're comparing the power ratings of two to four-cycle diesels. That's why, for around fifty years, Detroit Diesel was the engine of choice for power boats. Alas, no more.

First introduced in the mid 1930's, it was produced for over fifty years and there were hundreds of thousands of them in operation for many decades, and still are. Therefore, it's the one engine that more people know most about. This engine was known to achieve operating life spans up to around 8,000 hours between overhauls and have a service life of decades. There is one caveat, however: The original engine was produced at 165 horse power.

One of the best ways to estimate engine service life is by means of the displacement to horsepower ratio. That is determined by dividing the the horsepower by displacement in cubic inches. The 6-71 engine has a displacement of 426 cubic inches; at 165 hp, it has a displacement ratio of 0.38. This same engine was later souped up to powers up to 485 hp. At which point the engine's service life sunk to as low as 600 hours between overhauls. At 485 hp it has a ratio of 1.138:1.

My view is that ratios greater than 1:1 indicate an engine that has been souped up too much, and is very likely to suffer reduced service life. This formula was derived from 35 years worth of personal observation of how many hours various engines lasted between overhauls.

We can make this comparison for virtually any diesel engine and use it as a yard stick by which to measure potential engine longevity. For the simple fact is that one can squeeze only so much power from a basic engine block before this reaches the point of causing excessive internal heat and therefore rapid engine wear.

> **SideBar** What happens when the 1:1 displacement/hp ratio is exceeded. In order to get more power out of an engine, it needs to burn more fuel. Burning more fuel produces more heat. To take an existing engine and souping it up to burn more fuel, the service life will be dramatically decreased unless the additional heat created can be removed. Problems arise when the design of the engine cooling passages will not permit increased cooling, no matter how much the heat transfer rate is altered, say by increasing cooler size or coolant flow rates.

A well designed engine block is capable of maintaining fairly even casting temperatures. But when the power rating is jacked up by increasing the fuel burn, the ability of the internal cooling system to dissipate that heat can become compromised and the block is likely to develop hot spots, areas where the cooling system as originally designed cannot be adequately cooled. The end result will be heat distortion of the casting. A common problem with souped up diesels are cylinders going out of round due to heat distortion. The amount of distortion can be very substantial so that this can cause severe and very rapid wear on moving parts. This is what causes premature wear and failures in most high performance diesel engines. I've seen cylinder wall distortions in high performance engines as much as 1/16" or 2 mm.

Over the years, I have had the opportunity to evaluate hundreds of marine diesels, the result of which I have concluded that power ratios over 1:1 are likely to result in unacceptably rapid engine wear and low service life between overhauls. This assumes, of course, that there are not any major flaws in the engine design or marinization, which is a separate issue.

Of course, pleasure craft operation is vastly different than commercial operation. In pleasure craft, diesels are usually operated infrequently, and for relatively short periods of time. Note here that in terms of overall years, commercially used engines may not last longer. A commercial application may achieve 5,000 hours in only three years and becomes worn out, whereas the pleasure craft engine barely gets 500 hours, but in six years needs an overhaul at 1,000 hours.

The reason for this is usually the result of internal corrosion and other problems caused by too infrequent use and often poor maintenance. The bottom line is that the more an engine is used, the more operating hours one will get from it. All things being equal, the costs are the same, but the service life between overhauls will be longer in terms of operating hours, but not necessarily in terms of years.

Therefore, the practice of evaluating engine longevity in terms of engine hours alone is not a good one, for this omits many important considerations. It neglects the fact that the more you use the engine, the more one will get from it. Our problem is that pleasure craft are usually used insufficiently to be able to make good use of the engine hours yardstick. That's why I recommend using the horsepower to displacement ratio as a better means of estimating service life.

For example, let's say a ten year old engine with 1700 hours has a ratio of 1:1. Its horsepower is on the high side, but the 1700 hours indicates average or slightly above use. All other factors being satisfactory, one should not accept this engine with total confidence that it's going to continue running without a cash infusion in the near future because it does not fit the profile for probable long life.

Another example: A twelve year old engine with 1800 hours and a ratio of 0.85:1. With a much lower power ratio, it becomes much more reasonable to expect that this engine will have a longer service life, assuming that it shows evidence of good care because it does fit the profile.

Yet another reason why modern, high performance diesels aren't as trouble free as the myth suggests has to do with engine weight. Back in 1960, road vehicle weight wasn't as important as it is today for government mandated fuel economy reasons. Therefore, diesel engines back in those days were heavier, often a lot heavier. By way of example, consider that the Detroit Diesel 6-71 engine at 426 c.i. weighed in at about 3,000 lbs. The comparably sized Cat 3126 (442 cubic inches), yet higher horse power engine, is only half the weight, 3000 lbs. vs. 1592 lbs. The Cummins 5.9 L engine comes in at only a third, 1100 lbs.

What this means is that the basic engine blocks in more modern engines are substantially lighter, and having less cast iron means that the blocks are weaker and do not stand up to stresses as well as their predecessors. While lighter weight makes for higher boat speeds, it also means that the penalty is reduced engine life. To get these engines to perform reasonably well, it is necessary to take greater care with more frequent maintenance, particularly the cooling systems.

Gas Versus Diesel

Many boat buyers agonize over the decision whether to they should go with diesel over gas power, finding it a difficult choice. The difficulty is almost always one of how to justify the much higher cost of diesel engines. The arithmetic of quantifying this economically is not difficult. On the other hand, if one just simply wants diesel power for the sake of having diesel power, and for a few other reasons, then the decision is simple and need not to be justified by any other basis other than cost. If you can afford diesels, great. If not, there's no reason to fear gas engines.

Beware that the cost of diesel ownership can be substantially higher over gas engines, particularly when buying used. Here's where you need to apply the hp/displacement ratios when making a decision.

A typical situation looks like this: A buyer is considering a number of eight to ten year old boats, several with gas power and several with diesel, each with different engines of differing horsepower. At this age, engine hours will tell us precious little about the condition of the engines, though for gas engines, one can assume that they're on their way out. Of course, we could get comprehensive engine surveys on all these boats, but the cost and time factor of doing that will be high. What we want to know is how to make a good decision to start with, thereby avoiding wasting time and money.

The first thing to do is to take a look at your budget for ownership costs. No matter how diligent we are, it's always possible to encounter a streak of just plain bad luck in the form of an engine that goes BANG! for no reason that could be anticipated. Even the smallest diesel engine is going to cost around $20,000 and the mid-size engines on up to around $35,000 to replace. Assuming that there is no warranty and that insurance will not cover whatever happened to it, the question to ask is whether you could afford this sudden and unpredictable expense. Most likely, you wouldn't want to have to take out a second mortgage on the house to cover it.

Now, let's take a look at the replacement cost of gas engines. Replacement cost for a 350 block engine as of this writing is about $8500, a 454 engine about $9,500. That's a complete engine with all the components. Or, let's say your engine threw a rod or swallowed a valve; the block has to be replaced but all the old components are still useable. The overhaul cost in this instance is likely to be under $6,500 for a 454 engine and even less for the 350. Most boat owners could put those kinds of expenses on their credit card, without having to mortgage the house or dip into the kid's college fund.

Here you were probably thinking that the reason you wanted diesel was to save money over those outrageous gasoline prices at nearly two bucks a gallon, so let's take a look at that reasoning.

The average boat owner in a long season climate (but not 12 month) puts about 150 hours per year on his engines. A pair of medium horse power gas engines will burn around 32 gph at cruise speed, but chances are he'll spend more time idling than cruising, so we'll reduce that by about a third to 22 gph. 22 gph X 150 hours = 3300 gallons. At $1.80/gallon he'll spend $5,940 on gas.

By comparison, a similar sized pair of diesels are going to burn say around 26 gph at cruise for an estimated total fuel burn of 18 gph over 150 hours for a total of 2700 gallons (adjusting for idling time), so that with diesel generally priced at a dime less than gas ($1.70), he'll be shelling out $4,590 per year for fuel.
That is a significant savings of nearly $1500 for fuel. Now, for his diesel powered boat, he's going to spend at least $30,000 and probably more for diesel over gas engines on the price of the boat. If we amortize the fuel cost savings over the increased cost of the engines, it's going to take fifteen years to amortize the additional costs. And we haven't begun to consider the much higher costs of maintaining diesel engines.

Thus the myth that diesels are more economical than gas engines falls apart when examined closely. The reason, of course, is that high performance diesels are actually much more costly than their gas counter parts. It is certainly true that 150 HP diesels pushing a trawler yacht at eight or nine knots will get great fuel economy and long life. Yet boaters have continued to equate the benefits of these applications to high performance engines in high speed boats.

To summarize, the following are some of the recommended criteria for choosing diesel power when vessel size supports either option:

> Vessel weight in excess of 17,000 lbs.
> Particularly deep vee/ high drag hull
> Fuel range is a major issue.
> More long distance running than short hauls
> Above average annual operating hours
> Estimated maintenance costs are within budget.
> Fuel economy is more important than speed.
> Won't be harmed financially by uninsured catastrophic engine damage.

Choose gas when:

> You're stretching your budget to buy a boat.
> Can't afford uninsured catastrophic engine damage.
> Boat weight 17,000 lbs. or less
> Boat used seldom or infrequently, less than 150 hours annually
> Operating periods are short and infrequent.
> Cruising distances are short, with much idling or low speed operation.

The Safety Issue

But, you say – or they say, "diesel engines are a lot safer than gas engines. Gasoline is dangerous and can explode." True, it certainly can do that, but how often does it? Back as far as the 1960's, boat explosions were fairly common but since that time, improvements in systems standards has reduced the risk of gasoline explosions to far less than the risk we experience on the roadways every day.

Gasoline explosions in boats are quite rare these days, yet they are also very spectacular and almost always make the evening news when they do happen, a fact that gives us a skewed perception of the true risk. Conversely, the numbers of fires caused by faulty exhaust systems on diesel boats about negates any truth that diesel boats are safer than gas boats. That's particularly true in light of the fact that gas boats outnumber diesel by at least a 10:1 margin.

Gas Engine Longevity

I will start here by saying that I do not recommend salt water cooled gas engines, most especially in used boats. Make note here that salt water cooled engines make for a much more difficult time of resale and will disproportionately affect the resale value. Using outside water is fine for cooling engines so long as it is not salty or full of silt, as in some rivers. Sea water cooled engines typically have a service life of about six to eight years and 800 hours. After that, the castings are so corroded that they shouldn't or can't be rebuilt.

Closed cooling system gas engines, with good care, are known to last as long as 20 years and generally up to 2,000 hours with great care, though that certainly isn't the norm, which would be closer to 10-12 years and ten to twelve hundred hours. They are, of course, rebuildable at any point because there is no sea water going through the block.

Sea water cooled engines are generally okay for dry stored boats with flush out systems that are *used.* The problem arises at resale time since sea water cooled engines are a lot less desirable and the buyer is likely to doubt that the engines have been flushed after every use because there is no way of knowing short of taking the engine apart. They are also okay in fresh water environments so long as you intend to resell in the same environment. The owner who brings his raw water cooled engines to Florida and tries to sell will have a more difficult time of it.

Diesel Maintenance Issues

No one would want to fly with an airline that operates by the *if it aint broke, don't fix it* rule. Unfortunately, that is the philosophy by which most boat owners operate. The reason, of course, is because most of us can't truly afford to own what we own. If we could afford to perform preventative maintenance the way the manuals recommend, we'd do so.

Diesel engines are significantly more costly to maintain for several reasons. Because of the higher internal operating temperatures and pressures, cooling and oiling systems maintenance is far more critical than for gas engines, and there is much more of it to keep up. Diesel engines have the following cooling systems: Heat exchanger, oil cooler, fuel cooler and intercooler (turbo air) and usually a transmission oil cooler, all of which are larger and more costly items than those found on gas engines. That's two more coolers than the typical gas engine. The more power the engine turns out, the bigger these coolers (and pumps) need to be in order to dissipate the heat generated.

Cleaning of the heat exchangers and intercoolers is needed every two years at an absolute minimum, though few boat owners ever clean them at all until an overheat condition develops. Unlike gas engines, diesels are intolerant of overheat conditions and will succumb to severe internal damage.

Dirty intercoolers are one of the most common causes of overheats. That's because as the cooling vanes get dirty, they stop cooling. And when the turbo is feeding, hot, uncooled air into the engine, this results in a great loss of power and incomplete fuel burn. What is also happening is that the engine is running on the very edge of an overheat condition, so that just about any other minor problem in the cooling system is going to cause alarm bells to ring. Most often, after dozens of hours searching for the

Fig.9-1. A diesel engine heat exchanger core or tube bundle. Salt water flows through these small tubes to cool the closed coolant side of the system. Tubes can get fouled with debris or suffer a build up of calcium, causing a loss in cooling ability that results in overheating. Cooling cores on diesels need to be pulled and cleaned on a regular basis that depends on the type and quality of water the boat is floating in.

source of the problem, a dirty intercooler is one of the last things to be considered.

Because diesel engines consume huge volumes of air, they are almost always fitted with air filters these days, not so much because we're worried about dust out on the blue, but salt mist that is extremely damaging to marine engines. If you've ever looked down the beach at the ocean when the surf is up, you've noticed a cloud of white mist near the horizon. That is salt mist; it can't even be seen up close, but it is there and your engine is breathing it. What comes in through the engine room vents is even more concentrated than that. More and more builders of diesel boats are adding filters to the engine room intakes, and not just relying on the engine filters. That's a good thing, because huge amounts of salt spray can enter through the vents.

Turbo chargers are the Achilles heel of the marine diesel, proving to be the most frequently overhauled and replaced piece of equipment. That is because they get so hot, are subject to severe vibration, and is the last item in the lubricating oil scheme, so they are lubed with the hottest oil. Thus, turbo bearings most commonly fail.

Fuel and oiling systems also require more vigilant maintenance. Diesel fuel systems, unlike gas engines, are totally intolerant of any kind of fuel contamination. The systems require filters that separate out the inevitable water contamination, as well as bacteria growth that routinely occurs in fuel tanks, especially when water is present. Moreover, bacterial blooms in fuel tanks are difficult to eradicate and frequently require fuel reprocessing by means of specialized service equipment.

Bacterial blooms in fuel tanks is caused by the presence of water. Fuel oil is an organic liquid that, surprisingly, a lot of bacteria and fungi like to feed on. When you find the sight bowls of fuel filters to be full of crud (be sure to look at them), this is usually an indication that there is a problem with water in the fuel tank. Water not only causes bacteria blooms, but can also cause corrosion in the bottoms of aluminum tanks.

Removing the water can only be accomplished by services that have specially fitted out trucks (or perhaps a water borne service) with recycling equipment. The fuel from the boat tanks is completely flushed, filtered and placed back into the boat's tanks free of water and bacteria. Such services are usually only available in major boating centers and the cost is reasonable.

Diesel Operating Issues

Not long ago I was on a sea trial with the boat owner on board. He became very upset when I tried to run the engines at full throttle for ten minutes, as is my usual procedure. He mistakenly felt that this was damaging to the engines. It's not, but it's also not a good idea to run high performance engines full throttle for hours on end, either.

Diesels operate best in the range of 80-90 percent of full RPM. One of the worst long period operating speeds for turbo charged diesels is in the idle speed range, or the range before turbo boost kicks in. The problem here is an issue of carbon build up that occurs at low speed, particularly carbon building up in piston ring grooves that causes rings to stick, or even hot spots on piston heads that melt the aluminum pistons. Avoiding prolonged idling completely avoids this problem.

So what does prolonged idling mean? Carbon build up begins at about one hour of idling. The fact is that most boat engines are faced with fairly long periods of idling and it is not a problem so long as that is followed by an equal period of high speed running which will burn most of the carbon off. Severe build up occurs when those periods of idling are not followed by high speed operation, but yet more periods of slow running. When this pattern occurs repeatedly over a long time is when serious carbon problems occur.

Engines with carbon stuck rings have low compression and incomplete fuel burn resulting in very smoky exhaust. The condition is discoverable by borescoping a cylinder through an injector port. A borescope is a fiber optic device that will permit a limited range of vision internally. The device is expensive, so the cost of the service will also be, but not unreasonably so.

Concerning fuel consumption rates, diesel engines are unlike gas engines in that they will burn a fixed rate of fuel at any given speed regardless of engine load. That's because the fuel delivery system is mechanically driven so that the amount of fuel delivered is entirely dependent on engine speed. This is unlike the gas engine which relies on manifold vacuum to the carburetor to draw fuel into the cylinders wherein the higher the load, the higher the vacuum and therefore fuel consumption. For this reason, reliable fuel consumption tables are available for diesels but not gas engines.

Diesels are far less tolerant than gas engines of infrequent operation and there are two reasons for this. First is the development of acids in the lubricating oil that occurs as the natural result of water condensing within the engine due to temperature changes from night to day. These acids attack internal engine parts, more so than water itself. Second is atmospheric corrosion that occurs due to gravity pulling oil off of cylinder walls during even moderate periods of disuse. Because some cylinders will be open to the exhaust pipes which are full of water, cylinders will actually rust in just a few weeks. That's why it's recommended that engines be run at a minimum of at least once per week (1) to lubricate the engine, and (2) to evaporate any water that has accumulated internally.

Diesels also don't tolerate being overloaded very well. This most often occurs as a result of improper propellering, causing the engine to run below its designed full speed. This tends to cause incomplete fuel burn with subsequent carbon build up that is death to high speed diesels.

Who Really Needs Diesels?

From the foregoing discussion, candidates who should NOT own diesels should begin to become obvious: those who do prolonged idling and those who will use their boats less frequently. Clearly, boat owners who will use their boats more than the average will most benefit. The more you use them, the more you get from diesel engines. The truth is that marine diesels rarely ever wear out. The demise of most is due to neglect and disuse that results in corrosion.

The issue of prolonged idling does not generally apply to sport fishermen who do a lot of idling, the reason being that long periods of idling are usually followed by a long, high speed return to port which burns off the accumulated carbon before it accumulates too much. As waterways become increasingly speed restricted, this is a growing problem for many areas.

Boat Size and Weight

People often ask why we don't have convenient charts that we can refer to, that will tell us how much horse power is needed to drive a boat at certain speeds. Well, such tables do exist, but are not widely used or available because of numerous factors that render non expert use of such charts unreliable. Our problem is the very nature of that beast we call the rated horse power. Not all horse power ratings are cut from the same cloth, especially for gas engines, because manufacturers tend to be more optimistic in their advertising than they should. It's not that manufacturer ratings are false, but rather that nearly all ratings are derived from the top end of the engine speed curve. In other words, the power rating is at full, or nearly full RPM.

If we're smart, we don't run our boats at full speed for very long, thus, the useable horsepower is always going to be something less than what we are paying for. But there's another, even more important fact when considering gas –vs- diesel. Which is that cubic inch for cubic inch of engine displacement, diesel engines develop more useable power than gas engines do. That is true even when the horsepower rating of the gas engine is greater than the diesel, and the reason is this:

The horsepower rating tells only part of the engine power story. There are several other types of power ratings than can be, but are not normally used. One of these is torque, which is defined as the amount of foot-pounds of power delivered through a rotating shaft. Higher torque engines can turn a larger or higher pitched propeller than one with lower torque, thus yielding more power at lower speed.

Diesel engines deliver more torque and more horsepower at lower speeds for several reasons: (1) their greater mass develops greater kinetic energy deliverable to the shaft, and (2) the greater internal combustion pressures also deliver more power to the piston.

Examples: The Cat 3126 engine develops 350 hp at 2800 RPM yet delivers 349 hp at 2400 RPM, a difference of 1 hp over 400 RPM. A comparable gas engine delivers 350 hp at 5200 RPM but only 270 hp at a cruise speed of 3400 RPM. Thus while the diesel has no appreciable power loss between full and cruise speeds, the gas engine has only 77% of rated power at a normal cruise speed.

The end result is that diesels deliver greater power at slower speeds without an increased fuel burn. This makes the diesel engine particularly good for boats of a weight that is a bit too much for lower torque gas engines. Generally speaking, big block gas engines are capable of powering boats up to about 18,000 lbs. However, that statement is totally dependent on factors of hull shape. There are many 18,000 lb. boats with inefficient hulls that gas engines will not power satisfactorily. Conversely there are some 20,000 lb. boats with rather flat bottoms that do fine with gas power. It would certainly be nice if we could draw a hard and fast rule, but we cannot, for hull shape and hull efficiency play a major role in answering the question, at what point are diesel engines needed? As a rule of thumb we should become suspicious beginning at 35 feet and 17,000 lbs., from which point the boat buyer needs to research this issue closely if he has his heart set on gas engines.

The flatter the bottom of a heavy boat, the better it will perform with gas engines. Conversely, the deeper the vee, the more power it will take to push it. These are the reasons why we can't set a hard and fast line as to what size and weight boat must have diesels. In terms of boat styles, we'll find that larger, heavier express style boats will do better than heavy flying bridge sedan or so-called motor yacht style boats. One of the reasons is going to be the much greater windage of the later types that can easily whack a few knots of speed off.

Yet another factor which further clouds the issue is the matter of engine placement and boat trim. Rear engine boats, require more power to get up on plane because so much of the weight is positioned very far aft, rendering the boat poorly balanced. This causes the problem of many rear engine, express style boats having trouble, or at least being very slow to get up on plane, particularly with gas engines that do not have the greater lower speed power of diesels. Thus, while diesels are not likely to make the boat go overall faster, they can make the boat get up on plane sooner because they have more power at lower RPM.

Minimum Planing Speed Test

A very easy way to test for hull design efficiency is to test for the lowest possible speed at which the boat will plane. The lower the minimum planing speed, the more efficient it is likely to be. Minimum planing speeds vary not only based on hull shape, but also size and weight; for that reason I can't give any bench mark data to rely on. The only comparison that can be drawn is between different boats of similar size. However, we can say any mid size boat that planes well at 14 kts. demonstrates very good efficiency since most won't get up on the step and plane well until at least 16 to 17 knots. If it has leveled off and is running well at 18 knots, it's a reasonably efficient hull.

Diesel Engines

Diesel Power Ratings

As we all know, when it comes to advertising, the truth is rarely told, or at least not the whole truth. That is often the case with engine power ratings. It's not that engine manufacturers lie, but rather that the meaning of the power rating that they advertise has been manipulated to put their product in the best light.

Many boat owners wonder why another boat, with different engines, and perhaps of even slightly less horse power than their own boat, actually goes faster than theirs. Is it weight, engine tuning, propellers? Very often it's a matter of one engine manufacturer providing a more honest assessment of horsepower. The boat with a pair of 375's goes the same speed or faster than one with a pair of 400's because the power of the 400's is exaggerated or manipulated.

Brake -vs- Shaft Horsepower

Brake horse power is the power of an engine derived by applying a brake to the engine and measuring the power required to stall the engine. Normally, this rating is of a bare engine – no transmission, alternators or other peripherals – and therefore is always going to be somewhat higher than (typically 5-10%) than the deliverable power of engines in a boat. Before the engine power is ever transmitted to the propeller shaft, some of it is used up in the internal friction of transmissions, reduction gears, pumps and alternators. **Shaft Horse Power** is taken to mean the actual power delivered to the driven shaft, in this case the coupling at the transmission.

Some manufacture literature will not specify either term, but will state at what point the rating is obtained, for example the flywheel. In all cases, the power rating is taken under ideal conditions with a brand new engine, whereas actual operating conditions usually vary. The fine print on spec sheets will usually state the basis of the advertised rating. If no explanation is given, you have cause to be suspicious.

Continuous -vs- Intermittent Power

The intermittent power rating is the one most often used to exaggerate engine power. Intermittent simply means the power delivered at full RPM which, of course, is not the power we're going to be using all the time. Continuous power is the rating we're interested in because this rating is obtained at the recommended continuous operating (cruising) speed, usually around 80% of full speed. A manufacturer that rates his engines at wide open throttle (WOT) isn't being very honest with us.

The best way to get a good idea of an engine's useable power is to get a copy of the power curve graph. Such graphs show the power ratings at nearly all engine speeds. Most will also provide the fuel consumption curve on this or another graph as well. These graphs are available on the Internet for current model engines, and for older engines might possibly be obtained from dealers who will usually have data going back many years.

Continuous -vs- Intermittent Duty

If all this isn't confusing enough, some manufacturers rate their engine power by application. These are often defined as follows:

> **Heavy Duty** Continuous use in variable load situations where full power is limited to less than 80% of operating time. Displacement hull vessels, tugs, tow boats, trawlers and other commercial vessels.

> **Medium Continuous Duty** Variable load applications where full power operation is less than half of total operating time. Heavy planing vessels.

> **Intermittent Duty** Intermittent operation under variable load conditions. Full power operation is not more than 20% of total time. Yachts, pleasure craft and light commercial duty.

Fig.9-2. A pair of 435 HP 3208 Cats in a 37' Topaz. The port engine blew at 747 hours and was replaced. One hundred twenty hours later the starboard engine went. Here the engine is being torn down to try to find out what went wrong. This situation is very typical of high performance diesels at the upper end of the horse power spectrum. The way to avoid this is to keep the HP down to known reliable limits. This owner paid a big price to go real fast, over $70,000 for the two engines. The alternative is to buy mechanical breakdown insurance if you can get it.

As we can see from this description, the ratings are based on how one uses the engine since obviously some types of operation are much harder on an engine than others. What we usually find for engines so rated is that heavy, commercial duty engines will be governed at a lower RPM and have a lower horsepower rating since speed is usually not the issue. The power ratings will be lower for an identical engine mainly because engine speed is governed to much lower speeds.

Intermittent duty engines will have a higher RPM and greater horsepower based on the assumption that loads and operating duration will be less than for other ratings. Here we can glean part of the reason why we don't often see "thousands" of operating hours on pleasure craft diesels.

Revolutions Per Minute

Another very important consideration is the engine speed at which the power is rated. I don't mean full versus cruise speed, but how fast the engine actually turns compared to others. Manufacturers are increasingly upping the RPM of their engines. Historically, doing this has caused problems, bearing in mind that *diesel reliability is inversely proportional to engine speed.* I am personally very wary of any manufacturer that suddenly ups his engine speed by the likes of 400 RPM or more over earlier models of the same engine. If he previously felt that 2800 RPM was a comfortable speed, why does he now feel comfortable with 3200 RPM from the same engine? Maybe because he knows that the warranty runs out before the extra strain and wear caused by higher speed will become a problem. Your problem, not his. As a rule, more power at a lower speed is better than more power at a higher speed.

Diesel Engine Reliability Experience by Manufacturer

Despite the fact that virtually all diesel engines are manufactured by huge corporations who certainly do have the capital for adequate research and product development, serious design faults can and do occur. Unlike the problems with boat hulls, these are usually the result of "honest" mistakes, not penny pinching. Virtually all manufacturers have had their problems which almost always results from the same cause: The attempt to squeeze too much power from a basic engine block.

It is often the case that a manufacturer produces an engine that for a long time had a very good service record. Then, the manufacturer succumbs to the market demand for greater horsepowers and so soups up his old engine to deliver more power. Suddenly that old reliable becomes not so reliable any more. Virtually all manufacturers have fallen victim to this siren song.

Boaters want to go faster and faster with diesel power. They're no longer content to go the kind of speeds that would make nearly all diesel engines extremely reliable and trouble free. It is this desire for higher speeds that causes most of the problems, so be aware that if you want to go fast, it's going to cost you no matter how you slice it, whether you put bigger engines in your boat, or choose really souped up smaller engines. One way or the other, you'll pay the price whether it's bigger engines or more frequent repairs.

Detroit Diesel

The famed two cycle Detroit Diesel, manufactured by a division of GM, long the power plant of choice of the marine industry are no more. Falling victim to the dictates of the Environmental Protection Agency, it proved to be too costly clean up the emissions of these engines and Detroit Diesel dropped the line in 2000 after nearly 70 years of production which made the venerable 6-71 engine the longest running production engine of any type in history, 68 years.

Even so, large numbers of two cycle Detroit Diesels will remain in service for many years to come. Because there are virtually millions of them in use world wide, replacement parts will continue to be manufactured for the foreseeable future, so there need be no fear of obsolescence. As with gas engines, there are a number of resellers that offered souped up versions over the basic power ratings by the manufacturer. These included Johnson-Towers, Stewart-Stephenson, Covington and few others in addition to the standard Detroit Diesels sold by dealers.

Some of the great virtues of these engines are their eminent rebuild-ability and the ability to perform more thorough surveys on them. It is a very simple matter to pull inspection ports and view the cylinders, rings and valves. Parts prices are the lowest of all diesels and rebuilding costs are more reasonable than most.

The most popular engines are the 71 and 92 series. What these numbers signify is the cubic inch displacement per cylinder. All engines of a particular series have interchangeable parts, so that whether you have a 6-71 or 12V71, nearly all parts are the same. This is one of the virtues that made Detroits less expensive to service and overhaul compared to other manufacturers whose every engine model has a unique set of parts that is different than all others.

About Detroit Diesel Power Ratings The power of the Detroit 2 cycle engine is easily altered by making a few modifications. The most important of these are injector size and increasing turbo boost. Boat owners often play around with different size injectors trying to get more power from their engines. Therefore, power ratings advertised by sellers should always be considered suspect.

I highly recommend that an experienced engine surveyor be engaged and you should ask him specifically about the injectors and induction system, whether it's factory original or has been altered. There is an important consideration here, which is that installing over-size injectors can cause engine damage or at least premature wear. In order to burn more fuel, the engine needs more air, but also creates more heat. If air induction is not increased along with cooling capacity, both engine performance and service life will be compromised, so be sure to have this checked out carefully.

Detroit Diesels are rated shaft horse power with transmission at the shaft coupling. Ratings are intermittent at the higher RPM but continuous data is also published, usually at 1800 RPM.

6-71 In Line Six Probably the best marine diesel ever made, there are uncountable numbers of used boats with these engines and they remain highly desirable engines. However, their application in pleasure craft begins to fall way off by 1995 because they are so big and heavy. Most often found in sport fishermen and cruisers in the 40 foot range.

Very reliable in horse powers up to 400 hp, above which the service life between overhauls falls off dramatically. GM offered this engine with power ratings only up to 300 hp; anything above that is an after-market souped up engine. Engine weight is 3000 lbs. turbocharged.

Detroit 6V-71 The same displacement as the in-line 6-71, (426 cid) this vee engine had a rather short and turbulent history probably because even GM tried to squeeze too much power from it. GM sold it direct at 435 hp, proving my point that engines with displacement ratios at or above 1:1 tend not to do very well.

Detroit 6V-92 The redesigned version of the 6V71, it is nearly identical in appearance but with a displacement of 552 cid and weighing 3140 lbs. Improved cooling systems and keeping the power outputs at more reasonable levels, the 6V92 soon became the hot rod diesel of choice for the go-fast crowd. It proved to be an excellent engine, though at higher power ratings would require more frequent overhauls.

At 550 hp, time between overhauls drops to around 1,000 hours unless one happens to be lucky. The lower the power below 550, the better the service life will be. These engines have no known major design faults.

Detroit 8V71 One of the first V-8 marine diesels in existence, by 1980 the engine was obsolete due to heavy weight and rather low power output for such a heavy engine from a displacement of 568 cid. At a factory 435 hp, it has a rather poorly designed turbocharger and intercooler system. At this high power rating, its service reliability is spotty. Some engines do fairly well, others don't, most likely depending on the degree of care given. Out of production by 1979. At low powers and unturbocharged, these engines could last a very long time.

Detroit 8V92 Upon its introduction into the marine market, this engine had problems for about the first four years with valve rocker arm studs pulling out. This would cause the engine to swallow a valve and usually wreck the engine. This was one of the few times that GM was slow to correct a problem. Most of the engines that had the problem were either wrecked or the cylinder heads replaced.

The engine was in production from 1978-2000 at colossal power ratings up to 850 hp by after market modifiers. Typical engine weight is around 3700 lbs. These did not do well and its popularity in pleasure craft use fell off dramatically. Does best at powers of 600-650 hp.

Detroit 8.2 liter This less than spectacular engine is a rare GM four cycle engine that, during its brief period of manufacture, found its way into fairly large numbers of boats, particularly trawler types where its smaller size and power ratings was better suited. Typically rated at around 250 hp with a 500 cid displacement, it has much in common with the Caterpillar 3208 as both are throwaway blocks (no replaceable liners). I don't know of any instances where this engine was offered at over 300 hp, which may account for why so many are still around. It failed to gain much of a market, in part because this is a very noisy engine, and in part due to the unusually low power ratings for its weight.

Caterpillar Engines

When Detroit Diesel decided to drop its two cycle engines, the people at Caterpillar apparently decided to try to fill the void created by the demise of the two cycle engine. Heretofore, the only Caterpillar engine that was widely used in the mid-size pleasure craft industry was the venerable 3208, an engine which is rather large and heavy for its meager power outputs of up to 435 hp.

Caterpillar thus designed an entirely new series of in-line six cylinder engines to fill the gap, what is called the Six Series: 3116, 3126, 3176 & 3196. These, plus the 3208, are the Cat diesels found in mid-size pleasure craft. Unlike GM, Caterpillar does not permit their dealers to modify and sell their engines, so all Cat engines are theoretically "factory" power ratings.

Cat 3116 Making its appearance in 1988, the 3116 is no longer offered as a marine engine. The engine was fraught with serious valve train and cooling system problems about which Caterpillar did less than a commendable job on living up to their warranties. Virtually every boat with these engines that I did surveys on proved to have serious engine problems. Mark this one as an engine to avoid.

Cat 3126 Now the smallest Cat engine for the pleasure craft market, the 3126 is offered in power ratings ranging from 300 to 450 hp from a 442 cubic inch/7.2 litre block. A 2800 RPM engine (relatively slow compared to most lighter duty engines, it develops 350 hp at WOT and 347 hp at 2400 RPM, a difference of only three hp between wide open throttle and cruise speed. Used widely in pleasure craft for less than six years to this point, particularly by Sea Ray, so far the track record has been good. The power to displacement ratio is reasonably good for most models except the 450. Engine weight, 1592 lbs.

Cat 3176 Introduced in 1994, the 3176 is a 629 cubic inch engine usually rated at 600 hp for pleasure craft use. A slower turning engine at only 2300 RPM, it's found mainly in boats 50 feet and larger. I know of no major problems with this engine. Now increased to 660 hp, this engine is developing too frequent problems.

Cat 3208 One of the older Cat engines, it debuted in 1969 and as of this writing appears to be the only small V-8 diesel now on the market. It has a fairly large 639 cubic inch displacement and was commonly found in power ranges from 270 hp on up to 435 hp with an engine weight of around 1800 lbs. At the later power rating, the engine had a poor service record, which is strange considering that displacement ratio is nowhere near 1:1. So what was wrong? Though I haven't been able to prove it, the engine may have problems with uneven distribution of heat in the cylinder block. Or, to put it another way, the cooling system doesn't cool the block evenly. That's a problem many high performance diesels have that causes the block casting to distort and cylinder walls wear unevenly. Cat is now offering the engine at 450 hp and I can't help but note that their advertising states "Increased cooling and oiling capabilities." At powers of 400 and under, this engine performs admirably. Keep in mind this is a throwaway block without replaceable liners.

Caterpillar warranty response has been generally good except for the 3116 issues where customers were often told to keep running their engines until they went bang. Then,

Cat said, they would take care of the problem. That wasn't exactly reassuring to many owners.

Cummins Diesels

It's real easy keeping track of Cummins marine engines; there are only two basic engines, called the "B" and "C" block engines for the mid size marine market. Almost all of the boats that are the subject of this book would be suitable for the "B" block engine. There are four different models of the B engine ranging from 220 to 370 hp. Engine displacement is 359 cubic inches or 5.9 liters.

Cummins manages to squeeze a lot of power from these rather small engines, and does so in part by increasing RPM as the 220 hp engine runs at 2600 RPM while the model 370 runs at 3000 RPM. "B" block engine weights run a remarkably light 1100-1300 lbs. The block, heads and manifold are still cast iron. While the engine has not been without problems, those that it has had have been relatively minor. After nearly twenty years on the market, the overall service record is remarkably good. Warranty service response has also been good.

Next up are the "C" block engines, of which there is only one marine model the 450C. This is a 504 cubic inch engine rated by various standards from 430 to 450 hp. It's hard not to notice that Cummins does not publish horsepower/torque curves and that they offer various standards by which power ratings are derived. Considering the relatively high power ratings for such small engines, I suspect that they fudge a bit.

Cummins 6BTA5.9M The "B" block engine at 359 cubic inches turns out more power more reliably than any other comparably sized engine. At 370 hp it has a displacement ratio if 1.04 and stretches the envelop a bit. Even so, it has held up well in lighter boats but less well in heavier ones. If a heavier boat needs 700 hp or more to push it at respectable speed, I'd recommend going to a larger displacement engine. This engine is best for pushing lighter boats 35-42 feet at higher speeds.

Cummins QSM-11 A 662 cubic inch engine rated at 535 hp, it is unlikely to be found in mid-size boats. A long stroke engine turning 2300 RPM and weighing in at only 2475 lbs.

Cummins VT8-555 Long known as the "triple nickle", it develops 270 intermittent horsepower at 3000 RPM with 555 cubic inches. A weak ling for its size, it's a large bore, short stroke engine that's better for trucks than boats, the same for which can be said of the 903. This engine has been out of production since at least 1985. Engine weight, 2250 lbs.

Cummins VT8-903 The larger cousin of the 555, the 903 is also a large bore, short stroke engine that was used widely in older Bertrams. Developing 380 hp from 903 cubic inches, the engine had a rather poor service history. Engine weight is a whopping

3650 lbs. It proved no match for the smaller bore, long stroke Detroits against which it competed that were smaller and lighter, but put out substantially greater power. Piston melt-down was a common design-related problem.

Volvo Diesels

Volvo has long provided diesel engines to the pleasure craft market, but for some reason has never been a primary player. Everyone knows they exist, but few know much about them. Most likely they didn't become popular due to too many problems in earlier years combined with a relatively high price, and weak marketing.

Volvo engines have model names such as TAMD40. The alphabetic part simply stands for Turbocharged, Aftercooled, Marine Diesel. Designed in the European style with individual cylinder heads – one for each cylinder – they have cast iron blocks and heads with very little use of aluminum, and pump driven injection systems. Among European diesels, they are the simplest and least complex designs, and therefore lowest priced.

Most of the engines manufactured throughout the 1970's and 80's were not very well thought of, tending to be smokey, hard starting, rough idling and noisy. Beginning in around 1990, some major changes took place and the engines became quieter, easier to service and smoother running. Volvos are once again finding their way into new boats in larger numbers.

There are numerous reports of problems with the KAMD42 and piston failures.

MODEL	DISPL	HP	RPM	WEIGHT(lbs.)
TAMD 40B	220	165	3600	1047
KAMD42P	220	228	3900	1124
KAMDS44P	220	256	3800	1261
KAMD300	220	282	3800	1188
TAMD70E	410	270-300	2500	2005
TAMD73P	424	231-470	2600	1940
TAMD74P	444	473	2600	2304
TAMD63P	336	355-365	2800	1662
TAMD121C	731	370-408	2000	2910

Table 9-1

Fig.9-3. The Duo Prop drive. Is the high additional cost worth the small increase in performance?

The new Volvo Penta KAD 300/DP and KAMD300 series are the TAMD40 series engine connected to a Volvo DuoPro stern drive and rated at 272 hp. This power package, as with Mercruisers, is much too new on the market for me to have developed any information on the reliability of these systems.

Yanmar Diesels

Confined once to mainly the auxiliary sailboat engine market, Yanmar started converting light duty truck engines for power boats almost 15 years ago. Many people who own them, swear by them. On the other hand, there are a lot of people who loved British cars despite their terrible reputation for unreliability. Many others tend to swear at them. Yanmar is in a similar boat, so to speak; most of their engines find their way into niche market boats with very few popular production builders using their engines, which leads one to wonder why.

Extensive use of aluminum components may be one reason. The Yanmar 6 cylinder series engines use a cast aluminum combined manifold/heat exchanger casting, a configuration that has proved very troublesome for all manufacturers that have tried it, including Perkins and American Marine Hino-based engines. Galvanic corrosion is the main problem with the use of aluminum components. Aluminum is incompatible with other metals such as cast iron and the brass and copper used in heat exchangers. When all four of these metals are mated together into a single component, it's a prescription for disaster. Virtually every engine manufacturer has tried using aluminum components in their engines (especially components that are water cooled) at one time or another, with most abandoning the material. Besides, weight is not such a critical factor for marine engines as it is for automotive.

German Diesels

Smaller MAN, Mercedes or MTU engines are occasionally found in US built mid size boats although very few in number. Having very high initial costs, German diesels are equally costly to own. Parts prices are usually nothing short of outrageous. You're on your own if you buy a boat with one of these, so it's best to have deep pockets.

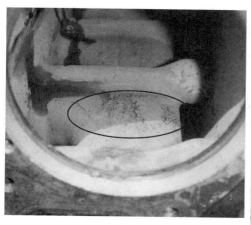 

Fig.9-4 & 9-5. The use of aluminum in marine engines has long been troublesome as these two views of a costly heat exchanger housing reveals. Most manufacturers abandoned the use of aluminum long ago though some few still continue to keep trying. LEFT: Severe internal corrosion created holes in the tank. RIGHT: attempts to patch the holes by means of welding or epoxy patches ultimately fails too.

Gas Engines

The virtues of the gas engine consists of their low initial cost, plus they are cheaper to maintain and repair. Parts prices are quite low due to huge production numbers. They are also more tolerant of poor maintenance than diesels. Gas engines are the logical choice of those seeking to stretch their budgets, and those who would find themselves financially crippled if faced with the very high major repair costs of diesels.

However, gas engines are less powerful than diesel engines in that the gas engine power rating is taken at the top end of their RPM range. This means that a comparably rated diesel engine is capable of adequately powering a boat that is larger and heavier than a gas engine could. This stems from the fact that diesels develop more power than gas engines at lower speeds. Thus, a 350 hp gas engine has nowhere near the useable power of a diesel.

GM Block Engines

Virtually all gas marine engines are marinized versions of automotive engines, converted by companies other than the basic engine manufacturer. This is in contrast to almost all U.S. made diesels being offered in a marine version by the manufacturer. The most popular engines by far are those produced by General Motors, long known for their amazingly reliable V-8 engines, that currently include blocks of 305, 350, 454, 496 and 502 cubic inch displacements. For many years, GM block engines have been the only ones on the market. We have to go all the way back to the 1970's to find Ford and Chrysler engines. GM does not sell marine engines under their own trade name.

All engines are marinized versions of the basic GM engine block, plus cylinder heads, and possibly intake manifold, carburetor and fuel pump. The remainder of the peripheral components will be after market products, and therefore there can be considerable difference among different trade names.

Since the year 2000, GM's engine line has been greatly modified with a new line up of engine displacements. We'll get to that in a moment. Less popular and reliable are the attempts by Mercruiser to use the small, V-6 block which simply does not develop enough torque to adequately power boats larger than runabouts.

This raises the question I'm sure some are bound to ask: Are car engines virtually the same as marine engines? The answer is usually not because the engines GM sells to marinizers are light duty truck engines, not automobile engines that may have distinctive differences such as four bolt main bearing caps, different heads and cooling and oil system design.

An Important Rule for Internal Combustion Engines

For greatest reliability and longest service life, it's better to have less horse power from a larger cubic inch displacement rather than getting more power from a smaller engine. The later is almost always a prescription for trouble.

For example, if you have a choice of 300 hp from a 350 cid engine or 320 hp from a 454 cid engine, the 454 is going to be the more reliable and stronger engine since it's delivering proportionately less power from a substantially larger engine block. In other words, the larger engine will be working under a lesser load than the smaller engine. There will be a far less tendency to overheat, and far less internal wear, plus greater valve life. This point becomes particularly important when considering used boats where the life of the engines has already been partly used up.

When it comes to new boats, a buyer may be telling himself that he doesn't really care because he doesn't plan to own the boat long enough for engine wear to be a serious factor to him. However, come time to sell the boat, he should be cognizant that it will be a major consideration for the person who considers buying his used boat. Particularly if the buyer elects to have an engine survey done. Over 75% of all 35' boats are surveyed; at 40' that jumps to nearly 100%.

What follows is a brief discussion of GM block engines of the past two decades:

GM 454 Cubic Inch V-8 Up to 2000, the 454 was the workhorse of the mid size gas boat fleet and is one of the most finely balanced and reliable engines ever developed. Normally a four-bolt main engine, I've seen Mercruiser versions with only two bolts, completely unstabilized bearing caps. That's because GM has manufactured different versions of the 454 for cars, trucks and high performance. This engine is capable of turning out about 400 hp with light loads, but is more commonly found at 320-340 hp where the engine has the best service life with heavy loads, doing very well in powering boats up to 36 feet and 17,000 lbs. Above those parameters, service life begins to decline substantially.

Originally introduced in 1980, these engines are remarkably durable and large numbers of them continue in service after nearly twenty years. Experience has proved that engines by Crusader Marine are the best and most durable marine conversions. Watch out for poor quality cylinder head gaskets that tend to leak on Mercruiser engines.
Typical engine weight, 1150 lbs. w/gear.

GM 502, 8.2 Litre This engine was introduced in 1997 and was eliminated from production in 2001, testifying to its less than stellar reliability record, turning out 380 hp in carbureted versions and 414 MPI versions. This engine has a demonstrable history of troubles. It is apparently a bored out version of the 454 that could not stand up to the amount of power extracted from it. My advice would be to avoid these engines. GM replaced it with the all-new 496 engine that should do a lot better.

GM 350 Cubic Inch V-8 Here's yet another GM engine which has a long history of trouble-free service, depending, of course, upon whose marinized version we're talking about. Again, those engines offered by Crusader have proved most reliable. Horse power ratings of this block typically are in the 250- 270 hp range which is a good balance of power-to-displacement.

GM 305 Cubic Inch V-8 The 305 has been in production since the 1970's and still is. This long production life testifies to the reliability of the engine. It is usually found in horsepowers up to 230 hp. The only problem with this engine is that too many boat builders have used it to power boats that are too big and heavy. It's often found in boats where the 350 engine should have been used. This engine will not withstand very heavy loads as it was designed mainly as a passenger car engine, and not for light commercial vehicles. It's found mainly in runabouts where it does fine.

GM 262 Cubic Inch V-6, 4.3L First introduced in the late 1980's, the V-6 has proved to be a great road vehicle engine but a less than spectacular marine engine. Pound for pound, this little engine develops a lot of horsepower for its size. Unfortunately, it does so at rather high RPMs so that when it is subjected to heavy loads, like any engine that is overloaded or is run very fast, does not hold up well.

There is nothing wrong with this engine so long as its limitations (220 hp tops) are recognized. It's best for powering smaller, lighter boats such as large runabouts, and small express boats in the 30 foot and under class. Mercruiser is one of the few who have marinized this engine, along with Volvo, and has had a notable problem with exhaust system design and gaskets.

Engine	Displacement	HP*	Heads	Brg.Caps
Vortec 4300	262 cid/4.3 L	223	Iron	2 bolt
Vortec 5000	305 cid	250	Iron	2 bolt
Vortec 5700	350 cid/5.7Litre	295	Iron	2 bolt
Vortec 6000 Comp**	364 cid/6.0L	350	Alum	6 bolt
Vortec 8100 std. Comp**	496 cid/8.1L	375	Alum	6 bolt
Vortec 5000	496 cid/8.1L	420	Iron	4 bolt

Table 9-2

* HP rating as offered by General Motors; engine marinizer may alter this power rating.
**Composite powder metal

Beginning in 2000, GM redesigned its big block V-8 line up with the Vortec series, named after what they call a new induction system design, with the models in Table 9-2.

All of the above engines have cast iron blocks. The 364 and 496 have multi port injection standard; the 305 and 350 are the two older engines in the current line up and have throttle body injection with optional MPI.

Engines offered by various resellers may have notable differences, such as the Crusader 350/5.7L being offered in a carbureted version at 270 HP and an MPI version at 330 hp. Heretofore, the old Crusader division of ThermoElectron Corp offered this engine at a mere 270 hp and it did well at that power rating. I have my doubts about whether similar good service life can be obtained after cranking another 60 hp out of this old reliable. If you're buying new, I think you're best advised to jump up to at least the 364/6L block or better yet, the 496/8.1 block if you need to squeeze this kind of power out of a V-8.

Note that the two new engines, the 364 and 496 both have aluminum cylinder heads except the 496 high performance model. Historically, aluminum engine components have fared poorly in saltwater marine applications, even in closed cooling system engines. Only time will tell how well aluminum heads work out on these engines. One thing we do know for sure is that these two engines will be a lot more sensitive to overheating. I'd recommend an extended warranty for these engines, and get the seller to pay for it. Aluminum heads are not proven in marine applications, and you don't want to be the beta tester at your own expense. Tell the dealer exactly what I've told you and tell him you aren't buying until he reduces the price by the cost of the warranty. Then you're covered if the dirty stuff hits the fan.

These GM marine engines are not complete marinizations and are only sold to marinizing companies such as Mercruiser, Marine Power and Crusader who add additional parts such as manifolds, risers, bell housings, cooling systems and water pumps. You'll need to get the specifics from the marinizer of the engines you are considering. Note that the quality of the castings and other components can vary substantially between product offerings.

As of this writing, Volvo offers only stern drive packages in 4.3L and 5.7L engines, the later at 280 and 320 hp engines. These are all duo-prop drive systems.

Marinizing Companies

Mercruiser

This brand is a division of Brunswick Corporation which is also the parent company of many boat builders including Sea Ray. Mercury Marine (outboards) and Mercruiser (stern drives) were once separate companies that were recently merged (again). This is one of the reasons why we find so many boat builders whose boats only have Mercruiser engines without any optional choices. It's part of the never-ending effort to consolidate the marine industry into the Big Three of boating: Brunswick, Genmar and American Marine.

The independent engine marinizers, Crusader, Marine Power and Volvo, are slowly being squeezed out. And now we have Mercruiser jumping into the diesel engine market in a big way, no doubt hoping to marginalize all the other manufacturers by providing only Mercruiser diesels in Brunswick products. If the engineering and reliability standards Mercruiser has applied to their gas engines are applied equally to diesels, that's a strategy that is unlikely to work in my estimation. For the track record of this company's products have something less than a stellar reputation, and has occasionally been the target of insurance company actions based on losses they've had to pay on faulty products. My attitude toward Mercruiser diesels is that they have to prove to me that they can produce a reliable product before I'd have anything good to say about them.

Historically, Mercruiser seems to have tried to dominate the market by providing the lowest priced product to boat builders. It's hard not to notice that a complete drive package is sold to builders at a cost that is less than one half than the replacement cost of the individual parts suggesting that power packages are sold to builders for near cost, while they expect to make their profits on replacement parts sales. Moreover, the less than high quality design of many of their parts and systems reinforces this notion. We might also consider the fact that Mercruiser is rarely the engine of choice when repowering.

Fig.9-6. A typical Mercruiser exhaust riser gasket. The very thin webs around the water jackets will not seal for long and are responsible for most of the premature failures of these risers and resulting engine damage.

And, of course, the replacement cost of stern drive packages and parts is astronomical. Hundreds of thousands of boats at this moment are permanently parked on the hard, shoved off in the corners of back lots because the owners cannot afford to replace broken drive units that cost up to $7,000 apiece.

Aside from stern drives, Mercruiser engines have historically suffered from several chronic problems. The first of these is poor quality gaskets, including cylinder head and exhaust riser gaskets on salt water cooled engines. The marinization of an automotive engine requires that the automotive gaskets be replaced with marine gaskets that can withstand saltwater running through the cooling system. Head gaskets on Mercruiser's 454 engines frequently were known to fail in 5-6 years. In many cases, faulty exhaust risers were blamed, the risers changed, and yet the problem of water getting into the cylinders continued because no one checked the head gasket.

Premature failure of exhaust risers and riser gaskets has been and continues to be another problem. Mercruiser risers often require replacement in as little as two to three years. Compare this to Crusader risers that typically last 8-10 years. Of course, no cast iron part with salt water running through it, is going to last forever, but we should certainly expect more than three years from a riser.

Mercruiser riser gaskets also frequently fail prematurely. This is basically a function of poorly designed risers wherein the web between cooling passage and exhaust passage is too narrow to allow for an adequate gasket seal. The 4.3L V-6 and 5.7L V-8's were particularly known for this problem as shown in Fig.9-6 above.

Beginning in 2001, Mercruiser began offering a diesel stern drive package which presumably will show up as optional power choices in new boats by builders that routinely offer Mercruiser engines standard. As with any new product on the market, there hasn't been the passage of enough time to get feed back and properly evaluate how it's doing.

Fig.9-7. The components of the conventional inboard straight drive system are made of bronze and high grade stainless steel for which corrosion is rarely ever a problem and maintenance is quite easy and low cost. Marine growth is not harmful and is easily scraped off.

Volvo Gas Engines

Volvo's participation in the gas engine market, much like with their diesels, has been spotty. Normally, boat builders offer them as a premium engine over the Mercruiser standard, and as such, they do not appear in large numbers.

Volvo also uses GM block engines that are marinized with their own peripheral castings for manifolds and risers. Often times these closely resemble Mercruiser components. Over the years I haven't seen anything that would lead me to prefer a Volvo over a Mercruiser other than, of course, Volvo's superior stern drive units. As far as I know, Volvo engines are only sold mated to their drives and not as straight inboard drives. While that doesn't seem to make much marketing or business sense, no one ever accused Volvo of having a great marketing program. The engines seem to be primarily a vehicle for selling stern drives.

Transmissions

Twenty years ago, transmissions were often problems, undergoing frequent breakdowns. Today, these problems have been greatly reduced for a lot of reasons that the reader probably doesn't want or need to know about. Suffice it to say that gear box manufacturers do a lot better job of not allowing too much horse power to be connected to a particular model gear box. This becomes more possible when a wider range of rated transmissions are available as they are today.

Reverse-Reduction Gears

Borg-Warner is the manufacturer whose products appear most often in mid sized boats. They are found with both stern drive systems and straight shaft drive systems. The advantage of the Borg-Warner box is that it is small and contains the reduction gear

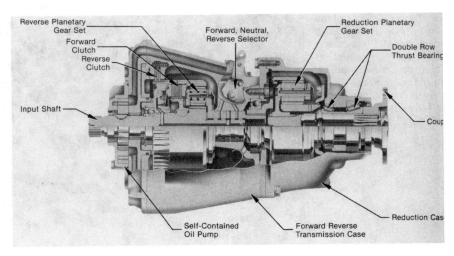

Fig.9-8. The Borg-Warner Velvet Drive is the oldest and one of the most reliable marine transmissions, shown here coupled with a 1.5:1 reduction gear (left side).

outside the transmission proper. This allows one gear box to be mated with numerous drive ratio reduction gears that can readily be changed. Both components are relatively low cost.

Borg-Warner Transmissions are a division of General Motors. They have been making the same basic gear boxes for longer than most people can remember. They are therefore highly perfected and when the properly rated box is mated to the right engine, these gears have held up very well. Borg-Warner gear casings are cast iron, not aluminum.

Another very popular gear box is the Twin Disc, an independent company that offers a huge line of gears from a few tens of horse power to thousands of horse power. Their gear boxes have proved very reliable when properly selected. Twin Disc gear casings are cast iron.

Z-F Transmissions

This German manufacturer markets a lot of Italian-made products (MPN) under its own name. Most of these are cast aluminum housing gear boxes that have racked up an impressive string of failures after boats collide with floating or submerged objects resulting in the gear housings breaking apart.

Heretofore, it was unusual to ever see a gear case broken to pieces because a boat ran aground or hit a floating object. After Z-F's introduction of cast aluminum housings, boats sustaining shattered gear casings became rather common. I personally handled dozens of such insurance claims. Finally I decided to have a metalurgical analysis done on the metal, which concluded that the material was Class D casting aluminum, the lowest grade. Because of this, I cannot recommend these transmissions.

Fig.9-9. This is why aluminum gear boxes are not a good idea. This has happened far too often.

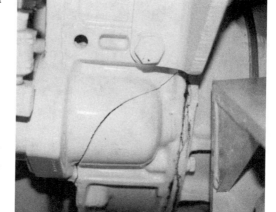

Vee Drives

Twenty years ago, there was only one vee drive available, the Walther Vee drive, and to say that people had trouble with it is an understatement. The Walther vee drive is no more, replaced by at least four other manufacturers, including Borg-Warner, Hurth, Twin Disc and Mercruiser. All of these seem to be doing fairly well with few reports of failures.

Stern Drives - The Bete Noir of Power Boating

The first production stern drives made their appearance in the early 1960's. The repair shops have been real busy ever since, and the back lots are loaded with dead boats, the owners of which can't afford to replace or repair these extremely expensive and fragile drive systems.

Stern drives are found on large numbers of boats at the lower end of the mid size boat range. There is a limit, however, as to how much load aluminum housing stern drives can carry, which explains why they usually aren't found on boats much over 12,000 lbs.

Good thing, too, for there are two problems with stern drives, (1) they are made of cast aluminum and, (2) with a stern drive, you are essentially dragging your engine's transmission and steering system through the water. Assuming that you never hit anything, that's fine, but there is an awful lot of stuff out there both on and under the water.

The differences between conventional propeller shafting and a stern drive unit may seem overly obvious until one looks at it more closely. Of course, the stern drive combines the elements of transmission, shaft, strut and rudder all into one unit. Turning the whole drive provides the steering. Less obvious is that the water pump and water pick up is located within the lower unit, so that when the drive snags one of the millions of discarded plastic bags out there, the water supply to the engine is cut off.

Equally less obvious is that when the prop inevitably picks up fishing line, the line gets wrapped around the shaft, works its way through the shaft seal, allowing the gear oil to leak out and water to leak into your transmission. And that's one reason there are so

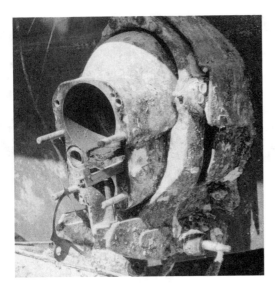

Fig.9-11. When a stern drive picks up fishing line, it usually winds it into the shaft seal, damaging it and letting water into the gear case.

Fig.9-10. Marine growth in salt water is the nemesis of stern drives.Once they get this bad, it's almost impossible to successfully recoat them.

many dead stern drive boats sitting around out in fields across the nation.

But the biggest problem with stern drives stems from the fact that they are cast aluminum so that corrosion and fouling is the biggest problem. Corrosion because metallurgists are not able to achieve for casting aluminum the same corrosion resistant alloys that can be obtained with rolled plate. And because drives must necessarily mix dissimilar metals, galvanism and stray current creates maintenance and corrosion problems.

No stern drive unit comes from the manufacturer with an anti fouling coating. Instead, they come with glossy paint, which makes it very difficult to get anti fouling paint to adhere to these things. When barnacles and oysters grow on a stern drive, these cannot be scraped off without also breaching the paint coating which is designed to protect the metal from corrosion. And unlike outboard motors, stern drives do not fully tilt up out of the water, so they remain mostly submerged on all boats left afloat.

Naturally, stern drives do a lot better in fresh water than salt because fresh water is less of an electrolyte and because barnacles and oysters do not occur in fresh water.

For these reasons it is my opinion that stern drives are best suited for boats that are used in fresh water, or boats that are dry stored, but are poorly suited for boats that are left afloat in saltwater. And for complex reasons that I'll not explain here, a stern drive boat with a shore power system is particularly vulnerable to electrolysis when docked at marinas with other boats that make use of the shore power system.

Alternative Drive Systems

These would include surface drives, Z-drives and various water jet drives. The truth is that it is very hard to improve on the advantages of conventional shafting drive systems, the virtues of which are simplicity and relatively low cost, as well as resistance to damage. The one weakness of conventional shafting is that the angle of the propeller shaft directs the propeller force at somewhat of an upward angle instead of the exact direction of travel, thereby diminishing useable power by around 10%.

Surface drives such as the Arneson are very efficient at high speeds but less so at lower speeds. The greatest weakness of this system is the loss of low speed maneuverability plus the danger of having partially exposed propellers. Backing up with this system can be an interesting experience, and you certainly don't ever want to fall off the back of one of these boats. Surface drives are not a viable or safe alternative in my view.

Jet Drives such as the Jacuzzi and the KaMeWa systems have been with us for a very long time, yet have failed to make much of a gain in popularity. That's because the drawbacks of these systems are considerable, including poor low speed maneuverability, and the problem of how to deal with the problem of what to do when the enclosed propeller gets jammed up with foreign matter such as ropes, plastic bags and other debris. Because components are aluminum, they also have serious problems with corrosion and marine growth and are more of a maintenance problem.

Z-Drives, which occasionally appear on larger yachts, present most of the problems of stern drives.

Engine Surveys

Diesel Engines

In my view, it's foolish not to have all used diesel boat engines surveyed by a professional engine surveyor. Unfortunately, professional engine surveyors are to be found only in the major boating centers where there are enough boats to support their business. Lacking a professional surveyor, the next best thing is a check out by an engine mechanic.

The difference between a professional surveyor and a mechanic is that the surveyor is trained, or has trained himself, to find not only existing problems, but also to look for potential future problems. Keep in mind that a mechanic who works for an engine dealer is not likely to advise you about negative aspects of the product that his employer sells. At least not if he wants to keep his job. Generally, you'll get more for your money by hiring an independent person.

Many boat buyers prefer to avoid the cost of engine surveys and save a few hundred dollars. This does not make good sense in light of the cost of potential difficulties and the value of the engines, even gas engines. The reasoning usually goes like this, "But it's only two years old and only has 300 hours on it. Therefore the engines should be fine." All you have to do is read the boating forums to find out why this argument won't hold up. I'll add to this by assuring you that I find plenty wrong with even new engines.

A thorough diesel engine survey should check the following in addition to visual inspection:

Four cycle engines:

Digital RPM measurement
Pressure test cooling system
Transmission slippage
Turbo charger boost
Manifold vacuum
Exhaust system back pressure
Infrared temperatures taken at critical locations
Manual oil pressure
Engine mount test

Note: Borescoping and compression tests are normally carried out only after a recommendation by the surveyor based on questionable condition.

Two cycle engines:

Digital RPM measurement
Pressure test cooling system
Transmission slippage
Turbo charger boost
Exhaust system back pressure
Manual oil pressure
Infrared temperatures taken at critical locations
Pull inspection ports and check piston rings, valves.
Air box pressure
Engine mount test

An open water sea trial is an integral part of any survey. Open water means just that, a sustained run of fifteen minutes or more in unrestricted waters. It does not mean a brief burst of speed up a canal, river or Intra Coastal.

Gas Engines

Surveying carbureted gas engines is a fairly straight forward task. For computer controlled MPI engines, it gets more difficult and costly. The reason being that there is usually so much peripheral junk hung on these engines that it gets hard to find the engine itself, for its hidden under all that stuff. To say that I'm not a big fan of these overly complex systems is an understatement. When it comes to boating, the essence of reliability and reasonable cost is simplicity.

Carbureted and throttle body injection engines are easy to assess since they lack all that stuff hung on them and the surveyor can actually see the engine. So, if the head gaskets are leaking, he should be able to find that.

Compression testing is the best diagnostic tool we have for the gas engine, and most of the time it's easy to accomplish – except when the engines are stuffed into a boat with a shoehorn, leaving no space to work on them. Some surveyors do engine surveys and compression tests while most don't. Any marina or engine mechanic can do them; the only caveat is that I'd recommend that you not use someone who is a dealer for that particular engine brand.

Gas engine sea trials should follow the same basic procedures as diesel engines, including most of the system checks outlined for four cycle diesels.

Chapter 10

The Engine Room

*Have you ever wondered why you don't see
a lot of over-weight boat owners?*

In this chapter I provide enough information for just about anyone to perform their own survey. That, however, is not my main purpose which is to arm you with more than enough information to size up any used boat that you may be looking at and rather quickly decide whether you wish to make an offer on it. Of course you can also use it to counsel your surveyor on specific points you might like him to check or give emphasis to.

Like the kitchen of a house, the engine room is the most expensive part of the boat with the components located there involving up to one-half of the boat's value, particularly when diesel engines and generators are involved.

The engine room is also the one area of the boat that a majority of boat owners least like to get involved with. After all, we see boat owners happily cleaning all other areas of their boats on Saturday morning, but how often do we ever see anyone cleaning the engine room? Judging by the appearance of most used boats, the answer is never. This is where we begin to discover that large boats aren't quite the casual recreation the marketing people would have us believe. After all, we're dealing with sophisticated machinery and electronics here, stuff that ought not to be approached causually unless one has buckets of money.

Most likely this is because the buyer has little knowledge about machinery or systems. If that happens to be you, I'm not proposing to make an expert of you, but do suggest that you not be intimidated by what you might see. So drag your body down there and

Fig.10-1. A real nightmare, it doesn't get any worse than this. Two engines crammed into a space that is far too small will likely mean service and repair costs will be double what they should be. It is almost impossible to get the spark plugs out from the inboard banks. This situation is very common with stern drive boats.

have a look around. And since you use common sense in everything else you do in life, you can apply it here as well.

Regrettably, most boat builders take the same view of the engine room (or compartment,

Fig.10-2. This engine room is spacious because the designer and builder made a conscious decision to not sacrifice serviceability for interior space. Naturally, it's a higher priced boat because it won't sell as well as competitors that don't embody this philosophy. Either way, the boat owner will pay a price.

Fig.10-3. A study in contrasts with the engine room shown on opposite page. Installations don't get much cleaner than this. A big complaint with this one is that there is no deck between the engines to stand on, leaving one to stand in oily bilge water.

as the case may be). They know that the layout, neatness and general access for service does not sell boats at boat shows and so the engine room simply becomes a place to put stuff with little regard for how it is done. Typically making it as small as possible so as to create larger living spaces, the machinery is usually crammed in like sardines in a can.

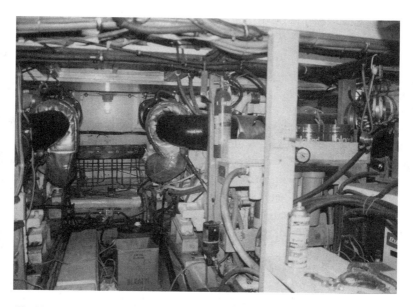

Fig.10-4. The engine room on this fifty footer is badly cramped. To complete an engine overhaul, a large part of the salon had to be dismantled and rebuilt, increasing the normal cost by nearly 70%. Smart boat captains avoid taking jobs on boats like this. To be a smart owner, one should avoid buying one.

Fig.10-5. Many express and open boats have whole deck sections that are hinged and lift up on only one end. Often, they don't open far enough as is the case here. In order to actually get into this engine room, one has to crawl on one's belly over the engines. That's painful even when the engines aren't hot.

However, this general disregard begins to change as boats get bigger and more costly. Sport fishermen tend to be an exception.

A very simple rule of thumb can be applied here; if things don't generally look good, then they probably aren't. But before we get into details, let's consider engine room layouts. For a very long time boat builders paid no attention to whether anyone could reach something in order to repair or service that something. They'd just take all the machinery and systems and cram them into as small a space as possible so that they could give mom the spacious interior she desires.

The ability to service components is especially important if you are a do-it-yourselfer, but it's also important if you pay someone else to do all the servicing. The reason is that the labor hours you pay can be double or triple, even quadruple over what you'd pay were a component or systems easily reachable. Not too many years ago, a National Marine Manufacturers Association survey indicated that too many people were giving up boating because the cost of service was too high and the quality of service too low. In addition, I've made this issue a near crusade on my web site because in many cases not only can one not reach components for service, often times one cannot even *see* them.

This causes a world of hurt for just about everyone associated with such a boat. If a repair man cannot easily reach a component for servicing, this adds to his labor time which you pay for. But for a boater who does most of his own work, this can really sour one's enjoyment of boating, especially when that breakdown occurs on a cruise or week end away from home port. For these reasons and many more, the layout of the engine room is very important.

Fig.10-6. Older boats will usually have large removable deck hatches that are often leaky and can cause serious water damage. Note that with two big diesels and a generator, working on this 32 footer is also a nightmare.

Engine Room Access & Serviceability

If one can't easily get into the engine room, the greater the likelihood that maintenance will not be up to snuff. After all, who wants to get all bruised and scraped up trying to worm your way into a tiny space with lots of sharp metal ready and waiting to hurt you? The more budget minded one is, the more important it is to have reasonably good access.

Fig.10-7. Clean installations like this allow minor problems to be discovered before they become big problems, as well as facilitating easy repair and maintenance. Things that can't be reached easily don't get maintained.

Fig.10-8. Blackfin boats are famous for having raised motor boxes. These serve to keep the cockpit low while giving excellent access to the engines. They also make for a good lounge and table.

Not many boats have serious engine room entry problems but there are enough that the subject deserves comment. So why should this be a subject worthy of consideration? Well, let's take the case of a flashy, forty-five foot luxury express cruiser. This boat not only had a large helm module, large wet bar, but also a large, circular lounge in the aft cockpit. I measured up eleven yards of upholstered seating in the cockpit of this boat. It's not hard to see where this leads to; no space for ready access to the engine room. To start with, one had to remove a large circular pedestal table, followed by part of the circular seating just to get the hatch open. If one had an emergency out at sea, this would obviously pose a serious problem, for we had to put all these removed components on the dock just to get the hatch open. With the hatch open a ladder dropped straight down six feet between the engines but to get around the ladder one had to remove it and hand it up to someone on deck. This is what one has to do just to check the engine oil! Ridiculous!

Other serious access problems are posed by the electrically or hydraulically opening deck sections that contain large seating modules above. Very often the electric deck lifters aren't powerful enough to handle this much weight and so frequently break down. In one case, it took four 200+ pound men to lift a hatch and shore it open with timbers. Test the hatch openers and if they groan and sound like they're straining, chances are there is going to be problem with failure.

Another thing to check is how far the hatch opens. I've seen some that open up only 18" or so, making it very difficult to get in. In others it's like climbing into an alligator's mouth and over his teeth as you have to crawl over the tops of engines and generators on your knees. This can be painful, to say the least. Particularly when the engines are hot, so you end up burned, cut and bruised. This does not make for "pleasure" boating. Some are so bad that it's more like enduring a special forces training camp.

Fig.10-9. Both the fuel filters and sea strainers are items normally serviced by the owner. Even on this small boat, both are front and center for easy access.

There are numerous boat builders that scrounge up the last few dollars of profit by not even putting a deck in the engine compartment, causing the owner to have to stand directly in the oily bilge. Not only is this dangerous, but you'll end up tracking oily sludge all over the place.

One of the worst aspects of badly cramped engine rooms is what it does to the cost when it comes time to overhaul an engine or two. What should be done at a reasonable cost now becomes exorbitant. Pay attention to this when buying older boats where the need to overhaul engines becomes a distinct possibility.

All About Engine Hour Meters

The biggest problem we have when we attempt to estimate remaining useful engine life via electric engine hour meters is that old misnomer, the "average" engine. There is no such thing as an average engine, average boat or average boater, and besides we should be talking about the median. An average is a mathematical construct, whereas a median denotes a specific number of a specific category.

The other problem is that no one has ever done actual surveys to determine how long engines do last. The information that I provide herein is based on a 35 year career involving large numbers of engine failure analysis as well as surveys. Even so, my experience covers only a small percentage of the total, and only in one region, notably one with a 12 month boating season. Experiences can and will vary in different climates. A boat located in the desert Southwest is subject to vastly different conditions than one in Florida or Alaska, so we need to be cognizant of these factors.

Most boat buyers would be delighted to find a five year old boat with only 150 hours on the meters. But the reality is that people tend to place far more credence in low hours

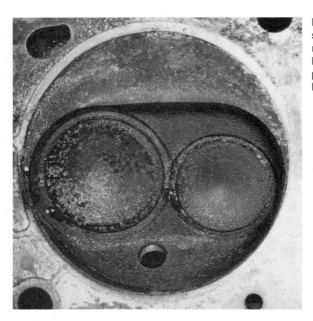

Fig.10-10. The effects of ingesting salt spray shows up in the pitting of these valves that results in reduced engine compression and loss of performance. Photos on opposite page reveal external evidence that this is happening.

appearing on a meter than is warranted. Not me, for I shudder when I run across engines with unusually low hours, and the reason why is gravity and moisture. Few people are aware that what prevents an engine from rusting up inside is a light film of oil. They're also unaware of the fact that when an engine stops, there are always a couple of cylinders that have the exhaust valves in the open position. That means that the cylinder and valves are exposed to the heavy moisture within the water-filled exhaust pipe. Moreover, rocking and rolling action of the boat serves to move this wet air around in the system because of water surging within the pipe.

If you were ever in the military, you know why they made you clean and oil your gun every single day – because it will rust otherwise. Most people know what will happen to a hammer if you leave it outside, even if it doesn't rain. There is that stuff at night called dew, and it will form on the hammer long before it forms on anything else, just as it does with the upper surfaces of your car. Condensation of atmospheric moisture occurs with temperature changes. Rapidly rising temperatures can cause cold pieces of metal to sweat, particularly when the metal has become very cold.

Normally what prevents the insides of engines from rusting up is a light coating of oil. Unfortunately, over time, not only does gravity pull that oil off of vertical surfaces, but oil also evaporates when there is a sufficient amount of air around it. Thereafter a very light surface corrosion will begin to form. It is not the rust, in and of itself that is the problem, but what happens after the engine is started. The oxide of metals is very abrasive and immediately acts like sandpaper, causing rapid wear. Repeated over and over again, through disuse, the engine can wear out prematurely.

A great deal depends on the particular environment, water temperatures and changes in daily air temperatures. The problem is more prevalent in colder climates than in warm

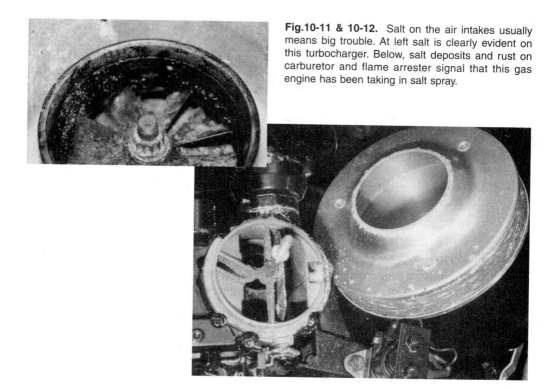

Fig.10-11 & 10-12. Salt on the air intakes usually means big trouble. At left salt is clearly evident on this turbocharger. Below, salt deposits and rust on carburetor and flame arrester signal that this gas engine has been taking in salt spray.

when a day can start out very cold and warm up quite rapidly. One mitigating factor is that boats in the north are usually laid up most of the year, so the time period in which this happens is less than in the south. Climatic and other considerations get a bit too complicated to deal with, but suffice it to say that one should be very wary of engines with unusually low hours. This does not autmatically mean they are in superb condition when in fact they may have corrosion damage

Premature engine wear is prevented by frequent running of the engines which relubricates all internal parts and evaporates any condensation in the crankcase that may have accumulated. Consider that an engine should be run at least once per week. If run for 30 minutes each time, in year that would account for 26 hours alone even if the boat never left the dock.

Conversely, high hours don't necessarily mean a worn out engine. The more frequently and longer an engine is run, the more total hours between overhauls will be obtained. Thus, above average hours may mean more frequent operation without excessive wear. The only way to really tell is through a professional engine survey.

Gas Engine Longevity

Gas engines would typically last twice as long as they do but for neglect and infrequent operation. The first casualty of infrequent operation are the exhaust valves that corrode, resulting in lowered compression which, in turn, causes excessive carbon build up that hastens ring wear and damage. Leaks in gaskets around the cooling system components are another major cause of the demise of engines. The biggest killer of engines is corroded cast iron exhaust risers that leak water into the cylinders.

Big block engines tend to last longer than smaller displacement engines mainly because larger engines tend to be stressed less since small block engines are often pushing boats close to their limit, and are run faster and harder to achieve more desirable speeds. When faced with the choice between big and small block engines where longevity is concerned, the big block engine is the better choice. It is always better to have more power and not use it, rather than use all the power from a smaller engine and percent of total load is the reason why.

With proper care, gas engines should go for around 2,000 hours before overhaul. In reality, few do so that people tend to be suspicious of high hours. However, my experience is that I find proportionately more high hour engines in good condition than I do engines with only a thousand hours or so. That is probably because high hour engines have been better cared for to last that long.

Overhaul costs for gas engines are sufficiently low that high hour engines shouldn't be rejected out of hand. Instead, one should compare the differences in cost between a high hour engine and a boat with much lower hours. One can look at it from the standpoint that with having freshly overhauled engines, you can be much more confidant about what you've got. Whereas with engines in the middle time range, you'll always be wondering just how much time they have left and not knowing.

Most buyers look at this from the standpoint of not wanting to deal with the hassle of going through the rebuilding process. After all, who wants to buy into a restoration project? Actually, this is not a lot of hassle since gas engine overhauling is fairly quick, easy, and not terribly expensive. A pair of engines are easily done in a week and will be almost as good as new.

As of this writing, the overhaul cost on a single 454 engine will run $3500 - $4,500 based primarily on the number of parts that the rebuilder recommends be replaced. Most that will give a warranty on their work will insist on replacing things like risers and oil coolers that could be old and fail. It's always wise to follow their recommendations.

Okay, let's say you do buy a boat with clapped out engines and decide to spend $9,000 for overhaul after negotiating the price downward an equal amount, but ultimately the final bill is $11,500. Let's say the mechanic found a few other things that we didn't anticipate needed to be replaced. Where are you in terms of other choices you could have made? Evaluate this situation in terms of total dollars spent plus the derived benefits of each and you'll probably come to the conclusion that the overhaul deal is the better one.

Diesel Engines

Would a physician look at a young person and assume that because he is young, the youngster is disease-free? No, and neither should you assume that low hours means no problems with diesel engines, even new ones.

Diesel engine costs are so high that it is not wise to place much credence in hour meters which can be changed, run backwards, or simply stop working for periods of time. Again, if you're going to place your faith in warranties, be prepared for some of the trials and tribulations that manufacturers have developed a history of putting boat owners through. The sad story of the Caterpillar 3116 in recent years is as good a case in point as I can make.

I recommend competent diesel engine surveys even for brand new boats just to make sure that the engines are set up right, because if they're not, the resulting problems can be expensive and involve much unhappiness between owner and manufacturer. For the cost of a few hundred dollars, such problems are usually nipped in the bud at the expense of someone other than yourself. Or, you avoid buying into a problem.

Propellering

Improper propellering can have an enormously detrimental effect on engines, particularly diesels which are designed to run at only a specified maximum RPM. When accomplishing the sea trial, it is very important to ensure that the engines turn up exactly to the specified RPM. If not, one must investigate the reason why. Most often the reson is improper propeller size, as boat owners are notorious for messing around with propellers, trying to sqeeze out that last extra knot of speed.

Ventilation

Engine room ventilation is something very few people consider, yet its adequacy and design is extremely important to engine longevity. Perhaps you've noticed that engines

Fig.10-13. After all these years, it's finally been recognised that good quality air filters are mandatory to protect diesel engines from ingesting atomized salt. Most engine manufacturers now supply them standard but on most older engines they will be lacking. The Walker AirSep is one of the better filters available. If your boat doesn't have them, be sure to put this at the top of your priority list.

are rated at a certain horsepower at a specified temperature. That's because the hotter the ambient temperature, the lower the power output will be. Most engine manufacturers state 125° as the maximum ambient temperature. Make sure your surveyor checks the engine room temperature and pressure.

Engine room vents need to be large enough to feed the engines enough air, yet be designed in such a way as to not allow salt water spray in. That is no easy task, which explains why some designs fail to achieve this goal. Poorly designed vents that bring spray in rather quickly begins to show up as excessive rust and corrosion on machinery and components. In salt water, not only does this cause heavy corrosion, but salt spray is also ingested by the engines, something that can greatly reduce engine life.

This is why most diesel engine manufacturers now provide sophisticated filtration systems as either optional or standard equipment. Systems such as the Walker AirSep and similar knock-offs, these are to be highly recommended on diesel boats. If they don't come standard, by all means purchase them as options.

Gas engines still don't have anything more than flame arresters, and although these may look like air filters, they are not. You can check for excessive salt spray ingestion by pulling the flame arrestors and looking at the butterfly valves in the throats of the carburetors. If they are rusted, then you probably have a spray intake problem. If they're clean and shiny, then all is well.

Federal regulations require all engine rooms to have blowers. Unfortunately, there is no mandate that blowers be adequately sized to do any good, so most of them aren't; instead, they have the bare minimum to meet the law. Blowers can do more than just fulfill the law; high capacity blowers can evacuate heat from the engine room that would otherwise radiate throughout the interior of the boat and reduce efficiency of air conditioning. This is particularly important for boats that have the engine room under the salon sole. It's a lot less important for express cruisers where the engines are under an open deck.

Things needed frequent servicing

Among the things that need rather frequent servicing are:

- Drive belts and water pumps at front of engine, so there should be adequate clearance to reach these components.

- There should be adequate clearance above the engine to reach the cooling system. I find numerous boats where one can't get the cap off the heat exchanger because it's only an inch or so below the deck. For gas boats, one should be able to reach the spark plugs on the outboard sides of the engines.

Fig.10-14. Water and rust trails are a dead giveaway to exhaust pipe leaks.

Fig.10-15. Exhaust riser leaks are the most common cause of serious engine damage. Rust trails on the outside mean water leaks on the inside. If it hasn't already happened, engine damage will occur unless the problem is corrected.

- Gas engines: Are the oil filters in a reachable location? The standard automotive filter is at the bottom of the engine. A marine conversion requires a relocation kit, usually placing them at the rear of the engine where they're easily reached.

- Batteries should be located for both ease of access and removal. The so-called maintenance free battery can be translated to mean batteries that don't last very long. I still prefer high quality lead-acid batteries where one has to check the fluid level periodically and add water. At least that way, I *know* what's going on with my batteries, whether or not they're being overcharged.

- Coupling/packing gland: Almost all boats since 1998 will be found with the so-called dripless packing glands, these things do not last forever and will require occasional overhaul. Some builders now regard these things as something that can be hidden or covered over. Same goes for the transmission/shaft coupling. You'll really pay the price on labor when it comes time to make repairs if these items aren't fairly easily accessible.

- Generators: Smaller boats with generators require special consideration, mainly for generator placement as well as its relationship to overall engine room accessibility. Some boats are obviously not designed for generators and so what we find are generators that are crammed into very tight spaces. This is not good because not only is it often extremely difficult to service the generator, but it can also block access to the main engines. Typical examples are generators located between the main engines, or behind the engines but too close.

- A good generator installation is one that allows good access to the generator, i.e. Adequate clearance on all sides, and does not block access to the main engines. Keep in mind that if one designer can create a nice engine room layout, they all can. It's no excuse to say the boat is too small, so that one has to suffer with these problems. All it takes is a bit of consideration during the design stages.

Sizing Up Condition of Used Boat Engines

For a trained eye, it is easy to tell what kind of maintenance a used boat has had.

> Cartridge type oil and fuel filters are rusty.
> Coolant in cooling system is low.
> Plastic coolant recovery bottles are dirty inside.
> Shaft packing is leaking and has been throwing water around.
> There is diesel soot in engine room.
> Engines have excessive amount of rust.
> Engines are very oily and otherwise dirty.
> There are oil trails under the engines.
> Bilges are more than slightly oily.

The list can go on and on particularly the older a boat gets, so we'll consider this in greater detail.

Boats for sale are often on the market for periods of time up to a year. During this time the vast majority of boats covered by brokerage contracts are not being used by the owners. That also means that no maintenance is being done, so we have to try to discern

Fig.10-16. Diesels have many more components that require occasional servicing than a gas engine. This intercooler had never been cleaned after 7 years of service and is completely clogged with salt and sludge. Ultimately, it led to the demise of the engine.

Fig.10-17. The effect of prolonged idling is heavy carbon build up. The upper ring is already stuck in the groove and this piston would soon start slapping the cylinder wall and eventually melt down and fail. To prevent this, idlling times should be alternated with long cruise speed runs. A sea trial or compression test will usually discover excessive carbon build up. Symptom will be oil burn and heavy smoking.

whether conditions we're looking at stem from short term or long term conditions.

Conscientious owners often will write the date of changes on oil and fuel filters, but most often not. Atmospheric corrosion, that caused by a damp, salty atmosphere will not normally cause rust on painted iron and steel engine components in the short term, but it will after a decade or so. Thus, the level of rust on iron and steel parts is a very good indicator. A typical steel filter will start to rust through the paint in about a year's time (assuming it's not directly gettting wet), so even slightly rusty filters are a good indicator that changes haven't been recently made.

In conjunction with rusty filters look for dirty cooling systems, low coolant and leaking water pumps which are usually found at the lower front of the engine. If the pump brackets are all rusty and the pumps themselves green with corrosion, all these are indicators of poor short-term maintenance. What do we mean short term? Figure about two years or so.

Next up in severity are cooling and exhaust system joints. Here much will depend on the age of the boat. All these joints have water traveling through the pipes and hoses, often salt water. Look for evidence of leakage at all joints, either orange-brown rust on steel or green oxide on copper based pipes. On a well maintained boat, there shouldn't be any corrosion showing, but if the boat has been sitting for a time while for sale the lack of maintenance may show only minor halos of corrosion around joints.

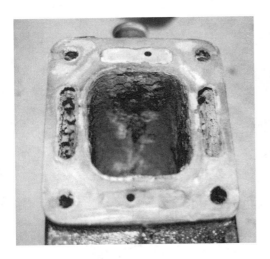 

Fig.10-18 & 10-19. LEFT: The Mercruiser riser while at RIGHT is the Crusader riser. Note how the coolant passages of both have slowly narrowed with rust scale, both of which are conditions that lead to overheating. Note how narrow is the casting wall between water and exhaust passage on the Merc riser. This is the design fault that causes such frequent riser failures and engine damage. The gasket area isn't large enough to effectively seal for very long.

Water and Oil Trails

Trails are the discolored path left by leaking, dripping oil or water. These may be prominent on or under the engine, so if you don't see them on the engine, look at the bottom of the hull under the engines. Any time something is leaking enough to leave trails, this means that it is a heavy and active leak.

Engine Rust

Rusty engines are always a bad sign that indicates either a previous or currently existing condition. As a buyer taking his first look at a boat, he'll be hard pressed to answer this question. The cleanliness of machinery is, of course, largely relevant to age. The newer it is, the cleaner we should expect it to be.

In the past, engine room vents were often so poorly designed that the vents would bring salt spray into the engine room, thereby not only causing damaging corrosion, but also usually resulting in premature component failures, including the engines themselves. In the last decade, this problem has become more rare. The general level of corrosion within the engine room should tell the story. At one to three years old we should expect to see almost no corrosion; at four to six years, only light corrosion. At six to ten years, expect to see rust on all sharp corners where paint has been knocked off. At this point you should not see substantial paint flaking and general rust all over.

For boats with engines under hatches in open decks, water leaks from above are a common problem, one that can cause serious damage to the engines and various components.

Fig.10-20. Most of the past problems with diesel engine risers have been solved by a combination of better materials and design.The lone exception is when it comes to larger and older engines where it becomes difficult to maintain integrity of very large pipes and risers. This riser system is 8 feet long so it only takes a small amount of engine movement to create a huge lever arm. Leaks tend to be a frequent aggravation, particularly on high performance boats. Note the high temperature sensor (arrow). This installation lacks a flex bellows at the hose joint connection that would solve part of the problem.

With careful observation, decks leaks from above usually become obvious by rust occurring in one or more localized areas. Conversely, if it's a mid engine boat with the hatches inside the cabin, expect that the machinery should be completely free of rust.

Sources of excessive engine room corrosion

The following is a list of sources that often cause excessive engine room corrosion:

- Leaking shaft packing glands that throw water around via the rotating shaft. Rust tends to be localized at rear of engines.

- Salt spray in through engine room vents. Rust tends to build up outboard and toward aft end.

- Leaky hatches. Engines tend to be more rusty on top. Look for rusty water puddles on top of engines.

- Leaking cooling system at front of engine gets onto pulleys and belts and is thrown around. Engines tend to be rusty at front ends. Look for corrosion damaged alternators, leaky water pumps, bad gaskets or leaking hose joints.

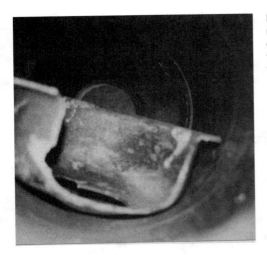

Fig.10-21. Broken baffle inside of a muffler, pointing up the fact that boat mufflers don't last forever. The danger here is that the loose baffle will completely block the muffler resulting in the build-up of pressure blowing the exhaust system apart or causing engine damage.

- Leaking exhaust system components. A leak in the exhaust system aft of the riser will throw a fine spray of water around, usually causing a lot of damage. On diesel boats, the exhaust will leave a sooty residue throughout and the sulphur dioxide emissions will leave all copper, brass and bronze components very green. Soot combined with green brass-based components is a definite sign of prior or existing exhaust leaks.

Gas engine exhaust leaks generally do not leave much soot nor turn brass and copper green. Instead, one has to look for water trails and general corrosion.

Generators are very often the victim of serious leaks, often leaking shaft glands because the generators usually sit between and behind the engines. However, they're just as likely to have water thrown on them when located at front and between the engines by rotating belts and pulleys.

Very rusty generators should be treated as though they have been badly damaged unless and until it has been proven otherwise. The same goes for corroded alternators. Electrical apparatus does not tolerate water damage very well, and what may be working today is likely to stop working tomorrow, so regard all serious corrosion on these components as a death certificate.

So what if the generator on a used boat looks like a ball of rust but it still runs? If there is a lot of rust on the outside, you should anticipate that there is also corrosion damage on the inside, particularly the electrical end. Also bear in mind what all those rusted up bolts and other parts will do to repair costs that you, the new owner will end up paying. My recommendation is to approach a very rusty generator as though one day you'll end up paying for its replacement, probably sooner rather than later. Even if it does work fine at the moment.

The Drive System

The drive system consists of the engine(s), transmission, engine mounts, couplings, shafts, struts as well as propellers. This section focuses particularly on the engine mounts and shafts as these components are occasionally troublesome. All components must be in the correct alignment for the drive system to function properly and avoid damage resulting from misalignment. Both the engine mounts and strut bearings are subject to wear that can cause misalignment. Therefore, these components need to be checked out by a surveyor on a sea trial.

Engine Mounts

Good engine mounts are quite expensive, say around $200-$250 apiece. For this reason, many boat builders opt to use the cheapest mount possible, which is the Bushings, Inc. mount shown in Fig.10-23 on next page. In my experience this type of mount is good for between 4 to 8 years which is what accounts for so many used boats needing engine mount replacements.

We can determine when this type of mount has failed by simply looking at it. Over time, the rubber in the mount degrades and compresses, causing the engine to settle or sink down a bit. Or we may find that the mount studs become cocked at odd angles, indicating that the engine is moving. In either case, this means defacto that the engine has gone out of its original alignment so that mount replacement is recommended. Mounts are replaced by jacking the engine up one corner at a time. After the new mounts are in position, the engine then has to be realigned with the shaft.

Alternately, on the sea trial the surveyor will conduct a stress test on the mounts to make sure that excessive engine movement isn't occuring. I perform these tests even on

Fig.10-22. We know for certain that the engine mounts have gone bad when we see the propeller shaft moving fore-n-aft in the strut bearing.

Fig.10-23. Bushings,Inc.,mount the least expensive and shortest lived.

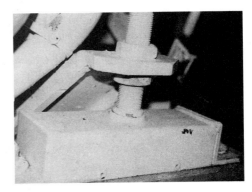

Fig.10-24. The Ace mount has the best record of performance over 30 years history. Also has the least insulating ability.

Fig.10-25. Caterpillar mount supplied with the companys engines since mid 1990s appears to be effective and reliable.

Fig.10-26. European mount most commonly found with European engines Volvo, MAN, MTU. Failures with vulcanized rubber are known to occur.

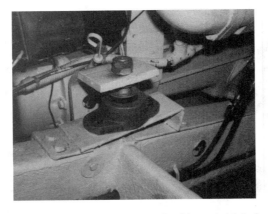

Fig.10-27. Mounted on an angle, this mount failed within a year because the angle puts a constant stress load on the rubber insulator. Mount base should be horizontal like all the ones shown above.

new boats because I find many of them where the original selection of mounts was inadequate to do the job.

Vibration Problems

Propeller technology has advanced to the point where most of the high vibration levels accepted in the past are no longer with us. It's fair to say that all boats should run nearly vibration-free although that is certainly not the case. There are numerous causes of drive train vibrations from propellers to engine mounts. All boat owners should have some understanding of the straight inboard drive system, so I'll start at the beginning with the engine mounts.

Engine mounts are a critical and frequently troublesome component of the drive system. The reason we have so much trouble with mounts is the compromises that are made between dampening engine noise and securing the engines. It seems to be often forgotten that the mounts have to carry the driving force of the engines without permitting much movement. After all, we have a fast spinning propeller on a long shaft that has to be held steady.

The most common type of mount, though certainly not the best, is a metal stud set in a rubbery base. Engine loads are primarily forward and backward plus the downward pull of gravity, engine weight and the effects of hull slamming. Thus, a 400 hp engine weighing 2,000 lbs. exerts those loads on our flexible mounts. Needless to say, if those mounts are too flexible, the engine will be subject to movement and when this happens it will go out of alignment with the propeller shaft. If, for example, a diesel engine has a high center of gravity, this can also induced a sideways component into engine movement that vastly increases the potential for damage.

The total length of the drive train is from the propeller end of the shaft to the front of the engine, a considerable distance. The shaft is held at the strut(s), of which there may be one or two, and anchored at the forward end by the coupling to the transmission. Thus, if there is any flexing of the hull along this foundational length, that flexing will also be telegraphed to the engine and shafting, resulting in yet more movement. This is why very rigid hull stringers are so important.

But bulkheads are also critically important because, whereas stringers prevent the hull from bending lengthwise, bulkheads prevent the hull from wracking or twisting, a force that occurs when putting the boat into a hard turn, among other things.
Okay, so now we have a general idea of the forces acting on the drive system, and we can see that these forces are very substantial. A boat traveling at 30 knots that smacks a wave results in more than force exerted against the hull, the impact also affects the drive train, and most especially the engine mounts. Of course, if the builder chose engine mounts based on low cost, we're likely to run into trouble, particularly with much heavier diesel engines. The photos on the opposite page show the variety of the

most common mounts, from $60 cheapies to mounts costing $300 or more apiece.

Yet price is not the only issue for engine mounts, for price alone doesn't equate with a mounts ability to hold an engine steady. I've already found a number of very expensive mounts on European diesels that do not hold the engines steady, most notably Volvo mounts. My advice is that the effectiveness of engine mounts should be checked by a surveyor, though as near as I can tell, few ever do. Here's what happens when engine mounts aren't right.

- The weight of engines plus slamming forces causes rubber-type mounts to crush. This causes the engines to settle downward, throwing the shaft out of alignment.
- Mounts that are overly flexible can result in excessive upper engine movement, which is sort of like a pendulum causing the engine to swing through an arc transversely, when this happens not only does misalignment occur, but can cause shaft bending. This is one of the most common causes of chronic or repeated shaft breakage without apparent cause.
- Excessive engine movement causes very high loads on the transmission output shaft and sometimes to the engine crankshaft. It is one of the more common causes of transmission oil leakage and failure. The true cause of transmission failure is almost never correctly traced to engine movement so the transmission gets wrongly blamed.

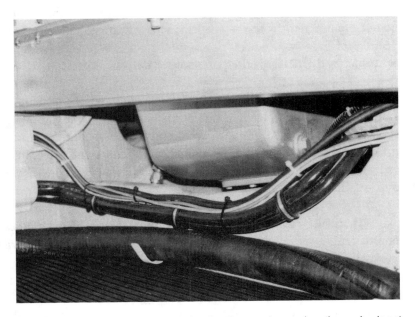

Fig.10-28. Engine oil pan clearance is sometimes an issue when the engine is set too close to the bottom of the hull. On gas engines and small diesels, the pan is usually stamped steel. If it comes in contact with bilge water, it's likely to rust out, causing a loss of engine oil and catastrophic engine damage. Pay particular attention to this on vee drive boats where the pan may be right over the stuffing box.

Fig.10-29. At first glance this engine room might look pretty good. That is, until you realize there is no deck in it and no place to stand except on top of equipment that is going to be damaged if you do. How thoughtless can a designer get?

- Sagging engine mounts results in rapid wear of shaft seals, wether the lip seal type or flax packing.
- Sagging mounts and engine movement causes the shaft to go out of alignment with strut cutlass bearing, resulting in rapid wear.

Consider the issue of engine alignment tolerances. Ask any boat yard and they will tell you that they use 0.003" as the maximum tolerance to align engines to shaft couplings. Then ask yourself what good does it do to align to 0.003" when engine mounts allow engines to move 0.250" or more? That's how shafts get bent without owners understanding why.

This is yet another good reason why you should have a qualified surveyor check out new boat purchases. On a recent new boat check survey of a 55' Carver, I found that the Volvo engine mounts were not only incapable of holding the engines steady, but were responsible for bending two shafts even before the boat was delivered to the owner. They blamed defective mounts and replaced them twice, but that did not solve the problem. Finally, I insisted that they change the mounts to a different style (Ace) and that completely eliminated the movement problem. Yes the Ace mounts did increase engine noise transmitted to the hull; but the final decision had to come down to trading a problem of constantly bending shafts or a bit noisier engines. Ace mounts permit very little movement but are not as good at preventing vibration transmission into the hull.

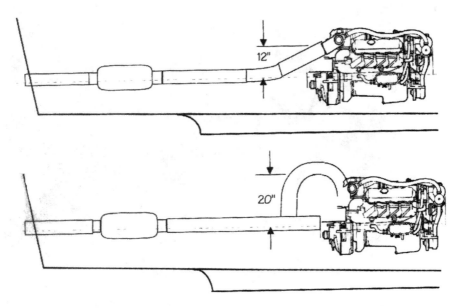

Fig.10-30. Exhaust systems must have a means of preventing water from backing up through the pipe and into the engine. This is usually accomplished by a combination of risers and mufflers with baffles. The top illustration shows an inadequate system while the bottom is a proper installation.

Exhaust Systems

There is one important difference between boats and road vehicles that boat owners should be aware of. This is that exhaust systems in boats are contained entirely within the vessel whereas with road vehicles it is external to the passenger compartment. Obviously, this poses some rather serious risks, especially with gas powered boats and the carbon monoxide danger. Diesel engines produce very little carbon monoxide so that the risk is substantially less. Everyone knows that steel exhaust systems on cars only last so long and then have to be replaced, the cost of which is nominal. But it is a considerably different story for boats that utilize a variety of different materials in these systems from cast iron, to stainless steel and fiberglass.

The two primary functions of the exhaust system is to (1) safely remove exhaust byproducts from the engine and, (2) prevent water from flowing back into the engine. Of course, the exhaust coming out of the engine is very hot and therefore the water from the engine cooling system is dumped into the exhaust system to cool it.

Except for cast iron exhaust risers on gas engines (discussed in detail below), some of the parts of exhaust systems on boats can last indefinitely while others do not. Rubber-based sleeve connectors and frequently stainless steel risers can have a limited life span. Keeping in mind that exhaust systems are full of water and therefore very heavy, there are considerable forces acting on it in a bouncing boat. This can cause joints to open up and result in leaks. Moreover, engine overheating due to a loss of cooling water can overheat fiberglass pipes and mufflers, degrading these parts, also causing them to leak.

Many of the problems we've had in the past with exhaust systems have pretty much been eliminated except for improper exhaust system design that ends up allowing back surge of water into the engines. This problem is directly related to the height of the engines above the water line, something that designers seem to overlook once in a while. The illustration in Fig.10-30 will help you visual why this can be a problem. For some builders, this occurs with considerable regularity, most notably Sea Ray Boats which often tries to get so fancy with their systems that they end up shooting themselves in the foot.

Be wary of underwater exhaust systems. Running the exhaust out the bottom of the hull poses much greater dangers of back surge than running exhausts out the transom when the boat is at rest. It happens that boats with underwater exhausts go for years with no problem at all, then suddenly for no apparent reason it ends up with an engine full of water.

This tends to happen when a boat at sea loses power or the engines are shut down with the bouncing boat causing water to surge back up through the exhaust system. In other words, it requires the right circumstances for this to happen and the problem goes unnoticed until those circumstances occur. This is why the problem often is baffling as to why it occurred. Worst of all, when boats have improperly designed systems, the problem will often reoccur when the cause is not recognized.

The idea of underwater exhausts in smaller boats were borrowed from large yachts, most of which have this type. The system works fine in large yachts that have the space

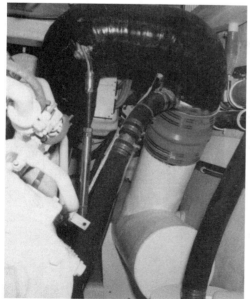

Fig.10-31 & 10-32. Exhaust system configurations can vary greatly. At LEFT is a very high riser with a surge extension. There is no chance of water backing up into the engine with this system. ABOVE is a sophisticated baffled muffler system, the primary purpose of which is to keep water out when there isn't adequate height clearance for a high riser.

for the massive antisurge chambers that are required. Unfortunately, a number of builders tried just making a hole in the bottom and running a pipe out. This won't work because small boats simply don't have the space needed to install a proper system. Therefore, be very skeptical of boats under 50' that have underwater exhausts. Numerous Sea Ray boats in the thirty foot range with various model names have underwater exhaust systems that have resulted in hundreds of cases of engine damage. Be extremely wary of these boats.

Diesel Engine Risers

Diesel risers are normally of welded stainless steel. They can be either water cooled or the dry insulated type. The problem with water cooled type is that welded stainless pipes are welded from one side only, a situation that makes them prone to developing pin hole leaks at the welds. Dry insulated risers have no water coolant, and have much less of a problem with this, though pin holes leaks do occasionally occur. In any case, pin hole leaks are easy to repair by means of simple welding.

A more serious problem with exhaust leakage occurs at the point of joining the piping to the engine which is probably on flexible mounts. In that case, engine movement tends to loosen the joint of whatever type and cause exhaust soot leaks. These are very easy to spot because of the sooty trails. The point here is that unless the designer has given adequate allowance for engine movement, such as with bellows hose connections, leaky joints are bound to occur. Chronic leakage is often a problem when connections are made with heavy exhaust hose because the joint is less forgiving of engine movement.

One final note, diesel exhaust system problems increase proportionate to size. The longer and heavier the piping, the greater the tendency for trouble and the greater the cost to fix.

Mufflers

Mufflers serve to not only quiet the engine noise but are one of the means of preventing water backsurge into the engine because mufflers have baffles. The important thing to know about them is that mufflers don't last forever. Not only are they subject to heavy low frequency vibration, but also from high temperatures when engine cooling system faults occur. Most often this results in baffles breaking loose, at which point the muffler has lost its ability to protect the engine from backsurge. Damaged mufflers are usually detectable by sighting up the exhaust pipe.

Gas Engine Risers

Gas engines usually have cast iron risers while diesels have stainless steel risers, so we'll deal with each separately. There is a concerted effort lately to market stainless steel risers for gas engines. This has been tried in the past wherein it was discovered that crevice corrosion problems made it less reliable than cast iron, and far more costly to replace. Fortunately, stainless risers are mainly found only on race type boats and almost never on cruisers.

Risers for gas engines are relatively cheap, running around $150 - $300 each. That's not true for stainless diesel risers that typically cost $1500 or more. Prior to the mid 1980's most risers were of the water jacketed variety, which means that they always had water standing in them - salt water. The weakest part of a welded stainless riser is the weld which is very vulnerable to corrosion. Weld joints very commonly develop pin hole leaks along the weld lines. Therefore, any little rust trails on the outside of a riser are an indication of a leak that is only going to increase over time and will eventually end up spraying saltwater and exhaust emissions around the engine room.

Fortunately, the dangers of water jacketed risers were recognized so that this type is not used any more, but may still be found on older boats. They were replaced instead with either insulated pipes or what we call down-side cooling water injection designs. Down side injection risers do not have water jackets, instead dumping the cooling water from the heat exchanger into a downward angled pipe to begin the cooling for the wet exhaust system.

While this does not eliminate the potential for leaks – for weld corrosion is still a problem – but it does mean that leaks will not go into the inside of the pipe and enter the engine. Instead, a pin hole leak goes to the outside of the riser, but typically only leaks very small amounts of water. Thus, when we find small water trails around riser welds, what we have found is the beginning of a problem that can be quickly and easily repaired. Pin hole leaks on welds can easily be repaired by a small plug weld without replacing the whole riser, except when risers become very old and full of holes, at which point they should be replaced.

Cast iron risers are such a common problem on Mercruiser engines that it's hard not to come to the conclusion that the manufacturer must design them this way in order to sell lots of replacement parts. Mercruiser risers have failed at very rapid rates ever since the beginning of my career over thirty years ago and since then nothing has changed. This has not proved to be true of most other manufacturers, though we cannot escape from the fact that cast iron risers are high maintenance items that will only last so long.

Crusader Engines, at the time they were owned by ThermoElectron Corporation, had among the best riser designs that usually lasted 6-10 years. Since the company was sold in 1999, they changed the riser style to a cheaper style, but we do not yet know how well they perform. By contrast, we routinely see Mercruiser risers failing within three years and sometimes even less.

Because there is salt water flowing through cast iron at a heat transition zone where the metal quickly goes from uncooled to cooled, the iron tends to corrode at very rapid rates, much the same way exhaust systems on cars do. Expansion and contraction from extreme heating and cooling makes it very difficult to maintain tight gasket joints at the base of the riser. Thus, leaking riser gaskets are a very common malady, but also one that should not be ignored.

The reason leaks at the riser gasket should be immediately addressed is this: The gasket is mated to a cast iron surface that separates the exhaust chamber from the cooling jackets. Rust trails on the outside of the gasket means that the gasket is leaking, and if allowed to continue, this will errode the gasket surface of both the riser and the manifold. If this happens, no gasket will ever seal again, and BOTH parts will have to be replaced. Exhaust manifolds are a lot more costly than risers, so one shouldn't ignore this yellow flag. Evidence of leakage should immediately be repaired.

This is the long and short of the cast iron riser situation. If there are any rust trails at all, that means that it's going to cost some one some money, and the longer it has been let go, the more it will cost. Bear in mind that these are water jacketed risers that retain water inside when the engine is not running – salt water that is. If ignored long enough, eventually the leak will go through to the inside exhaust port, and at that point water will enter the valves and pistons, wrecking the engine.

Other Quick Checks

We know today that if a human being is constantly breathing dirty air, that person is going to have health problems. It is no different for engines, gas or diesel. If engines have been breathing dust or salt spray, their life span is going to be reduced. Fortunately, there is an easy way to tell whether engines have been breathing clean air or dirty. Simply look down its throat and see!

Well, that really means to look at the air filter if it has any, and if not look deeper inside, all of which is visible up to a point. For gas engines this is very easy. All gas engines should have flame arresters, which are in essence metal filters that will trap larger particles of dirt but not smaller ones. The cleanliness of the flame arrester will tell a lot about maintenance, but looking down a throat of a carburetor will tell even more. Whether it's carbureted or fuel injected, the throttle body will have a steel butterfly valve. If the engine has been breathing wet, salty air – or worse, there was a water spray leak in the engine room – the butterfly valve is going to be very rusty. If so, this is a very bad sign indeed. You can make these same checks on generators as well.

Many diesel engines only recently have been fitted with air intake filters as standard equipment. Older engines often have nothing so the condition of the intake orifice will often be revealing. On the other hand, if it has filters and they are badly fouled, this is a sign of poor maintenance. Fouled filters means that the engine hasn't been getting enough air which results in incomplete fuel burn that can cause excessive carbon build up that, in turn, causes other kinds of internal damage.

Intercoolers are like radiators fitted between the turbocharger and the engine, the purpose of which is to cool the hot air that the turbo rams into the intake. If the air doesn't get cooled, this will reduce engine power. All turbocharged diesel engines have them. If there is no air intake filter, or the filter hasn't been doing its job, any dirt getting into the intercooler will stick there and reduce cooling efficiency. Many engine overheating problems that are hard to trace usually end up being due to dirty intercoolers. An after cooler is much the same thing; only its placement determines what it is called.

Turbo chargers have aluminum bodies on the air intake side so that if you can get at the intake orifice, corrosion found in this area is another bad sign. So are turbocharger vanes that are corroded (white deposits, for these are titanium) or fouled with soot and grime. Try spinning the vane with your finger; if it is stiff and does not spin freely, the shaft bearing is damaged.

For older carbureted gas engines, take a look at the carburetors. Much can be told about the physical appearance alone. Over time, the gaskets in carburetors age, shrink and start to weep gasoline. This condition is plainly visible in the form of yellow-brownish gum that forms on the outside of the units. By touching them and they feel sticky, this means that a carb overhaul is needed. Of course if you see a lot of corrosion (rust on the steel parts, white oxide on the aluminum), that's not a good sign.

The Cooling System

Remove the cap from the heat exchangers and look at the coolant. It should be clear and green or pink. If you see black carbon floating on top, this indicates a very serious problem. So too does any kind of sludge or crud appearing on the bottom side of the cap.

Antifreeze and other cooling system coolants that are alkaline are very good at removing paint. Thus, coolant leaks are usually denoted by water trails where the paint has been eaten away. If you can't get the caps off the heat exchangers then look at the plastic coolant recovery bottles. The cleaner they are the better, but when they are brown or black with sludge – beware for this is a sign of poor maintenance and possibly other serious problems.

Look Under the Engines

It's probably hard to see this area but it's definitely worth the effort to look at the bottom of the hull under the engines. After all, this is where anything that leaks out of an engine will end up. It may be that this area has been recently wiped up and cleaned, in which case you're left with the question as to why. Most likely that was to remove evidence of oil leaks, in which case look at the remainder of the bilges for signs of excessive oil.

Gas engines typically have leaky valve cover gaskets, a condition that will leave an oil drip trail at the rear of the engine block. However, leaking rear crankshaft seals will do the same thing though the later is a lot more serious than the former. To determine which it is one needs to look inside the flywheel housing. If that is wet with oil, then one can be sure that the crankshaft seal is leaking. Leakage from the front seal is easier to detect as it is unlikely that any other source would leave an oil drip trail at the front of the engine.

Fortunately we do not have anywhere near the problem with leaking transmission seals that we did years ago. Even so, it does happen and is expensive to repair. Transmission seal leaks are usually evidenced by an oil spray pattern thrown by the coupling. Depending on gearbox design, that doesn't always happen, so look also for a drip pattern on the hull bottom.

Vee Drives can pose problems since the stuffing box is so close to the transmission that any water leakage is likely thrown by the shaft or coupling up onto the underside of the engine. This can cause sever corrosion of the coupling (meaning that it may have to be cut off and replaced the next time you have to do an alignment or change a shaft), or worse, corrode a hole in the engine oil pan (particularly if it is stamped steel) resulting in loss of lube oil and a wrecked engine. These points obviously need to be checked carefully.

Shaft Seals

Next to leaking exhaust risers, leaking propeller shaft seals cause more engine room damage than anything else. That is because a rotating propeller shaft, when it is leaking, can throw salt water all over the engine room. This can result in the engine intake sucking salt spray into the engine. When this happens, engine life decreases dramatically. For over 60 years, the standard shaft seal (called a stuffing box or packing gland) used braided fiber (called flax) impregnated with a type of wax to make the seal. The problem with this type of seal was that if it didn't get any cooling water, the shaft would heat up, melt the wax, and would start leaking.

Ten years ago, new types of seals were introduced that were generically termed "dripless" seals. These are of a variety of differing designs, some better than others. On balance, I

Fig.10-33. Tides shaft seals for propeller shafts and rudders. One of the better types, they are very expensive.

find that most are superior to the old flax packing. Although better, they are not fool proof and don't last forever. If a shaft gets bent or an engine out of alignment, such seals may become damaged and leak.

The down side of this improved seal is that to service them, the shaft has to be disconnected from the coupling, which greatly increases the cost. And if the coupling is frozen onto the shaft -- which they often are -- it can cost well over a thousand dollars just to replace one shaft seal. This begs the question of whether these new seals really are an improvement when the cost can be so high.

Installation of Other Components

Fuel Filters

Diesel boats require high quality, high capacity water separator fuel filters. Engine manufacturers specify minimum fuel filter types so there is rarely a problem with builders skimping. But for gas boats, it's a different story since gas boats often have nothing more than spin-on cannister type filters. I have never considered these to be adequate for boats mainly because one cannot monitor what is happening within the filter.

While water contamination of fuel is a fact of boating life, the majority of problems from this can be greatly minimized with the right kind of fuel filters. The right type are the two stage separator type that have sight bowls that let you see what the filter is doing. By occasionally checking your filters, larger problems can be avoided. Experienced boaters expect these filters to be prominently mounted so they can check them as religiously as checking engine oil and coolant. They are of little value when mounted in a bad spot.

Fuel Lines

The safety requirements for both gas and diesel fuel systems are basically the same. Even though gasoline is more dangerous, diesel fuel under certain circumstances can be equally dangerous.

While fuel lines not being the right material is rarely a problem anymore, the manner in which they are installed can be. Fuel lines, be they copper pipe or flexible hose, need to be routed in such a way as they are not subject to accidental happenings. For example, they should not be located where they get stepped on. Fuel lines should not be routed with, or attached in any way with electrical wiring. However, we often see fuel lines tied together with the main battery cables, and to a surveyor this is a real horror. The reason why is that should the engine starter motor solenoid ever hang up, this can cause the cable to overheat and even melt down.

Fuel lines also should not be routed near or above batteries or stuffing boxes.

Fuel lines are also required to be supported at intervals sufficient that they will not bounce when the boat is pounding. They should never be left laying in the bilge.

Fig.10-34. LEFT: Disastrously cheap: This 50 cent plastic vent fitting is not only incapable of keeping water out of the fuel tank, but the plastic deteriorated in only three years and broke off. The end result was chronic water contamination of the fuel and engine failure.

Fig.10-35. BOTTOM: both of these two stainless steel fittings are effective.

Fuel Tank Vents

Hull side vents are occasionally the cause of chronic water contamination of fuel tanks. And discovery of that fact is always the last thing anyone ever considers, often involving months of frustration and expense. To check this, simply locate the fuel tank vent on the outside of the hull. The vent opening should be facing down and aft, and be located well aft of amidships. If it is too far forward, it may be constantly submerged by the bow wave and spray.

Now check the vent hose on the inside of the hull. It should have a riser loop in it. This is the added protection to make sure that no water can be pushed back through the vent.

Batteries

Battery installation is important because batteries have to be inspected and maintained. If you buy into that 'maintenance free battery" nonsense then you are an easy mark. All batteries require some degree of maintenance. The terminals must be kept clean and free of corrosion and the tops above all dry. That is because dirt, water or electrolyte laying on top of the battery can cause current leakage. So can batteries sitting in boxes full of water, as they often are.

Fig.10-36. Looking down into a battery compartment. Not every boat has the space for a dedicated battery compartment like this Bertram, but this gives you a good idea of what a clean battery installation should look like. The high quality battery boxes not only have a top cover, but a hinged hatch that provides for easy inspection and service without having to remove the whole cover. Note how neatly the main cables are laid out.

Proper battery mounting is not easy, as testified to by how often my pants fall apart due to coming in contact with battery acid. It is best that they be mounted in heavy duty covered boxes and secured so that a boat can be laid over on its side without the batteries crashing through the side of the hull or taking out a sea cock or strainer if they come loose. Only the more expensive, high quality boxes will meet this requirement, something that in the vast majority of boats is highly substandard. Typically what we find are those el cheapo plastic boxes that are secured with those horrible belt-buckle straps that are next to impossible to get on or off. If you're looking at a boat that has these things, I'd recommend you save yourself a lot of future frustration and plan to replace those things.

If batteries are not properly mounted and covered, the results can be costly. Leaking acid not only ruins clothing but causes nasty corrosion damage to nearby components. When battery tops become dirty and wet, stray current results that prematurely discharges them, as well as causing electrolysis damage elsewhere. Last but not least is what happens when some piece of metal accidently contacts both terminals. This is not an uncommon occurrence, resulting in either injury, fire or damage to various electrical components.

Batteries should be mounted in a place that is relatively easy to get at, and never near aluminum fuel tanks or have fuel lines or water hoses nearby, especially above. Why? Because the hydrogen gas emitted while charging is extremely corrosive to aluminum and rubber-based materials.

Water Heaters

The most common problem with water heater installations are that the steel casings are mounted directly on a flat deck that often is running in water. This rusts the water heater out until it eventually fails. The simple solution for this is to shim the unit up on plastic or teak blocks to that it won't be in contact with water, i.e., the heater sits above any water that floods the deck.

The same goes for virtually any kind of pump; if it's mounted up on a 3/4" riser block, then water can't get at it, and it won't rust away to nothing in no time.

Battery Chargers

Most battery chargers meet their demise because either they were mounted near a leaking propeller shaft that threw water on them, near the edge of a leaking hatch, or near an engine room vent that is taking in salt spray. Otherwise, chargers should last the life of the boat.

Fig.10-37. Foam insulation has long been a big problem in boats because it disintegrates after six to eight years. This insulation from an engine room has turned to dust.

Insulation

In the last twenty years or so many boat builders have taken to using a type of foil covered foam insulation that is glued on with contact cement. This stuff tends to last not more than six to eight years before the foam begins to crumble. But long before that the heat in the engine room loosens the contact cement and the insulation is falling down all over the place. This stuff is usually put in before everything else so that things like wiring, plumbing an other components are mounted on top of it. This makes the task of attempting to replace deteriorated insulation a physical and economic nightmare. Not only does the crumbling foam make a terrible mess of the engine room, but can get into and damage engines and other components.

Therefore, if you run across a boat with bad insulation, never think that this is a minor problem that can be quickly and cheaply corrected.

There are other problems with insulation, particularly when this involves leaks from above. Even if it is mechanically fastened, the foam can absorb water and become very heavy, thus pulling it off in any case. Even worse, there have been many instances where the insulation on the under side of a deck spread the leaking water all over the engine room, including into the engines.

When going into the engine room, be sure to look up! Foil covered foams do not readily reveal leaks so you have to look closely for signs of water stains and corrosion on other components. Water can leak into the insulation in one place, but leak OUT six feet away, making the locating and stopping of leaks a very difficult proposition indeed.

Other types of foil/foam insulation are attached with foil tape. This doesn't work much better than contact cement, and after a few years will also start to go adrift. The more conscientious builders are attaching insulation panels with mechanical fasteners (which is no problem when screwed into the bottom side of a cored deck or hatch) so that if it does have to be replaced, the job becomes very much easier.

Since around 1995 or so, the quality of foam/foil insulation has improved so that we don't see crumbling foam as often on later model boats, or at least hasn't shown up yet.

Chapter 11

Electrical & Plumbing Systems

Electrical and plumbing systems comprise the heart of a vessel's operating systems, and because we are dealing with boats that float in salt water, it is imperative that such systems utilize the highest quality materials and be designed and installed by competent professionals. Therefore, this chapter will give you a detailed overview of these systems.

The good news for later model boats is that they don't have anywhere near the kind of electrical problems that they had only fifteen years ago. One reason is that electrical systems have become much simpler in overall design but, unfortunately, that also often means a lot less flexible. Another reason is premanufactured panels that more or less cause the builder to follow a preconceived scheme. Still another is that industry seminars have been helpfull in better educating builders, designers and installers about basic standards.

This subject may be of little concern to the casual boater who doesn't travel much, doesn't overnight and who relies primarily on his home dock system for most of his power demands.

As demands for electrical power continues to increase, the ability of most 125 VAC to meet those demands declines. Twenty years ago, many boats in the mid size class had multiplex high voltage systems. A duplex system is one that has one shore power line plus a generator; a triplex system two 125 VAC lines plus generator. Moreover, a boat's internal system may have, one, two or three legs. That is, certain items of electrical equipment can grouped into circuit A, B or C.

A multiplex system is one that allows us to choose which power sources operate which branches of the system. For example, let's say we have shore power line #1 line #2 and we have the generator. This gives us a boat on which half of the electrical equipment is on one line, the other half on the other. With a pair of rotary switches, it is possible to wire the system so that we can switch between power sources for any circuit. We can put all on generator, all on shore, or one line on each, shore and generator.

> Shore power voltages will vary from around 110 volts to 125 volts depending on the actual voltage received from the power company at any location, and because of this AC power can be referred to as 110, 115, 120 and 125, as well as 220, 230, 240 and 250. The reason for this is that there is voltage drop from the power company to your location.
>
> The numbers used here are the ratings of cables and connectors.

The advantage of such a system arises at those inevitable moments when either the dock doesn't supply enough power, or there are not enough dock outlets are available for us to plug in both lines, and so on. Thus, one leg could be run from shore, the other on generator. This kind of flexibility is a great thing to have since while cruising, it is common to run into problems of inadequate shore power.

Unfortunately, for lower end boats, this degree of flexibility has been decreasing, rather than increasing. That's because sophisticated electrical systems are expensive and builders of "price" boats can cut costs by skimping. When it comes to mid size cruisers with relatively high power demands, it's far better to have two 30 amp, 125 VAC lines than a single 50 amp, 125 VAC line. With the single 50 amp 125V line (which s what we are seeing with increasing frequency) we've got 20% fewer amps (50 versus 60), plus we are reduce to reliance on only a single power source.

Would it be preferable to have a 50 amp, 250 line? Generally yes, but while you're now limited to that one line, there is usually no shortage of 250V available, plus it proves to be far more reliable. Of course, it's better still to have one 250V and two 30 amp 125 lines because this yeilds four potential power sources including the generators. This is the type of system that most of our better quality boats will have.

Note here the distinction between 50A, 125 and 50A, 250 VAC. The later can be split off into two 50 amp, 125 VAC legs for a total of 100 amps, whereas there is no 30 amp, 250 VAC service. With 50 amp 125, fifty amps is all you've got. Actually, on a dock there are no wires carrying 250 volts; instead, there are two wires carrying 125 volts each. As when two batteries are connected to give double voltage, so too with the dock system and on board a boat. Thus, a 250V shore cable has two 125V positive conductors whereas the 125V cable has only one.

The 250V shore cable is particularly versatile because those two 125V lines can be split right off the cable ends with the use of a splitter. Note that a 50 amp, 125V line cannot be split as it is a single hot wire circuit and thus has no such versatility.

Fig.11-1. Anatomy of a well-designed panel. This one is large and divides the AC and DC sections, eliminating confusion. It is set at eye-level height for convenient access. Two sets of meters monitor generator and shore power sources that can be used concurrently.

There are a couple of reasons why that single 125V, 50 amp line may not be as desirable as you think: (1) You live or die by that 50 amp line. If that 50 amp line goes out, the breaker on the dock takes a dump, or 50 amp sockets aren't available, you're stuck unless you want to run off generator alone. (2) Two 30 amp lines gives you 10 more amps plus two 30 amp lines are a lot easier to handle than those huge, heavy 6/4 50 amp lines even if you do have a Cablemaster. (3) Two 30 amp lines are more versatile when it comes to dealing with dockside shore power problems such as the usually bad, burnt up receptacles so often found at transient marinas.

There are a wide variety of adapters for shore cables available, often called pigtails or splitters. For example, the 250V splitter is a highly versatile device that can be used on either end of a 250V cable. It takes the 250 volts and splits them into two 125 volt lines. Thus, one can run two 125V lines *into* the 250V cable or take two 125V lines *out* of the cable, increasing your versatility even further.

Flexibility is in the Switching

Nowadays one can pretty much judge the quality of a boat by looking at the electric panel alone, for it's real easy to tie up a lot of money in electrical systems. Needless to say, price boats tend to have systems that are engineered down to bare bones, which usually translates to a lack of power source versatility. A typical system with two 30 amp lines, one leg is usually dedicated exclusively to the air conditioning, though not always. No matter what the amperage draw is, if the total draw for the air conditioning is 16 amps, you've got a wasted 14 amps that can't be used because the AC is the only thing on that leg.

Since air conditioning is one of the biggest power users, how it is wired up becomes important. An alternative to that described above is to divide the units up and place them on both circuits, that is, to not devote an entire line to just air conditioning. If the total AC demand is close to 30 amps, then it won't matter much. Multiplex switching systems offer the greatest flexibility between appliances and power sources. Keep in mind that we can have three power sources consisting of two shore lines plus a generator. Our ability to have the greatest flexibility is dependent on the extent of switching the builder has provided.

For example, the builder can simply throw everything together on one or two primary circuits, fixing each to a shore power line with the generator feeding both equally. Hopefully, you have a lot of kilowatts available from your genny. We can make the system a lot more versatile by dividing up our internal systems into two main circuits (exclusive of air conditioning) and permitting switching from all three power sources independently. This is the way most large yachts are wired because large yachts usually demand more power than most docks provide. Therefore, it's nice to bring your generator on line to meet the shortfall by switching it into the circuit that needs the juice.

Multiplex switching allows one to feed any power source into any circuit. This is a feature that becomes increasingly desirable the larger and more complex a boat becomes. For boats in our subject range, the following panel diagram illustrates the most sophisticated system that can be made use of in a 45 footer. For smaller boats with lesser power demand, this degree of flexibility is not normally needed. The break off point is 30 feet or so.

AC Power - How Much is Enough?

The power demands aboard boats today just keeps climbing and climbing, but the truth is that there are very few boats afloat today that can meet all the power demands of their owners, either AC or DC. It has been true nearly from the beginning of boating that boaters have had to make do with what they've got. Not only can most generators not supply all the A.C. power boaters want, but neither can most dockside systems. This is not because it is not possible, but because it becomes very expensive to wire docks for very high power, not to mention the accompanying hazzards. Marina operators are wise to keep a cap on power limits for everyone's safety.

A typical 35 foot express cruiser gobbles up power with the following:

Air Conditioning	15 amps running, 35 amps start up
Water heater	8 amps
Battery charger	6 amps
Refrigerator	6 amps
Icemaker	4 amps
Stove, 1 burner	10 amps

Microwave	9.8 amps
Television	1.5 amps
Coffee maker	7.5 amps
Total	67.8 amps

As we can see from the above listing, we can quickly run through all available 30 amp shore power, never mind a 7.5 kw generator which theoretically will supply 62.5 amps peak power but realistically far less than that on continuous load, usually about 80%. Now you know why boaters are so good at blowing dock breakers. Their power demands are insatiable.

I haven't included computers and the myriad of little appliance transformers we all have plugged into every available outlet, from cell phone chargers to laptop computers, all of which when added up draw some serious power. Note here that one could easily wish to run all this equipment at the same time, which couldn't be done even with a dual 30 amp system. Most boaters simply accept this reality as a fact of life and operate appliances judiciously. While a few builders offer higher capacity systems, most do not.

The typical 30 -35 footer sports a 5 kw to 7.5 Kw generator. For offshore needs, this is usually enough where the main demands are refrigeration and air conditioning that the generator can easily meet. That is, so long as Sister Sue isn't aboard with her hair dryer and other electrical demands. It's our dockside demands that cause us the greatest problems. Because they're hooked to the dock, people tend to think that all they need is immediately available. A little experience quickly disabuses us of that notion.

Therefore, when we're into the 35 foot cruiser range we need seriously consider whether that standard single 30 amp shore line will be enough because it would be very costly to attempt to retrofit a boat for twin 30 amp lines. Increasingly, the size of boat that starts out with 50 amp service is growing smaller. With new boats, there may be some shore power options available such as single or twin 30 amp circuits or even 240 VAC or any combination of these two. Boats in the forty foot class often have both or even all three, e.g. two 30 amp, 125V lines and, and one 50 amp 250V Line.

The better solution is always a 50 A, 250 V line since a 50 amp, 250 VAC line is equal to two 50 amp, 125 VAC lines for a total of 100 amps at 125 VAC. In reality you will not find 250 volts of power on any dock because of the danger of very high voltage. Even your home is wired that way. What docks have is two 125's joined together for total of 250V like a battery in series. When you bring 250 volts aboard, what you really have is two 125's joined to a common buss, but the boat has to be set up for that.

Most smaller boats that have 250VAC service have few, if any, 250V appliances but simply make use of the extra total amperage. Exceptions would be electric stoves which function rather poorly on 125 VAC, though that is what most mid sized boats have.

One way to tell is that 250 VAC appliances will always have dual pole breakers which are really dual 125 breakers joined together.

The 250 VAC power connections on most boats are really just two 125VAC lines, the only difference is the higher amperage of 50 amps per leg. One can connect a dual 30 amp system to 50 amp, 250 service by means of a Y splitter, but you can still only get 30 amps per line because that is all your boat lines are rated for.

The key to A.C. power demands is of course air conditioning. The typical 35 footer is going to need two units of the self-contained type, so we're looking at minimum of 20 amps running and possibly a whopping 50 amp start up amperage. Here's where our boat fitted for multiple power sources really pays off. Most boats with twin 30 amp lines usually devote one of these exclusively to air conditioning. The reason for this is the high start up amperage demand. Were we to spread the AC units to both circuits, when running other appliances turning on the A.C. would likely trip the breaker. When working with 30 amp systems this is a frequent problem because, working at near the maximum rating of the breaker, it tends to run closer to its trip temperature and so a

Fig.11-2. Bertram Yacht has long had one of the better designed panels. Note that on this one, there are four rotary source selection switches. This one handles two 30A, 125V, one 50A, 250V plus generator and permits the use of any combination of the three. The ideal in flexibility.

sudden start up of an appliance like a refrigeration compressor is far more prone to trip a hot breaker than a cold one.

This is where a multiplex switching system really pays off because it allows you to transfer basic loads to one of three power sources. Again, these considerations are most important in areas with high air conditioning demands such as the Florida and Gulf coasts. There is a good reason why no one lived in Florida prior to the invention of air conditioning, and that is because the heat and humidity are intolerable during the summers. It can be even worse out on the water, so be sure not to underestimate how much you will rely on air conditioning.

Shore Power Cables

It doesn't pay to buy cheap shore cables which are the majority of what we find available in the marine stores, particularly the chain stores that hawk low prices. Good cables are expensive and there is a good reason why. Shore cables get a lot of abuse, not to mention being dropped in the drink all too frequently. One of the main differences between cheap cables and high quality ones is that the cheap ones have end fittings that can't be serviced because they are molded in one piece. That means that if you drop it in the drink, it's going to corrode and there is nothing you can do about it except replace it when it either fails or starts a fire. Cable ends need to be serviced and cleaned at least once a year in order to maintain them in safe condition because once they get corroded

Fig.11-3. An inexpensive Marinco shore cable costing about $130 has unserviceable and irreplaceable end fittings. When corroded or damaged it cannot be satisfactorily repaired.

Fig.11-4. Intelligent design: these power receptacles are recessed and angled downward to relieve stress on the connections as well as helping keep water out.

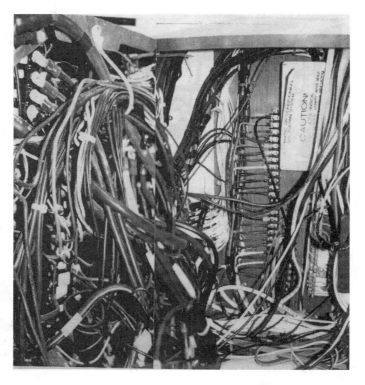

Fig.11-5 & 11-6. The way electrical systems should and should not look. Both of these photos are electrical systems that are on new million dollar plus yachts.

they become dangerous.

Better quality cables such as those offered by Hubble have end fittings that can be dismantled, serviced and easily replaced. I strongly recommend this type because in the long run, they are well worth the extra cost.

All shore power cables eventually get very dirty after being dragged around on docks for years, but dirt does not affect them; being immersed in salt water does. Cable ends should be opened and cleaned of corrosion once per year for maximum service life. The cost of the ends is equal to the cost of the cable, so it is well worth taking care of them.

Shore cable retractors by CableMaster are handy but expensive options. For the most part, the device works well and is reasonably trouble-free. The ability to install one will be limited by boat size as they take up a lot of internal space. Nowadays with 250 VAC systems they are considered almost mandatory because the cables are so heavy.

Shore Power Connectors

High resistence in the shore power circuit caused by corroded terminals and wire connections is the number one cause of boat fires. Because of this, the quality and placement of the connectors is critically important. Ideally, the connectors should be placed in a location that is not constantly doused with spray, nor in danger of being submerged – as we occasionally see when these things are mounted on hull integral swim platforms. If the receptacles are mounted on the platform, they should be located well above the point where they would be flooded with water when backing up.

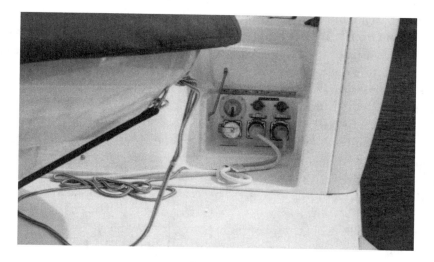

Fig.11-7. This ought to be a no-brainer, but even builders with stirling reputations make mistakes, in this a Tiara 40 with the shore receptacles installed less than 18" above the water line.

Another point to be wary of is circuit protection. The ABYC standard allows the main breaker to be placed as far as ten feet from the connector (we're talking here about the distance between main panel and shore cable receptacle). When receptacles are more than ten feet away, the standard requires an additional breaker at the receptacle. The reason is that when electrical contact points become corroded, this reduces the contact surface area very substantially. This causes more current to flow through a smaller area that will result in heating. It's the same thing as putting too much power through a too small wire. With a circuit breaker located too far away, it's not going to sense that heat build up and therefore will not trip. This is why we see quite a few builders placing fuses or circuit breakers directly at the shore power receptacle, which means that the receptacles have to be placed in a drier location such as the cockpit.

By far, the greatest danger is with having corrosion induced high resistence on the neutral connection of a 250VAC cable connection. This results in a line voltage rise of the neutral of one leg that then feeds back into the neutral of the other leg. Where you once had two 125 V legs, the other now becomes 250V (125 on the hot, 125 on the neutral combined make 250V). Since this exceeds the voltage of the appliance and its wiring, it will burn up the appliance and likely cause a fire. When purchasing used boats with 250VAC systems, be sure to have the cable ends and receptacles serviced whether it appears to need it or not.

Electric Service Panels

Service panels don't have to look like the cockpit panels of a Boeing 747 to be effective.

What makes a panel most effective is a convenient location. It's not convenient to have to get down on your hands and knees to see the thing — as is occasionally the case – nor to have to climb over or move furniture. When we encounter shore power problems, the boat owner is usually faced with the prospect of going back and forth between panel and dock connection numerous times, so my reasoning for convenient panel placement should be clear. Poor panel placement tends to be more of a problem with older boats than newer.

For this reason, quite a few builders will place the panel directly into the cabin companionway, but unfortunately in a location where sea spray will get to it if one forgets to close the door. Be alert to corroded panels on used boats where this has happened. A good surveyor will open up the panel and check inside for corrosion damage.

No matter how small the boat, if it has shore power, it should have an ammeter for each circuit, for one really can't monitor power usage without one. To avoid blowing circuit breakers, most boat owners control their power consumption by paying attention to the ammeters. If you don't have them, then, of course, you can't do this.

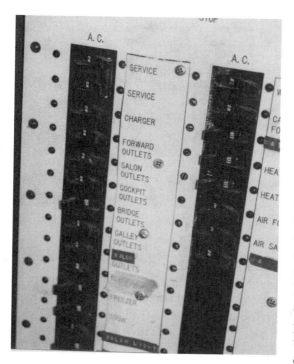

Fig.11-8. A portent of trouble, this panel has too many breakers that have been relabled. What lays behind this a severely jerry-rigged system.

Circuit Breakers

Something that a lot of boat builders are doing that they should not be doing is to use circuit breakers as on/off switches as well as power source selection switches. Circuit breakers are expensive and fairly sensitive devices. Like an old-fashioned autmotive distributor, they have electrical contact points in them. Whenever you throw the breaker lever, electrical arcing occurs across these contact points. Over time, frequent throwing of the levers results in eroded and high resistance contact points, as well as weakened internal springs. This causes the breakers to heat up and trip prematurely; this condition will become accumulative until the breaker is no longer useable because it is always tripping. This is often mistaken for a short circuit problem where none exists. Thus, for the want of a $6.00 switch, the boat owner ends up paying $60-80 for replacement circuit breakers that were used as switches.

Main panels that use circuit breakers for main power source switching are substandard and you will pay a price for that in circuit breaker replacement costs. Panels should have rotary power source selector switches. Their presence is always a sign of good engineering. Using circuit breakers for power source switching becomes particularly expensive because these are under high amperage loads and will deteriorate very rapidly. These large breakers, of course, are much more expensive.

Service Outlets

The number and location of service outlets in modern boats remains as frustrating as in older homes where there's never one where you need it. A minor annoyance, but perhaps something you may want to check on or have something done about. Most boats are deficient in this regard. Be alert for used boats where substandard additions have been made, such as the installation of add-on power strips.

Fig.11-9. When systems on older boats get this bad, a surveyor has no choice but to condemn it.

The ABYC standards require ground fault current interrupters (GFCI's) in the galley and head. If there are outlets in the cockpit, bridge or engine room, these should be GFCI protected as well.

Older Boats

Older boats often present serious electrical system problems, usually in the form of substandard repairs, additions and alterations similar to that shown above. When systems get this bad surveyors will usually condemn the entire system because there is too much wrong to ever get it straightened out. This makes the boat uninsurable, a factor that has a profoundly negative effect on its value.

The cost of rewiring a forty foot boat will run about $25,000 to $35,000 and possibly higher depending on degree of complexity and difficulty. Since estimating such jobs is extremely difficult, most electrical contractors will either quote a very high estimate, or will only do the job on time and material basis. Because of this, purchasing a boat in such a condition becomes financially risky.

Generators

The beauty of having an auxiliary power generator is that it makes your vessel self-sustaining electrically. Not only does it make it possible to air condition when away from the dock, but other forms of refrigeration can be maintained as well, a very important point for sport fishermen and cruising boats. The cocktail cruiser also gets to keep his ice cubes nice and crisp. Almost all boats in the mid size range have generators and not having one is a definite negative at resale time as it costs more to have one added than the OEM installation.

The vast majority of mid size boats do not have sufficient generator power to run everything on the boat. This is mainly a cost versus need issue and sometimes a unit size/space issue, i.e., not enough space for a larger unit.

The key to getting the right generator capacity usually lies with air conditioning as the single largest power demand, and the one that is most often used. Normally one wants to have a generator because one plans to rely on it, so it's a mistake to think that you will

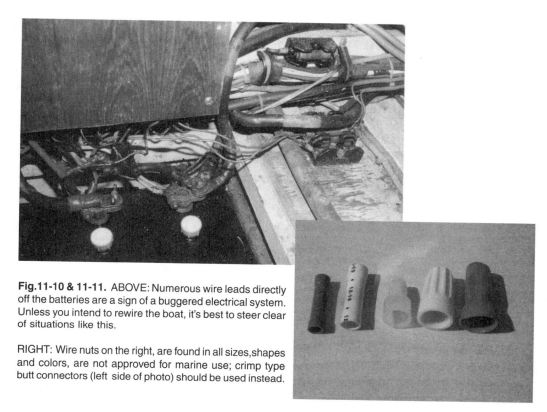

Fig.11-10 & 11-11. ABOVE: Numerous wire leads directly off the batteries are a sign of a buggered electrical system. Unless you intend to rewire the boat, it's best to steer clear of situations like this.

RIGHT: Wire nuts on the right, are found in all sizes, shapes and colors, are not approved for marine use; crimp type butt connectors (left side of photo) should be used instead.

Fig.11-12. A generator in sound shield located under a cockpit deck. This is all that can be seen of it, or accessed. Note that the removable door (right) can't be opened sufficiently, nor can it be removed from this hole, making it nearly impossible to even check the engine oil. While we don't run into installations this bad very often, one does need to be alert for this sort of thing. In the end, the sound shield had to be dismantled and discarded in order to service the generator.

only use it sparingly if that is not your thinking. A 30-35' boat with only a 5 Kw generator, air conditioning is likely to be under powered considering that it will need to run air conditioning, battery charger and refrigerator at minimum. To this you might add icemaker and water heater, microwave and stove. This is because when we add up the total wattage and though the total falls under 5 Kw, it probably still comes awfully close to 5 Kw and thus causes the unit to run at maximum load. This is not good for the unit, so what we need is a unit that has excess capacity so that at worst the unit is only running at a moderately high load or less, about 80%. This pretty much makes a 7.0 or 7.5 Kw unit a necessity.

The bottom line is that you can't use it if you don't have it. On larger boats, say 35 feet and over, the builder will usually supply an adequately sized unit. On smaller and lower priced boats generator size is typically where we find the builder skimping on, so be aware of this if you're shopping for bargains.

As with all products, quality of the product is related to price. Low price usually means short life and unreliability. When it comes to diesel generators, the fewer cylinders it has, the noiser it will be with more vibration. Anything less than three cylinders will be noisy and shake a lot. Two cylinder diesel units should be avoided.

Generators often get installed in bad locations where they either get wet, or become extremely difficult to service. The end result is usually frequent breakdowns and poor reliability. The generator manufacturer usually gets blamed for what is the boat builder's fault. Generators in smaller boats are inevitably more troublesome than in large boats simply because they too often get crammed into bad spots. The usual attitude toward them is out of sight, out of mind, with predictable results.

As for brands, I generally believe that the well known makers such as Onan, Kohler, Westerbeke and Northern Lights are the better choices. There are dozens of manufacturers that market generators, often at much lower prices than those just mentioned, but their products tend to be inferior. Then there are what I call the suitcase generators which are very small units installed in fancy boxes. Most of the ones I have

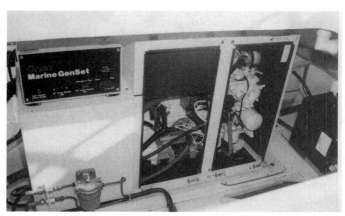

Fig.11-13. Sound shields can cause serious maintenance problems if there isn't adequate space. Decide whether you really need it before you pay the extra money for it. This one is installed in a 50 footer so acess space isn't limited.

Fig.11-14. A fiberglass, water-lift generator muffler. A good muffler but for the fact that (in this instance) it discharges into the main exhaust system.

seen are not manufactured specifically for marine use and I would not want one of these on a boat as they are very light duty and contain lots of dissimilar metals. The cooling systems also leave a lot to be desired. Most of these have been adapted from road vehicle generators. These include names such as Fischer-Panda, Ruggieri and Mace. Suitcase generators made a rather brief appearance in the early 1990's, but their record of performance was so dismal that by Y2K almost all builders stopped installing them. An exception may be European builders.

Gas or Diesel?

In a gas powered boats, only gas generators are available, and the same goes for diesel boats. While gas propulsion engines present no significant hazard, gas generators do. The problem here is carbon monoxide emissions that can possibly be brought back into the cabin spaces. It is generally not prudent to lay overnight, closed up with the air conditioning on powered by a gas generator. It is as dangerous as sleeping in a car with the engine running and the windows closed. There are just too many unanticipated ways in which exhaust fumes might find their way into the sleeping quarters.

Diesel generators unfortunately are noisy, but there is far less risk of carbon monoxide poisoning. Fortunately, there have been a lot of improvements made by the big name manufacturers (Onan, Kohler, Westerbeke, Northern Lights) so that most late model units are about half as loud as those manufactured in 1990 and earlier. Later generation diesel engines also run smoother. Most of this noise reduction comes about through engines with more cylinders that makes for a more balanced engine.

If you're looking at a boat on which the generator sounds excessively loud, check the generator's operating speed. A relatively small number of boats in the early 1990's were fitted with 3600 RPM generators which are extraordinarily loud; you don't want one of these. Most marine generators run at 1800 RPM which is what you want.There are also a few 2400 RPM generators currently on the market; I'd suggest you check carefully whether the noise level is acceptable to you.

Diesel exhaust has a very noxious element of sulphur dioxide. While it smells bad, it doesn't adversely affect most people with moderate exposure. However, breathing diesel exhaust greatly amplifies the tendency toward sea sickness. A few people, most often women, are made very ill by it. Some boats have more of a problem with station wagon effect than others, so if diesel exhaust bothers you, be sure to check it out.

From the 1980's through the early 1990's it was thought by some builders that dumping the generator exhaust into a main engine exhaust line was a good, money-saving idea. it turns out to be a bad idea because exhaust pressure of the main engine line often forces water in the generator exhaust line back into the engine, ruining same. Generator exhausts should not, as shown in photo at bottom of page 15, exit into the main engine exhaust pipes.

Does it make any difference whether generator output is 120 or 120/240? The only reason you would need 240 volts is if you have an electric stove that uses that voltage, or maybe a high capacity water maker. Otherwise, pleasure crafts don't have anything that uses 240V. The vast majority of 7 Kw and above units are 120/240 while under 5 Kw are single voltage only.

Is there a power advantage to 120/240 generator units? No, unlike a shoreline, you get the same available amperage from a generator regardless of voltage. For example, with a 7kW unit, you get 64 amps at 120 or 32 amps on each of the 240 lines, so the total available amperage is the same.

Almost all marine generators at 7 Kw and above are dual voltage, so the question really becomes a moot point.

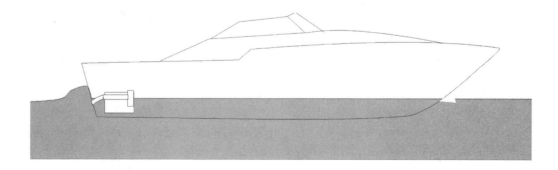

Fig.11-15. This illustration reveals why generators installed at or below water line require extra care on installation, such as high exhaust risers, to prevent water from backing up through the exhaust into the engine. The risk is greatest when backing up or laying at rest while at sea. Note how easily water can go up the generator exhaust.

Water Where It Shouldn't

Usually only generators in express, open or other rear engine boats pose an installation problem. Since generators are usually located at or below the water line, they must have an adequately high riser in the exhaust piping outlet, otherwise back surge through the exhaust could enter the engine. The problem being that the cockpit heights in most open boats don't allow for a sufficiently high riser. Specifically look to see if there is space between the cockpit liner and hull at the transom with an exhaust riser in it. A transom riser should be a minimum of 12" above the static water line.

If the generator is located on center line, check to see if it is adequately high above the bilge so that it won't get wet. This is a very common problem, and one that causes a lot of generators to become damaged , particularly on rear engine, vee drive boats. Sea Ray is one of the worst offenders in this regard.

On mid engine boats the generator is often located behind and between the engines, which usually means right between both stuffing boxes as well. THE STUFFING BOXES MUST HAVE SPLASH GUARDS on them to prevent water from being thrown onto the generator and ruining it. Don't be fooled by the so-called "drippless" type that never leak. There is no such thing as *never* on a boat!

I've heard many boat owners say that they only run the generator when they absolutely have to. The rule is: use it or lose it. Generators are meant to be run; they use very little fuel and you needn't worry about wearing it out. Its life is reduced mainly by the passage of chronological time rather than the hour meter. Don't waste all that money by not using it. It will just rust up and become unuseable.

Inverters: AC Power From Batteries

In recent years inverters have been very aggressively marketed as a substitute for generators. The usual advertising claim is that generators are expensive, noisy and maybe even dangerous. Generators are indeed all those things, yet they are also something else: much more effective and reliable than attempting to run high powered electrical equipment off of an inverter and batteries. Inverters are always marketed on basis of the good things they can do without ever mentioning the negatives, which are considerable.

An inverter may be an acceptable solution for anyone who simply can't afford a generator, but inverters by no stretch of the imagination should be considered a passable substitute. They are extremely hard on batteries and will cause the need for frequent battery replacement, so the notion that an inverter is any way an acceptable substitute ignores the fact that one either has to plug into the dock to charge batteries, or run the main engines. The later is not a good option, for alternators require a long charging period to fully charge batteries. Additionally, most boats in the 30- 40 foot range do not have sufficient battery power to run an inverter at a sustained rate, so increasing battery and charging capacity is likely necessary to install a properly functioning inverter system.

The vast majority of boats in the thirty foot range are fitted with inexpensive automotive batteries that are inadequate for this application. To reliably use an inverter for any serious power conversion one should have commercial duty batteries that typically cost two to three times as much. The differences are in the quality of the lead plates inside which you cannot see, but are always reflected in the price. The most effecive inverter systems use banks of 6 volt batteries. That's because two 6 volt batteries in series yeilds nearly twice the area size of internal plates that in turn increases battery power and life.

Inverters will not operate air conditioning systems and neither can you run an electric stove with one. DC refrigeration and water heaters run off engine cooling systems can take care of those needs when dockside power is not available. All that leaves for an inverter would be a small TV, computers and other small devices. In fact, small devices are what the inverter handles best, so if you have no need for air conditioning, and don't do any cooking, an inverter may very well fulfil your minimal 125 VAC needs. Again, as with all things marine, if you go for the cheapest one, you'll get equally cheap results. Heart and Trace are the two most respected manufacturers and their products are anything but cheap in quality or price.

Before purchasing an inverter, I highly recommend that a first class marine electrician be engaged to evaluate your existing DC system.

Fig.11-16. A DIYS inverter installation under a dinette seat. The owner has used substandard materials such as a household power strip and extension cords for the wiring, in addition to installing a battery in the cabin space where it should not be.

DC Systems

Where high voltage systems tend to be more or less the same, battery systems are likely to be very different from boat to boat. This all starts with whether the builder decided to skimp on cost by supplying minimal battery power. Unfortunately, most of them do because these systems involve a lot of cost and it's good place to cut corners.

Anything but a high end boat is likely to be furnished with inadequate battery power, but even that is no guarantee. A high price Cabo on a recent survey turned up only two 12 volt 90 Ah batteries for a hungry power demand. Nor was there a separate starting battery for the generator. Thus, if the main engine starting batteries went dead, the generator could not be started to run the charger. The new boat owner had to modify the system and install additional batteries to meet his needs at considerable cost. Since this was a new boat survey, he was able to negotiate a good part of this cost with the dealer in order to make the sale.

In most price boats the batteries can be expected to last only 18-24 months. When you combine poor quality batteries with undersize batteries, the result is inevitably unreliability. When it comes to low price or entry level boats, well over 50% of the boats that I survey have failed battery systems. I often show up for a survey where the engines won't start even though the battery charger is on. When it comes to the Regals, Silvertons, Bayliners, Carvers and the like, expect that the batteries will be second rate and likely undersize, particularly for new boats.

With many used boats we find that batteries have been upgraded by necessity. Builders like Bertram and Hatteras will tell you in the owner's manual exactly what batteries the boat was originally supplied with, but not so for lesser breeds.

Regardless of how small the boat is, battery banks are best installed in pairs for the reason that this doubles the available ampere hours and reduces heavy load drain on a single battery, thereby facilitating faster recharging. Furthermore, batteries do not recover as well from heavy draining as they do from light draining. Obviously, then, any boat that has only a single starting battery for each engine and no "house" bank is going to be seriously deficient and should be upgraded. Note that DC system battery amperage can be upgraded with no additional modifications to the electrical system other than making room for larger batteries.

All boats are required to have battery shut off switches though many will have combination shut-off/selector switches that will determine whether systems are being run off bank 1, 2 or both. This could allow one to start both engines off one bank or the other, or it may determine only which bank the house system operates from. How boats are wired can vary, but most such systems will switch the whole system over. Larger boats over 35 feet or so usually do not have combination switches but use both banks for the house system wherein the battery switches will be simple ON/OFF switches.

They will have battery parallel switches for engine starting in the event of low cranking power. The reasoning behind this is that larger boats with generators will normally solve the dead battery problem through the generator which has a separate starting battery and battery charger. One is only stuck if none of the three engines can be started or the generator doesn't have a separate starting battery.

When it comes to used boats, the most common problem is related to replacing batteries one at a time when they go bad. You know what would happen if you put one used battery and two new batteries in your digital camera. The used battery would drag the new ones down to its level and very soon you'll have four bad batteries. The same also happens a lot with boats. If you look at a boat's batteries and find them to be all different sizes and brands, expect a big battery replacement bill soon.

An important consideration with battery switches is whether turning the switches to the OFF position will shut off power to the bilge pumps. Builders have often made this wiring mistake, so you should be sure to check this yourself or have your surveyor check it out. The pumps should still function with the switches turned off.

Battery Chargers

The battery charger is one of the most relied upon but ill-considered pieces of equipment on a boat, perhaps because how they work is not well understood. Suffice it to say that all late model boats since around 1998 will have electronic rather then the old style ferroresonant chargers. The cheapest electronic charger is probably better than the most expensive ferroresonant chargers by virtue of their ability to adjust charge rates and sense when a battery can take no more charge.

The problem with ferroresonant chargers is their tendency to overcharge, which is very damaging and ruins a lot of batteries before their time. Therefore, if you're buying an older boat, it would be wise to consider upgrading the charger.

It's also a good idea to check out the location of the charger and make sure that it isn't located under the lip of a hatch (as many are) where it is likely to get wet and ruined. It should also not be located directly above or beside a shaft packing gland for the same reason. If so, it should be relocated or a protective cover provided.

Older Boats

Generally speaking, electrical systems do not degrade much unless they are getting wet. The most common problem with older boats is all the substandard, amateur wiring and jerry-rigging that is done by former owners. Over time, these shortcomings can accumulate to the point where the overall system becomes unreliable, so be alert to this for boats 12 years and older.

The first sign that all is not well usually comes in the form of an electric panel that has had numerous changes to the circuit breaker labels. This is a sure clue that there have been a lot of changes. The right question to ask is "why?" The answer is often something that you don't want to buy into. It is a serious problem that there are too many boat owners who can't or won't pay to make electrical alterations, additions and repairs to a proper electrical standard. Often times they'll patch new circuits into existing circuits with no consideration for the higher load this creates, thereby creating overloaded circuits and potential fire hazards.

Either you or your surveyor should generally inspect the wiring wherever it is visible, particularly behind the electric panel and within the engine room. The important thing to look for are jerry-rigged wiring and excessive numbers of wire splices that indicate that there has been a lot of patchwork going on. Splices are denoted by the presence of butt connectors appearing at other than the ends of the wire. Splices should never be insulated with electrical tape. Every wire splice poses a potential problem that is not inherent in a non-spliced wire, so the more of them there are , the less reliable the system will be.

Another thing we don't like to see, something that is all too common, is the use of in-line fuses that less than professional equipment installers frequently use to save on costs. A boat with a dozen or so inline fuses scattered throughout its length, plus numerous butt connectors, is a boat with tens of dozens of wire splices in its systems, all of which can potentially pull apart or corrode when coming in contact with water.

Not only do these pose short circuit and stray current risks, but when a piece of equipment fails, it is usually impossible to check out a 30 foot run of wire, so the best one can do is run new wires, making simple repair jobs time-consuming and costly. Therefore, it is wise to avoid boats with buggered electrical systems. The more a system appears to be original and without significant alterations, the better it will be for you.

Plumbing Systems

Plumbing systems on boats are a frequent source of problems on boats. The more optimistic among us would simply say that plumbing is a high maintenance category, the nature of the beast. Of course, the quality of systems and materials utilized plays a huge role in this issue, and so it is generally that the quality involved is usually directly related to the price of the boat; higher priced boats will almost always have higher quality systems.

There are two basic types of systems on boats, those that use internal fresh water only, and those that in one way or another are common with the water in which the boat is floating, be it salt or fresh. For the lack of a better term, I refer to all systems that make use of a through hull fitting as a salt water system. That includes things like heads, bilge pumps, shower sumps and even sinks.

Fig.11-17. This plastic bait well pump was installed by a builder, threaded directly onto a sea cock. Imagine what would happen if someone opened the hatch and threw a fender down into the bilge.

Fig.11-18. A top quality Perko bronze body sea strainer. Located for easy access, it is important that the sight glass be visible for frequent checking. The filter basket is easily removable from the top.

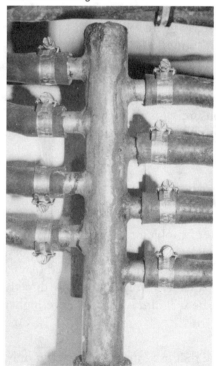

Fig.11-19. Stainless steel components in plumbing systems often prove troublesome as this stainless manifold reveals. Boats built in the orient often have a lot of stainless in the plumbing that fails after a number of years.

Fig.11-20. This bronze strainer is threaded directly into a plastic air conditioning pump housing. The leverage created by the strainer is distorting the pump housing and causing it to leak and malfunction. Connections like this should always be made with a hose section.

Sea Cocks

All boats are required to have sea cocks on all underwater connections, though not on above water line through hull fittings. While the logic of this is not exactly clear, the economics of it surely is. The typical thirty-five footer will have a dozen or more openings in the hull, all of which are potential sources of trouble. Sea cocks are used in an emergency, such as when a hose or other plumbing component fails, to close off the unexpected opening. They are also closed when boats lay afloat for long periods unattended, to reduce the risks of systems failure.

Over the years we've seen a huge variety of valves used on boats, many of which don't qualify as sea cocks. The most common of these is the brass gate valve which should not be used on boats because of the weakness of brass to corrosion, as well as inherent problems with the design of the valve, such as threaded valve stems and the potential for seizing up. Gate valves are most easily identified by their round top handles. I haven't found any builders that use gate valves anymore but you may find them turning up on used boats where they may have been installed by owners.

True sea cocks come in several varieties, including cylinder cocks and ball cocks. Their base material is bronze, hence they are more expensive, although ball cocks usually have a stainless ball set in a plastic seat. Because of their close tolerances, historically sea cocks have always had a problem with seizing up due to small amounts of minor corrosion. The use of plastic sleeves and seats (introduced only about 10 years ago) now virtually eliminates this problem. Cylinder cocks really tend to seize up hard and have rightly fallen out of favor. They're likely to be found only on pre 1990 boats. Most good quality sea cocks will bear the U.L label, so you might want to look for that.

Fig.11-21 & 11-22. The most common sea cocks today are ball valves like this one. Shown at right is the ball half open. The stainless steel ball is set into a nylon bushing which prevents corrosion seizing. Note the wide mounting base.

The cost of bronze ball cocks has come down so much in recent years that there is no longer any excuse for not using this good quality hardware.

Plastic Valves

Fiberglass reinforced plastic valves that go under the trade names Marilon and Forespar have been approved for marine use. These are not widely used because of a fundamental problem with seizing up that makes them no better than old bronze sea cocks. Due to stresses imposed on the valve body, they tend to distort, causing them to be extremely difficult to operate.

No other type of plastic valve should ever be used as a through hull fitting.

Sea Strainers

It is highly recommended that all systems that draw water into the boat from without be equipped with internal strainers. This is to protect pumps and other equipment from damage caused by debris in the water. Sea Strainers can be made of plastic, stainless steel or bronze, with the later being most highly preferred. Stainless steel, due to problems with crevice corrosion does not perform well in plumbing systems. Plastic is highly

Fig.11-23. A typical jerry-rigged, DIYS installation on a through hull. This one uses a plastic hardware store valve and a garden hose quick-connect fitting that is almost guaranteed to sink the boat sooner or later.

Fig.11-24. A bronze, ball-type sea cock that bears the U.L. lable. Note the wide flange or base plate. Pipe plug at center is for winter draining of the valve body.

vulnerable to breakage, leaving bronze the only sensible choice of materials.

An important consideration for strainers is the ease of access to and servicing since strainers require frequent cleaning. A proper bronze marine strainer will have a removable top with removable basket. Secondly, the whole strainer breaks down so that the plexiglass sight cylinder can be cleaned or even replaced. Keep in mind that barnacles can grow inside side strainers on the sight lens. When this happens, the lens has to be replaced, otherwise one cannot see through it.

Of course it is of no help if the boat builder installs the strainers in places that are very hard, even impossible to reach, so be sure to check this aspect out.

There are two main types of strainers: the internal and external types. External types are fitting on the bottom of the hull, over the intake opening. These are fine as a primary strainer with a proper strainer on the inside. However, to rely on external strainer screens is ill advised since these cannot be easily cleaned without hauling the boat. In areas where rapid marine growth is prevalent, these will tend to foul rapidly and likely causing engine overheating and the risk of costly damage. If a boat does not have good quality internal strainers, particularly for the main engine intakes, consider this a deficiency which the seller should bear the cost to remedy whether the boat is new or used.

Small plastic bilge pump strainers and plastic swimming pool strainers should never be used on through hull systems.

Plastic Components

The virtue of plastic is that in plumbing systems it doesn't corrode. One serious fault is that it is very weak material so that we have to be careful how we use it, if at all. Not all builders are, so be on the lookout for these points:

- Threaded metal male connectors should never be threaded into female plastic connectors. The reason is that all metals corrode and create oxides that expand and can fracture the plastic. This is a very serious problem, so be on the lookout for it.

- Strainers should never be suspended by a pipe or hose. All strainers must be rigidly mounted to a solid structure.

- Pumps, especially plastic pumps or those with plastic housings, should never be threaded directly to strainers or sea cocks. The reason is that this will put stress on the pump housing, eventually causing it to fail. ALL pumps must be connected to a strainer or sea cock with flexible hose. This is a common defect.

Fig.11-25. At top a plastic through hull nipple. Bottom, a bronze nipple. The difference in price at retail is about $8.00.

Fig.11-26. Sunlight damaged through hull nipple. Note crack on inside. They need to be replaced before they get to this state. Look for crumbling oxidation on the exterior flange.

- PVC pipe should always have glued and never threaded connections. When pipe is threaded, the threads literally cut the wall thickness in half, making the pipe highly vulnerable to breaking.

- PVC pipe should never be directly mated to any component, instead being joined by nipples and flexible hoses.

Plastic Nipples

Look down along the hull sides, just above the water line and you'll see a number of water exit ports. These are nipples to which a hose is attached on the inside that are also referred to as "through hulls." (Actually, virtually any type of hardware that brings water in or out of the boat is referred to as a through hull.) On the vast majority of boats they will be some type of plastic above waterline. More conscientious builders will use bronze.

This is a problem because more boats have sunk from broken plastic nipples than probably any other cause. First, most of these plastics are highly vulnerable to sunlight and second, they are naturally weak and will age and become brittle in any case. Bear in mind, too, that a hose filled with water will weigh up to four times the weight of the hose alone, and when combined with a slamming hull . . . . well, you can see the nature of the problem. Breakage, and being only few inches above the water line, there exists the potential for sinking the boat.

So why don't they put them higher up, you might ask? Well, for a fairly good reason. Water flowing out of an exit port will cause splash which in turn will cause a big discolored halo on the hull side, so they mount them low to reduce splash. Then why don't they use bronze ports instead? That's a good question, and since nearly everyone knows that broken plastic is a problem, then cost must be the answer. The plastic isn't likely to break until after the warranty runs out, so it's not the builder's problem.

Vacuum Head Systems

Also known as marine toilets, heads have long resided on the dark side of paradise. Fortunately, in recent years there has been significant improvements, particularly for the SeaLand vacuum head system, currently the only vacuum system on the market. Once a leaky nightmare, this system is now reliable and the most widely used. One of its benefits is that it doesn't smell like old fashioned heads do. The problem with pump heads is the large amount of water it takes to clear the system; people simply don't pump long enough to clear the lines and so waste sits in the lines and the smell escapes back through the bowl. That is especially true in locals where the use of holding tanks is enforced, for tanks are quickly filled with flushing water. The vacuum system goes a long way to solve this problem by greatly reducing the amount of water needed to flush the system.

The down side of these systems is that they are somewhat cheaply made so that system life expectancy will be in the range of 6-8 years before major system components such as pumps will have to be replaced. Fortunately, these parts are not terribly expensive. The good news is that so far these systems have proved to be more reliable than any other type of system.

Holding tanks are a problematical issue that is only going to get worse as time rolls on, for as surely as night follows day, we will one day be facing a ban on virtually any waste water whatsoever going overboard. That will include sinks and showers. As of this writing, only a handful of states rigidly enforce the use of holding tanks but that could change suddenly as water quality is once again on the decline.

Boating in a Sewer

The quality of boating life is directly related to the quality of water we go boating in. Nobody wants to go boating in a sewer, yet that is the way many people treat our waterways. Garbage disposers are often provided with larger yachts; though their use is not banned, as it should be, I ask you please, please, do not ever use a garbage disposer if boat has one. Do not ever pour any kind of waste down a sink drain. With so many boats and so many people boating, when everyone adds a little pollution, the total adds up to a lot.

Standard Electric Pump Systems

There exists a fairly large number of different types of pump systems, from the High quality Galley Maid to the Raritan Crown and various water "jet" systems to the cheaper inexpensive combination macerator pumps including those by Raritan and PAR or ITT Jabsco. Units that include the pump and motor in the head itself have generally proved to require frequent maintenance and overhaul. One of the more egregious problems with this type stems from the fact that the builder almost never ties the metal pump into the common bonding system and it thus becomes vulnerable to corrosion.

One of the worst heads ever made is the old plastic manual pump system by Raritan that has been electrified and driven by plastic cams and levers. Made almost entirely of plastic, this system has a nifty habit of grinding itself to pieces with great regularity. Fortunately, this unfortunate work of art is rapidly disappearing from the market.

Waste Plumbing Systems

These systems are pretty much standardized after 1990 to the point where the vast majority of boats will have near identical systems and they generally work well. Prior to 1990, there is a hodge podge of various designs and equipment that may not work very well.

Fig.11-27. This bilge pump has three feet of static head without any riser at all (black hose running vertically at center). Since the discharge is in the transom, it's not hard to see why this is a problem. This installation did, in fact, sink this boat.

The main fault in system layout occurs in the piping or waste hose runs from the head to the pump, be it vacuum or otherwise. Low spots in the run, or piping that has to run uphill will cause pumping problems, resulting in waste remaining in the line with resultant odors. These can be quite unpleasant, so you'll be sure to check. If a boat smells bad, ask your surveyor to check out the piping system for faults since the cost of correction can be fairly high.

Bilge Pumps

These are some of the most important devices on a boat, and probably the most ignored. Think of bilge pumps as serving TWO major functions; first they remove small amounts of water as it accumulates in the bilge. Secondly, they are emergency devices that can mean the difference between sinking and swimming.

Some people get the idea that a bilge should never have any water in it at any time: that's unrealistic. Most boats have minor leaks that are not worth the effort to try to stop. Besides, rain water always finds its way into the bilge.

It's amazing how many boat owners never even consider the possibility that their boats might become endangered to sinking. It's usually boats belonging to people who think this way that do. Why? Because they never even bother to check whether their pumps are working, yet alone doing any kind of maintenance on them.

Adding to the problem is the fact that most builders don't provide adequate bilge pump capacity to begin with. Most provide enough pumps just to remove normal

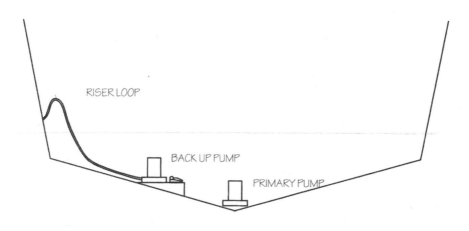

Fig.11-28. The proper set up for a primary and secondary bilge pump arrangement.

accumulations, not for emergency purposes. Unfortunately, we can't come up with a quick and easy rule to figure how many pumps a particular size boat should have since this also depends on the configuration of the boat plus how many separate compartments it has.

This important point stresses my earlier statements that boats that do not provide access to major areas of the hull pose serious risks to the owner. To illustrate, as this was being written, I surveyed a 36 foot, rear engine boat that had bilge access only to the rear engine compartment. The remaining 75% of the hull had no access whatever, a situation that is completely unacceptable.

The criteria to follow for pumps is that they need to be large and powerful and well made. Because they live in such a harsh environment, this is no place to be economy minded; this is sort of like shopping for the best price on a pacemaker.

Back up pumps are so important that many builders provide them as standard equipment. Pumps usually fail for one of two reasons: either the wire connections get wet and corrode, or the float switch sticks or something interferes with its operation. This is why back ups are needed. The back up usually has a float switch that is installed at a higher level, so that it kicks on only when the water level reaches that point. Or the pump itself may be installed at a higher level.

Very small pumps such as the Rule 500, 800 or 1000 are too small to be reliable; their small impellers are easily jammed with small amounts of debris. My recommendation is that a Rule 1500 is the smallest size that should be used in the over 30 foot class of boats.

The formula:

$$Length \times beam \times 8$$

will give you a rough idea of how many gallons of water will definitely sink your boat. In many cases, as with rear engine boats, that amount will be less. For these boats use:

$$Length \times beam \times 4$$

One needs to be able to remove that amount of water fairly fast, and since all pumps are rated by gallons per hour, we can easily figure this. For a 30' boat with a ten foot beam, this translates to 2400 gallons. Thus, two 1500 GPH pumps would take roughly 45 minutes. Is that fast enough in an emergency? Not with me on board it isn't. For the hundred bucks or so that it would take to install a third pump, that time would be reduced substantially.

Of course, we're not very likely to take on 2400 gallons all at once, but a 1-1/2" hole in the hull, such as from a lost propeller shaft or hose gone loose, can put in as much as 50 gallons/minute. Our 1500 GPH pump only puts out 25 gallons/minute under ideal circumstances; the real output is more likely to be significantly less, the reason being capacity is reduced by the amount of static head pressure (how high the discharge is above the pump).

Therefore, in the face of a fairly common emergency we're as much as 25 gallons/minute short. But, there are two 1500 GPM pumps on board you say. True, but one of them is likely to be up forward and the water is coming in aft and it will be a while before the water level forward rises to the point where that pump is a help and by then it will be too late. Now, if we had two 2000 GPH pumps aft and one forward, we're in a lot better shape aren't we?

As you can see, it's hard to ever say that a boat has too much pumping capacity, especially if you're doing any serious offshore cruising where the possibility of getting immediate help is unlikely. The following table will serve as a guide but is contingent on hull configuration and number of compartments:

Boat Size	No. Pumps	Total Capacity in GPH
25-30	2	3000
31-35	3-4	3500-4500
36-42	3-4	4500-6000
43-49	4-5	6000-8000
50-59	5-6	8000+

Fig.11-29. A clear illustration of an improper bilge pump discharge installation. This discharge is just a few inches above the water line so that water can backflow through the line. A simple riser loop will prevent this problem.

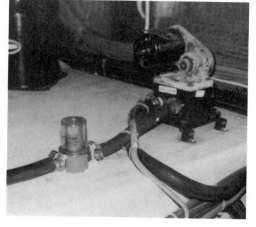

Fig.11-30. When centrifugal bilge pumps won't evacuate all the water in the bilge, it is often necessary to install a diaphragm pump such as this one. Diaphragm pumps always need to have a filter.

Where Does the Water Go?

Free communication is a term that means the ability of water to run from one compartment to the next. While you might think that it would be a good idea to have water tight compartments in a boat, actually it is not. A sad story recently illustrates. This fellow bought a brand new boat that the very first time he took it out nearly sank. It seems the forward bilge was filling up with water and neither of the two bilge pumps were taking it out because this particular compartment was sealed and had no pump in it. Miraculously, the owner managed to get in off the ocean before the boat went down bow first.

After pumping the boat out, it was returned to the dealer who repaired the water damage but could not find a leak. The boat was returned to the owner as being repaired. The owner took the boat out a second time and the same thing happened. After much head scratching, the dealer finally altered some plumbing that was thought might be the problem, only they weren't sure. Boat was again returned to the owner "fixed."

The third time the no longer proud owner took it out, the boat did sink, though both boat and owner were recovered. This time the owner called his insurance company that wisely hired an expert surveyor who spent several days investigating what happened. It turns out that the leak resulted from a crack in the bottom that was located inside a hollow stringer. The stringer had hole in it in *only that one compartment* which would fill up only while underway.

There was no bilge pump in the forward hull section which was sealed off from the aft section. With no free communication of water between compartments, the entire bow section flooded before anyone noticed what was happening. By the time the owner noticed that the boat was not behaving right, it was too late. As he slowed down, the bow sunk even further.

For safety's sake all major compartments need high capacity pumps; just because water doesn't "normally" accumulate in a compartment is no reason not to have adequate pumps in all compartments. What do I mean by "compartment"? Consider this to be any area that is separated by a bulkhead extending from keel to chine in height or higher. It is virtually any area that is dammed off by any kind of structure and could lead to the sort of thing that happened above.

Fresh Water Systems

These systems are fairly reliable and trouble free even though the majority of builders use low cost pumps. However, one trouble spot is the use of aluminum water tanks and diaphragm pumps such as Shur-Flo and PAR. Water in the tank causes a very heavy corrosion scale to accumulate on the bottom of the tank. This doesn't mean that the tank is failing; the size and amount of corrosion scale is way out of proportion to the actual damage to the tank. In other words, aluminum tanks make a lot of scale, but aluminum tanks actually hold up pretty well. But pumps don't when they are ingesting that scale.

Fresh water pumps therefore need to be fitted with good filters between pump and tank, and periodically cleaned. If the potable water system has a purification filter, chances are it hasn't been changed in a long time. It's generally a good idea for any used boat purchase to treat the water system with chlorine before use. Then drain the tank and fill with fresh water.

When checking out a boat, whether new or used, it's a good idea to check the system water pressure from the internal pump, especially if you plan on taking showers. Most single pump systems are inadequate for both hot and cold water systems where a dual pump system is needed to maintain adequate pressure. Larger boats are often deficient in this regard.

Most boats 30-35' have 6 gallon water heaters. Believe it or not that is enough for showering as long as you don't leave the water running while soaping up. At 35' and above, or for longer showers you need a 12 gallon heater. While you're at it, you may want to check on how that steel housing heater unit is mounted. Very often they're mounted on a flat deck where water collects that quickly rusts the water heater. If so, a quick remedy is to have the heater shimmed up on blocks as it should have been in the first place. That way if the deck gets flooded, at least the heater won't be sitting in water. Also, look to be sure the pressure relief valve has a drain pipe attached. Otherwise, the valve will discharge water onto the base of the tank and rust it out.

An amusing situation occurs when a builder decides, as many do, to install the water tanks in the engine room. You get hot water from both faucets whether you want it or not after the boat has been run! Since most boats have water pipes that at least run through the engine room (but the tank is elsewhere), the water on the cold side usually runs momentarily hot and then goes cold.

Fig.11-31. Lacking a proper drain hose, the pressure relief valve will discharge water onto the deck on which the steel heater is sitting and will rust out the base of the heater.

Dockside Water Systems

Connecting directly to dockside water is very convenient but this also poses serious risks. If a water line in a house bursts, at least the house won't sink; a boat will. Dockside water connections are required to have pressure reducer/regulators that reduce standard city water pressure from an average of 60 psi to about 30 psi. Neither the pumps or other components in a boat can withstand 60 psi so the proper functioning of the regulator is critical.

Air Conditioning Systems

Marine air conditioning systems are found in two basic types, the self-contained systems and systems that use remote compressors. The self-contained systems are installed within the living quarters of the vessel whereas remote systems place noisy compressors outside the living quarters, frequently in the engine room. Self-contained systems can be problematic from the standpoint of both noise and the potential for condensation damage since air conditioners create large amounts of water that has to be safely disposed of.

All marine systems use sea water for cooling the heated freon which makes them more efficient. They are also reverse cycle – the same type of system that in a home is called a heat pump – so they will make heat as well when the outside water temperature is 40 degrees or greater; below that, it doesn't heat so well. This means that they will have a sea water pump and a sea strainer to filter out debris in the water. If the flow of cooling water is interrupted, the compressor will overheat and a temperature sensor should shut the compressor down before it becomes damaged. Therefore, it is important to have a good quality strainer that is in an easily accessible location for cleaning needs may be frequent.

The most common problem with A/C systems is the loss of freon. This is usually due to strain on the coolant lines due to G-forces caused by slamming of the hull that results in freon leaks. This is especially true of units mounted in the bow of the boat. The second most common problem is a failure of the high temperature sensor to shut the system down so the compressor burns up. For this reason on used boats it is important that A/C units be clean and not rusted and corroded. Expect heavily corroded units be subject to near-term failure.

A/C units in boats are very often thoughtlessly and poorly installed. In very humid environments, air conditioning units can create very large amounts of condensed water that has to be safely gotten rid of. Among the worst of the faults is a failure to ensure proper drainage of the condensation pan which may overflow or water slosh out while underway and result in water damage if the pan does not drain completely. When it doesn't and the boat pitches and slams, rocks and rolls, the water sloshes out. Often times woodwork damage in a boat is not due to external leaks but a poorly drained A/C system. It is therefore important that the A/C units be carefully examined.

Yet another problem can be inadequately insulated ducts which cause condensation. Condensation can end up on the inside or outside of the duct, with different consequences in each case. Outside condensation usually results in rotting nearby wood structures with which the duct is in contact, along with increased mildew problems and associated odors - *despite the use of air conditioning!*

Look for a return air filter on the system. About half of all boats I see do not have a return air filter, which means that the condenser coils will eventually get clogged up with dust and debris and lose cooling efficiency. A typical unit without a filter will lose 50% or more in efficiency within two years. Moreover, some 90% of boat owners never bother to clean them even if they do have filters, so it's little wonder so many boats have A/C that cools poorly or not at all. The only way to clean dirty condensers is by blasting them with a hose, not something one would like to undertake in the interior of a boat.

In larger boats, particularly sport fishermen, A/C units are sometimes mounted up on the flying bridge, an idea that has proved problematic over the years. First, if the condensation pan leaks, the water usually ends up damaging the overhead in the salon. Secondly, the units often sweat in such a way that condensation pan does not catch the condensation. I often find ducting that is not insulated. A related problem is that because the ducting is on the outside, condensation can collect in the ducts. This can lead to the interesting situation of the boat suddenly rolling and a cascade of cold water pouring out from an overhead vent. That has happened to me more than once.

The output temperature of each system should be checked with an infrared pyrometer to determine adequate cooling. Air temperatures usually vary widely, but a well insulated and functioning system should put out air at a minimum of 55 degrees after running for an hour or so. Keep in mind that inside a hot boat it will take some time before the lowest output temperature is reached. If the output temperature is 60 degrees or above,

Fig.11-32 & 11-33. ABOVE LEFT: Cruisair has improved their A/C units recently by adding a condensation catch pan on remote compressor units that is clearly lacking on the unit shown at RIGHT where the problem is that condensation runs all over causing damage.

consider this unacceptable and that for some reason the system is not functioning properly. All of the ducting should be checked with an infrared pyrometer for leaks an adequate insulation.

Occasionally I find units installed in a compartment that is open to the bilge. This is bad news because the system will be pulling smelly air out of the bilge, possibly even the engine room and could be dangerous.

My experience is that surveyors will often overlook these points, so be sure to stress to him that you want the installation and efficiency of the AC system checked.

Assessing the Overall Systems

When checking out a boat, new or used, it cannot be overemphasized how important it is that both plumbing and wiring be neatly installed. It may be okay to have sloppy wiring in a house where it isn't seen or touched, but not on a boat that bounces and shakes. Wiring that is not properly secured can chafe, wire connections loosen or come apart. Water is heavy, and a hose or pipe filled with water is even heavier, so it should not be hard to imagine that in a slamming boat things can easily become damaged if not well secured. When we find hoses and pipes carelessly scattered about, draped across open spaces and so on, this is not a good sign of a boat builder who cares much about his product or the people who buy it.

Note here that the smaller and lower priced the boat is, the more likely it is to find sloppy installations. Sloppy and careless installations can also mean that when things are being worked on or serviced, those scattered hoses are likely to get stepped on and damaged. All hoses and pipes should be solidly secured against movement and ordered in a neat and intelligible way. Wiring should not be secured to hoses and vice versa.

Freeze damage is a problem for plumbing systems on used boats throughout most of the country. Freezing is particularly hard on plastic parts, though it can damage metal as well. This sort of damage is best found by operating the various systems and inspecting the plumbing for leaks while in use. Water systems should be inspected while pressurized. If the system won't hold pressure for long, and the pump cycles frequently, leaks should be suspected.

Convenience for Servicing

This is something you'll want to pay particular attention to if you're a do-it-yourselfer, for the access to plumbing for service and layup can turn what should be a relatively easy job into an ugly task. Even if you dont perform your own service, you'll pay more for labor if the job is harder and takes more time for yard personnel.

Sea cocks and strainers are the most frequently serviced items, so take a few minutes to check out their positioning. Engines, air conditioning and heads are the ones that get the most attention, so these especially need to be easily reached.

Check to see if any of the plumbing is labeled. When you find little plastic tags that tell you what a valve, pipe or hose is, you can be assured that someone cared enough to make your job a little easier. Note the location of the water heater and other pumps as follows:

> Fresh water pump, one or two?
> Saltwater wash down, if any.
> Air conditioning sea water pump(s)
> Head pump
> Shower pump
> Bait well pump

There's a half-dozen pumps that you probably never thought about. Each of these pumps should have an intake strainer or internal filter, and the pumps need to be located so that they can be checked on periodically. Six pumps, six strainers. Imagine what life is like when they are all very hard to reach! And that doesn't include the bilge pumps.

Chapter 12

Design Details

Many people who own boats have come to the conclusion that the term "pleasure boating" is a misnomer; that "work boating" may be more appropriate. In this chapter I'll discuss many of the reasons why boats can become more work than expected, mostly the result of the accumulation of little things that can make it so, what to look for, the rights and the wrongs, how to avoid them and possibly how to get around them when they appear unavoidable.

The failure to really think through the details of design elements of a boat often end up becoming costly problems to boat owners. While I can make you aware of some of the more egregious problems, we have to bear in mind that in the real world there is no such thing as a perfect boat. On virtually all boats we will find that the builder/designers have done some pretty dumb things as well as some pretty smart things. A thirty-five foot boat is a large, complex vessel that we expect to be able to purchase at what we consider a reasonable price, and it's just not reasonable to expect that it's going to be perfect. That, however, should not deter us from trying to get our money's worth, while at the same time avoiding the trap of trying to find perfection in a production boat.

As a result of millions of boats being designed and built over about 70 years of yacht building in the U.S., the industry does have a lot of experience and common wisdom that pretty much sets a generally accepted common standard on the way things should be. It is those deviations from the common standard that we'll be dealing with in this chapter.

Hey Man, It's Cool

In the interest of attracting inexperienced buyers, marketing people come up with a lot of cool ideas. Ideas that appear to be cool to the uninitiated, but would definitely get a cool reception by people who know better. We'll take a look at some of those cool things and explain why "cool" might turn to ice cold.

Important Changes in Boat Building

It goes without saying that improvements in technology and process take place over time. Since this book addresses fiberglass boats since the days when they were first built, we're looking at over four decades of change. During those years, change has tended to take place not gradually, but in a number of great leaps, quantum changes that obsolete all that has gone before it. The introduction of the molded fiberglass boat was one. The electronics revolution another. Perhaps surprisingly, some of the most important innovations have occurred quietly and with little fanfare or notice.

Computers, CCR & CAD-CAM

Beginning in the late 1980's the use of the computer in boat design and construction methods began to play a large role in how boats were designed and built. The most important of these was the CCR or computer controlled router. This basically consists of a router head mounted on a long hydraulically and computer controlled arm. The CCR carves a mold out of a large block of foam which becomes the plug for the mold.

Previously, all boat molds started with wood were shaped and built by hand. This was a laborious and time consuming process that was so costly that builders only made model changes when absolutely necessary. Today builders make style changes as rapidly as auto makers do, and it is the CCR that allows them to do this.

Not only has the CCR made mold making easier, but the process also allows for almost flawlessly fair molded surfaces. No longer do we have those ripply, wavy hull sides and other flat surfaces. It is easy to make a smooth curve but very difficult make a flat surface perfectly flat. Computer controlled mold making has allowed designers to be much freer with designs, which is one of the reasons why boat styles have tended to morph quite a bit.

By around 1990 a majority of boat builders were using this new process. This is what largely accounts for the heavily rounded shapes of boats compared to the squarish shapes of pre-1990 boats. Along with CCR came computer design programs that took the tedious design process off the paper and put it into computers and then put it back on paper. Known as CAD-CAM (computer-aided design, computer-aided manufacturing), this advancement contained both good and evil. Whereas before most boats over thirty feet were designed by people with degrees in naval architecture, now anyone who could learn to operate a CAD system could design boats. This brought the cost of design down but predictably caused some other problems.

It is often stated that the introduction of the computer into boat design freed designers from the constraints of traditional design that the use of wood posed. True, but in many cases it also freed inexperienced designers from the contraints of common sense, or at least marine common sense. Free-wheeling design occasionally goes beyond the bounds of mere common sense and borders on lunacy.

The computer program supposedly eliminates the need for the expensive naval architect with software that is supposed to do all those things. The obvious problem with that is that we now have people designing boats whose reliance is on the computer, which presupposes that the computer knows all it needs to know and can second guess the operator's intentions. Any bets on that one?

Eliminating Wood: Enter New Materials

The current drive to eliminate wood from the framing systems of boats resulted mainly from a handful of builders that used inferior quality woods in their boats, so that wood has gotten a bad rap. The elimination of wood is a great thing but for the fact that it drives up the cost of boats considerably as the wood has to be replaced with a more costly material. There is a common perception amongst boaters that wood is bad. This is unfortunate because there are a lot of very old quality boats out there with wood that has been soaking in water for twenty or thirty years with no problem. In the end, we pay more either way – for better wood or woodless construction.

New, space age materials are great so long as they've been tested. Unfortunately, the industry has a bad habit of not testing new stuff before they drop it into their production lines.

There are other improvements, too, such as improved electrical components, and more systems built "on the bench" instead of hand wiring in the boat. Bench wired systems tend to be more reliable and free of excessive numbers of wire splices, which are primary sources for potential problems. Molded plastic counter tops replaced mica on plywood, and plastics such as StarBoard polymer plastic has made teak trim a thing of the past. New methods of building interiors outside the boat and then dropping them in improves workmanship quality, often reduces weight as well as reducing cost.

Using plywood for upholstered seat frames had long been a huge problem for boat owners as the foam filled upholstery filled up with water and rotted the plywood. Plywood has now mostly been replaced with a new plastic material that doesn't rot. While this raises the cost considerably, it's nothing compared to facing the cost of replacing badly deteriorated upholstery which runs into the thousands of dollars. This is more of a boon to used rather than new boat buyers.

On top of this, there have been big improvements in the vinyls used for exterior upholstery that withstand the effects of weathering much better. Whereas previously seating could easily be worn out or become shabby looking after just a few years, now it's common to find upholstery easily lasting 6-8 years or more, depending on care and use.

Hardware is a mixed bag. Chromed die cast zinc has mostly been eliminated, though one may wonder about being replaced with plastic. Plastic door hinges, please! On the other hand, the use of aluminum to those applications where it is suitable has pretty much balanced out. Very few aluminum rub rails are found these days. Three big cheers for that one!

Other improvements in systems and components have helped to make boats more reliable. Other changes came about with electrical systems that became more standardized as a few companies sprang up that went into the business of making panels just for boats. This took much of the burden of design and manufacturing off the shoulders of boat builders and overall resulted in better systems.

When it comes to engines, we've seen a big migration from gas to diesel in smaller boats as diesels have gotten smaller and more powerful. Gas engines have undergone a conversion from carbureted to fuel injected engines with a lot more computerization.

Ultimately, the quality of a boat, the satisfaction and enjoyment that you get out of it, comes down to a matter of dozens, even hundreds of small details. Is a door hinge made of stainless steel, raw steel, aluminum or plastic? Are the deck hatch hinges recessed into the deck so that you don't cut your bare feet on them? Are electrical switches and other apparatus located so that they don't get wet? The list can go on and on.

In this chapter, mostly by means of photos, we explore some of the good things and bad things contained in the details of design, hardware and other important points. Whether a boat has been thoughtfully designed by someone with a lot of experience, or whether it's been hastily conceived and assembled is easy enough to spot by the trained eye.

High Maintenance, Low Maintenance and too Much Clutter

At this point, let's consider for a moment what factors account for both high and low maintenance. We know that low quality materials means that things will deteriorate more rapidly, things like plastic, aluminum, steel. And, of course, when things made of cheap materials go bad, all we can do is replace them. But quality material isn't the only factor that makes for low maintenance. Another important factor is the degree of difficulty of routine cleaning.

Fig.12-1. This is what I mean by a boat with too much clutter. Numerous and gratuitous styling features that make cleaning and maintenance doubly difficult, proving the point that looking good and being good aren't always the same thing.

If you really want to get a good understanding of the differences in maintenance levels that can be found on boats, I strongly suggest that you take a close look at any of the high quality sport fishing boats such as a Viking or Hatteras. and compare what you see to any of those stylish express jobs. One of the first things we note is the cleanness of lines and lack of clutter. There isn't anything there that doesn't need to be there. Looking around the cockpit, we find a lot of plain, white fiberglass, which is easy to clean. The less clutter the better because all that has to be cleaned and cleaned frequently. It's a whole lot more difficult cleaning areas that are cluttered up with all sorts of stuff that really doesn't need to be there. There isn't any decoration for the sake of decoration, which is the very thing that helps keep maintenance costs down and boating pleasure up.

We don't find any plastic or aluminum at all. In fact, there is likely to be very little hardware showing. That's because the owners want boats that are easy to keep clean. If you've ever tried to wash and wax the top of an SUV with luggage carrier on top, you'll know exactly what I mean. That is an exercise in masochism. Unfortunately, boats can be much the same way when there are dozens of nooks and crannies that collect dirt and have to be laboriously cleaned.

When it comes to cockpits, most people want to be able to clean them with a hose and not have to worry about having too many things that shouldn't get wet. After all, this is the exterior of a boat, though some designers treat it as if it were an interior. The less uncluttered and smoother the lines, the easier any boat will be to keep clean. And we haven't even considered what it's like compounding and waxing all that gel coat that within a very short time will become oxidized and dull.

Now you know why so few boats ever get compounded and waxed. It's just too difficult or costly due the endless clutter.

Ergonomics

Ergonomics is the study of product design as it relates to the scale of the human body. But it is also very much a matter of common sense. Typically we find that the more we use a boat, the more important having a good, ergonomic design becomes. A problem for many mid size boats often results from a builder who attempts to put too much in a too small space, thereby creating a layout that is inconvenient or even downright uncomfortable. A good ergonomic layout is one that allows people to move around freely without excessive restrictions or bottlenecks. But marketing people often try to woo buyers by loading a boat up with extra features, typical examples being a small bar or extra berth added to a space where it doesn't really fit.

If you're new to boating, you may want to think about traffic patterns, which is the means by which you get from one end to the other. Ease of movement may not mean all that much for typical day cruising, but becomes increasingly important when we spend longer periods of time aboard. The best layout typically has a linear traffic pattern that allows one to move from one end to the other without a lot of twists and turns, without having to maneuver around obstacles. And then it's not just a matter of one person, but several trying to move in the same space at the same time.

Many boats have unnecessary bottle necks caused by the placement of too many objects in the cockpit. This results in narrow passages where passengers are apt to stand. When it comes to express cruisers with large seating modules in the cockpit, you may want to decide whether an abundance of seating and restricted ease of movement is worth the trade-off of more open spaces. This is particularly important when it comes to docking, any kind of water sports, and even boarding.

Also give some thought to boarding, especially if you expect some older passengers such as your 70 year old mother-in-law. More than a few boats are designed with no thought given to the ease of boarding. On some, one can only board on one side without having to walk on upholstery. Others may have upholstery on both sides; still others expect you to board from the transom platform. If you know your dockage arrangements in advance, you'll be able to get a good idea of what kind of obstacles you face.

One of the obstacles we often overlook is the short dock. You know, the ones where the docks are only half as long as your boat and for some reason you can't dock stern-to. This means having to negotiate side decks. Unfortunately, far too many boats are designed either without side decks or decks that are far too narrow to be traversed safely. The time to consider such factors are before you discover the hard way that your young children or mother-in-law are in danger every time they try to board.

Fig.12-2. Mounting a dinghy like this is beyond stupid. It creates so much leverage being extended out so far that the platform brackets are starting to deform the transom and separating the hull deck join. Be wary of such arrangements.

Integral Platforms

Hull integral swim platforms began to appear in the mid 1980's and by the 1990's became pretty much standard on most boats, the lone exception being flying bridge sedans and sport fishermen where the bolt-on platform still prevails because the integral type is unsuited to these boats where a big cockpit is everything.

Hull integral platforms can solve a lot of problems, such as eliminating a lot of submerged metal hardware (support brackets), rust stains from stainless steel and so on. But they are also capable of adding additional problems when designers get too fancy without thinking things through. Ranking at the top of the dumb things list is the placement of shore power receptacles somewhere low in the platform area where they get wet.

Platform decks may or may not have doors on the transom opening. This is particularly significant if you have children or do a lot of entertaining. Think of what will happen if the boat accelerates when someone is standing directly in front of the transom opening. They'll probably be left behind, right? If there are no doors or gates, with a new boat you should demand that one be installed since this presents an unacceptable hazard.

Some builders, most notably Carver, has used bolt-on platform extensions that extend out well beyond the side of the hull. Some of these things cleverly house the engine exhaust ports. It's a bit less clever when the boat hits a piling while docking or undocking and tears the whole thing right off, as happens rather frequently. Nothing on the side of a boat should extend out further than the rub rail, which is supposed to be there to prevent this kind of damage.

Exhaust Ports

Having just mentioned exhaust ports, I should discuss this further at this point. Over the years, exhaust systems have posed a lot of problems. Mostly these problems come about as a result of the builder trying in some way to keep exhaust fumes from being pulled back into passenger areas as a result of the station wagon effect (the partial vacuum that forms behind a moving boat). The only method that has ever succeeded is the underwater exhaust system. Unfortunately, underwater systems can only be used with larger yachts that have adequate internal space for these bulky systems, along with high freeboards.

The fundamental problem with underwater exhausts stems from the high back pressure that can be caused by not getting the design just right. High exhaust back pressure will damage diesel engines very quickly. Further, if the design is not just right, there can be a very high risk of water backing up into the engine. Numerous builders have taken big hits from lawsuits over improperly designed systems. *If you are looking at a boat of any kind with an underwater exhaust system, regardless of its age, it is recommended that you have it analyzed by an expert before you buy it.* The damage plus the cost of correcting an improperly designed system can easily run $100,000 and more.

Fig.12-3. Here's one good reason why it is a bad idea to build an exhaust system into any part of the hull. When an engine's cooling system fails, the loss of cooling water burns the hull.

Side Exhausts

Exhaust ports on the side of the hull can either be a simple hole in the side of the hull, or may involve elaborate external ducting, as mentioned in the swim platform section above. The idea behind side exhausts is too prevent the station wagon effect and the transom from getting all sooty. Unfortunately, this design does neither and usually ends up sooting the transom and both sides of the hull.

If heavy accumulations of black soot are occurring, the problem is NOT the exhaust system, but an engine problem. The engines should not be creating these kind of emissions. Heavy black soot is the result of incomplete combustion, indicating that something is wrong with the engines. Old fashioned transom exhaust ports have been in use for nearly a hundred years and so far, no one has been able to improve on them no matter how fancy they get.

Unfortunately, diesel exhaust stinks because diesel oil contains a high sulphur content. This can only be minimized, not eliminated, by maintaining tip-top engine tuning, combined with precisely the right propellering. *The* most common cause of exhaust soot problems are the owner of the boat fooling around with propellers, or the builder didn't get it right from the start. Overloaded diesels *will* smoke no matter what you do until one gets the propeller load right.

Boats with external side exhaust ducting of any kind that protrude beyond the hull side should be avoided as sustaining damage to the ducts is inevitable.

Fig.12-4. Platforms that include side extensions like this that house exhaust ports often prove more trouble than they're worth. Note the judicious use of fenders to keep from tearing it off. Sooner or later the owner/ operator will whack a dock and do just that because it sticks out beyond the rub rail.

Platform as Patio

There area a number of builders who have designed platforms as though these things were patios. Carver and Cruisers, Inc. are two notable examples that include seating, carpeting, drink holders and audio speakers and whatever else they may think of. There are several problems with this idea, not the least of which is that it encourages people to go back there while the boat is underway. A design like this is a personal injury lawyer's dream come true when the first person, particularly a child goes back there and falls off and is chewed up by the propellers or simply lost overboard. There are no railings on any of these things, making it very easy for anyone to fall overboard.

Although there may be a gate on the cockpit pass-through, there's nothing to stop anyone from opening it and going down there while underway. Unless it is constantly watched, it can happen. Secondly, while very nice for swimming or diving, the operator of the boat cannot see this area and has no idea of whether anyone or anything remains in the water.

It would appear a sensible thing to do to put a locking gate on the pass-through. But if you look at figures 12-5 and 12-6 closely, you'll see that the only way to board this boat is via the platform because this boat is so high sided that no one but a gymnast could get aboard anywhere else (see the next paragraph for further discussion of boarding problems). This is incredibly bad design, and yet it's rapidly becoming a leading and accepted style.

Thirdly, anyone who understands the station wagon effect knows that salt spray and exhaust fumes are pulled into this area when the boat is underway. This causes the area to become very salty and sooty, making for a maintenance nightmare. Not exactly a great place for upholstery, hardware and electrical stuff.

Fig.12-5. The deck of this beauty is six feet above the water line with the only way to board being via the transom platform which is several feet below the dock. You get a massive interior with high ceilings in return for a boat that is extremely difficult to get aboard unless you are at exactly the right kind of dock. This is the sort of boat that only the inexperienced could go for.

Fig.12-6. The design of this boat is also such that it cannot be boarded from the side, made impossible by the superfluous design hump below the arch. Also note how far the platform sticks out from the sides.

Boarding Problems

During my daily work, I am constantly amazed at the lack of consideration given by designers to the ease of boarding. On numerous occasions, a client has brought along an aging parent for the sea trial, despite my attempts to discourage such things. It's often not the slightest bit amusing to watch the rigorous ordeals some of these people go through to try to get the less than agile on board.

Fig.12-7. Here's another case where style took precedence over common sense. Here you've either got to climb up three feet over an unnecessarily high side, or jump down onto a precarious platform with no hand holds. How would you get aboard with an arm load of stuff? Perhaps that davit ought to be on the dock!

It's hard enough boarding a boat without the designer making it even tougher by putting a lot of obstacles in the way. These problems are particularly prominent on express cruisers. In one recent case of a late model express, there was no reasonable way to board other than via the transom platform. That's fine if one can always be assured of backing into a low slip, but that's not a reasonable probability. What do you do when the tide is down three or four feet and you have a six foot drop to the deck? The following is a list of a few other design problems:

- Radar arch cuts off cockpit entry, causing one to have to duck under it.
- Boarding can only be accomplished by walking on upholstered seating.
- Having boarding ability from one side only presumes one can always dock to that side.
- No reasonable hand holds for boarding.
- Available boarding via the platform only is a bad idea. What do you do when only a high dock is available and the tide is out? Apparently, get a ladder.
- Step up/down from cockpit is poorly placed. Step up causes one duck or slam head into arch.
- Cockpit is very high sided for style reasons only.

These problems are proliferating apparently due to the growing numbers of floating docks in non tidal areas, so designers feel free to become more free-wheeling in their designs without considering what this means when floating docks aren't available.

In some parts of the country, dock space is becoming in short supply, with finger piers getting shorter and shorter. I often encounter these things that are barely ten feet long, making them all but useless. Therefore, it's a good idea to have some idea of the kind of docks available to you before you buy a boat. Otherwise, you could end up with frustrating situation.

Cockpit & Under Deck Storage

Almost every boat has a number of large, bulky items for which some convenient storage is needed. This includes things like shore power cords, hoses, and fenders. Too many boats lack adequate, or at least convenient storage space.

Storing anything outside the cabin proper has always been a problem on boats because most areas where storage of anything is possible do not offer much protection from water, extreme heat and mildew. Even items that are not necessarily harmed by water – items like fenders, lines, cleaning supplies, etc. – do suffer from things like mildew which can turn nice looking things to really ugly things. Plastic is organic and most is readily attacked and eaten by fungi.

Cockpit areas are often fitted with various types of storage bins, cabinets and so on. More often than not when I look inside, what I see is an ugly mess of mildew and dirt.

This happens because most of these areas are not water tight and often actually channel water and dirt inside due to inept design. Being wet inside, when the sun beats down on it and heats it up, the end result is inevitable. Either we have to perform a lot of maintenance keeping these things clean, or just let it rot. Therefore, when you may be delighted to see all that gleaming new storage space, this blessing may turn into a curse a few years later. Cabinets need to have a drip ledge along the top to keep water from running into the top door gap.

Particularly troublesome are the in-deck storage wells that consist of fiberglass tubs that fit into hatch openings. These things are never water tight because they're dependent on gutters never overflowing, which they often do. The value of exterior storage is proportional to the amount of ventilation it gets, which is usually very little. Some of the designs we see where a sort of "trunk" is built into the faux transom work out considerably better as long as they get some ventilation.

The area under an open cockpit deck suffers basically the same problem. There is water in the bilge and with the sun heating up the deck, the humidity is very high. This area, however, has better ventilation than most above deck compartments because it is usually integral with the engine room. It is usually a better place to store fenders and ground tackle than above deck and in-deck bins. The shortcoming is usually a matter of a lack of decking or provision to keep things from fouling the steering gear.

Large cockpit seating modules usually offer abundant storage opportunities, although one does need to check on the ability of these areas to stay dry. Will it withstand pressure water from a hose during wash down? With respect to cabinets, check to see if they have a drip ledge across the top to prevent water from entering. Most do not. Is there a gutter for top loading lockers?

Fish Boxes

In-hatch fish boxes are a convenient way to avoid cluttering deck space. The only thing that distinguishes a fish box from a storage box it that the fish box has a drain, but the fish box can be used for either purpose. The drain must be connected to an overboard pump because if fish slime, scales and blood ends up in the bilge you end with an extremely foul-smelling boat. Very often fish boxes are connected up to a macerator pump to help solid waste move through the drain.

If boxes are self draining, it's a good idea to check how it is plumbed overboard. Many older boats have the box simply connected to a through hull with a length of hose. Since boxes often have to be removed for servicing stuff in the bilge, what often happens is that on removal of the box, the hose or one of it's fittings gets damaged or the hose is pulled off without anyone being aware of that. Then, because the drain is open to the sea, the hull starts flooding at some unsuspected time.

Unfortunately, there is no fool-proof way of draining fish boxes without creating this hazard, so this plumbing must be treated with care and checked regularly. One builder when questioned about this told me, "Well you should keep the sea cock closed when not in use," but that makes little sense when you have to haul that huge box out of it's hole just to do that. Neither was there any information provided to the owner that that is what he should do.

Yet another fault I occasionally encounter on smaller boats is that the drain is not installed correctly and while running the box fills up with water. That's because the drain was installed on the bottom of the hull and when underway water is pushed back through the drain. The drain should be through the transom.

Exterior Upholstery

The byword here is that the less of it there is, the better off you'll be. If there is a lot of upholstery, you either have to spend a lot of time covering it up, taking the covers off and putting the covers away, as well as cleaning – or you just let it sit out and deteriorate as many do.

Seating upholstery should be closely examined for how or even whether it drains when rained on. Bucket type bucket shaped seats are particularly bad because these can trap large amounts of water. Rolled, tucked and pleated type upholstery doesn't belong on a boat for reasons that should be readily apparent. Keep in mind that exterior upholstery frequently gets wet despite the best efforts to keep it dry. It also gets very dirty and has to be cleaned frequently. Complex upholstery is not easy to clean, so once again simple is better, less is more.

Sunbathing deck cushions are yet another form of upholstery, the value of which is dubious. These things can suck up huge amounts of water and cause all sorts of problems. Though they may be fitted with covers, such covers rarely help much. Not infrequently do I pull the covers off to find them sitting in a pool of water with moss and weeds growing out of these cushions! The area becomes a marvelous dirt trap.

Upholstered trim panels are widely used in the cockpit areas of entry-level boats, mainly to provide a jazzy appearance. These also suck up lots of water and tend to deteriorate quickly. Rarely do I ever see any boat owners replacing this stuff, so that by the time the upholstery is wasted away, the rest of the boat is pretty much shot too. As the number of deteriorated items piles up, so does the cost of replacements to the point where the owner is overwhelmed. At that point, most maintenance stops and the boat rapidly slides down hill until it gets shoved off in a back lot somewhere. That is the reality of snazzy, jazzy upholstered boats. Once the upholstery is shot, there isn't much left to motivate maintenance.

Fold-Down Cockpit Seats

A new boat consideration, these things seem like a nice idea, right? Well, you'll probably change your mind about that when you see what happens a few years later when that folded up seat collects water and dirt and becomes a mildewed, ugly mess. This is what usually happens when people don't use these seats very often. It's probably best to determine how often you might use these things; if you want a wide open cockpit more often than seating, folding chairs would probably be the better solution.

Hardtops

A new boat consideration, increasingly builders are offering hardtops as options, albeit expensive options. Hardtops are viable choices (1)when operating in a climate that is more unfavorable than favorable, i.e. where enclosures are removed infrequently, and (2) the top will fit the lines of the boat, particularly express cruisers where there is a conflict with radar arches. Some of these hardtop installations are pretty awkward, to say the least. Don't understimate how much ungraceful design can affect resale value.

Hardtops on open boats are ultimately more cost effective than soft tops. particularly when a hailstorm hits and you have a high deductible! Consider a hard top if you're unlikely to ever put a soft top down.

Transom Doors

Found primarily in sport fishermen, on post 1990 boats there is little likelihood of structural problems but before this time there are often problems with structural weakness around doors. These are almost always shown up as severe cracking around the lower part of the door sill, both on the inside and on the transom itself. A structurally weak door design is essentially unrepairable at a reasonable cost owing to the close proximity of the cockpit liner to the hull that allows no internal access to this to make repairs from the inside where it is needed.

Another thing to look for are loose hinges and hinges that are standing proud with sharp corners that can cut people. The hinges should have been bolted, but if they've come loose they're probably just screwed on so that making a permanent repair is impossible unless one can get it bolted through from the inside.

Cockpit Scuppers

These are often a sore spot on sport fishing boats, especially smaller boats where decks are much closer to the waterline. The idea is to let water run out, but not in , as when a wave comes either over the transom or through an open cockpit door. But in reality it's usually a two-way street. To be truly effective, scuppers must be fairly large, for we're relying on gravity to take the water out.

First we need to look at the cockpit angle relative to the trim of the boat. Boats that have crowed decks will have superior drainage to flat ones. Try using a water hose and testing how the water flows . . . or not. We want to be sure that we don't end up with a boat with poor trim so that cockpit water runs forward and puddles. Take note of the fuel tank status since fuel state will have great effect on trim. I've seen a lot of boats where, when fuel gets low, the stern rises causing a bow-down trim resulting in cockpit decks that don't drain.

The other problem with scuppers is the great difficulty the builder has in joining the inner line with the hull. There is usually very little space between the cockpit liner to the hull itself. Normally an oblong fiberglass tube is glassed in place to create the overboard duct but a worker can't get his hands in this narrow space to do a good job of it. Or, some builders simply glue the duct into place and hopes it holds. That's why we see so many boats with large cracks all around the scuppers. The danger here is that these things leak water into the hull being so close to the water line. Again, I turn to the water hose, blasting the area, then going down below to check for leaks.

Windshields and Wipers

Here's a real sore spot, particularly for boats with racy styling and low, swept back windshields. All too often the windshield becomes nothing more than a style element where any practical reason for it's existence is forgotten. What good is a windshield that hits you chest high when you're standing up, or has only 6" vertical height because it is

Fig.12-8 & 12-9. Both the Bertram 30 (left) and Tiara 3100 (right) have superbly laid out panels replete with space for flush mount electronics and properly placed controls. Both are tucked up under tall windshields that do what they're supposed to do. Note the positioning of switches off to the side on the Bertram. A clever Tiara owner had a clear plastic cover made for his helm to futher help keep the salt off. Both builders opted for the vertically positioned large wheel. It is consistently good design like this that has helped make these companies so successful.

Fig.12-10. While stylishly correct, rakish windshields are just about useless. The helm panel is so high that it is nearly above the windshield so that neither the delicate instruments, nor the operator or passengers, have any protection from spray. The panel is also subject to glare from direct sun.

laying at a 30 degree to horizontal angle? I've seen some of these that, while under way, the only thing one could see through it was the foredeck because the bow was riding so high. While it may be exhilarating for a few minutes to have the onrushing wind in your face, it very quickly gets old. It's not only you, but your passengers that are affected. Many boat owners are dismayed by the fact that they are abandoned by their passengers and left to stand alone at the helm, not seeming to realize that everyone else went below to escape wind and spray.

Such things may not be a big deal for fresh water operation, but in salt water on a bad day with blowing spray being smeared around by some el cheapo windshield wipers is a real party pooper. As mentioned previously, Tiara is one company that has mastered the design of a high, practical windshield that still looks reasonably good style-wise. Having surveyed hundreds of their boats, I've grown to greatly appreciate these windshields simply because they do what windshields are supposed to do: keep you dry and the wind out of your face.

If you're serious about seeing where you're going, then you need to be serious about windshield wipers. Fortunately, there has been a lot of improvement in the designs of electric wipers, though some pretty shabby types will be found on entry-level boats. However, all windshield wipers in salt water are nearly useless without a fresh water wash, and many of those that have it usually don't work very well. The problems are typically that they tried to force it to spray through a fine nozzle that easily plugs up, or it is controlled by a cheap electric solenoid that corrodes and freezes up. Water from aluminum tanks ends up with a lot of fine scale in it that will plug up fine nozzles.

The type that is most reliable simply uses a mechanical valve on the helm which you turn, allowing fresh water from the internal system to pour water onto the windshield, not through a nozzle, but just a small diameter copper pipe. Spray is not needed as the wiper blade will move the fresh water around.

Chapter 13

Steering, Controls, Systems & Equipment

The control interface between vessel and operator, called the helm station, is one of the most overlooked design features on boats. On sport fishermen we typically find the most thoughtfully and ergonomically designed helm stations of all, no doubt because avid fishermen are usually more experienced and demanding.

Some of the poorest designs are to be found on stylish express cruisers and others wherein style takes precedence over practicality. The importance of this point cannot be over stressed since the owner will spend more of his time at the helm than with any other boating activity, so if he gets stuck with a bad design, he's not going to be very happy about that.

Ergonomics at the Helm

Good ergonomic design includes the ability of the pilot to stand or sit at the helm station and control the boat comfortably for relatively long periods of time. Much will depend on the physical size of the individual, for most designers will, or at least should be, thinking about how the set up fits the average sized person. Therefore, unusually tall or short people are likely to have problems with this.

Check the set up simply by standing behind the helm. Place your hands on the wheel at what would be the normal position. There should be adequate clearance between the seat and the wheel. Whether the wheel is vertically or horizontally mounted, you arms

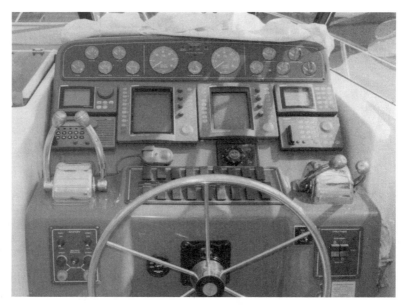

Fig.13-1. Experienced boaters tend to prefer the large destroyer wheels. A wheel in the vertical position does not require the operator to keep his arms extended, but can let them hang down naturally, which is more comfortable and less fatiguing. Control heads are Panish cable type.

should be able to rest comfortably on the wheel with hands in the normal position. If the wheel is too high, or low, this will cause discomfort over longer periods of time.

Note that on many flying bridges, the helm is placed very low where it is comfortable for the sitting position but not the standing position. This is backwards: the wheel height should first be set for a comfortable standing position and the helm chair adjustable to that height because the reverse of this is not possible.

Getting adequate clearance between the seat and the wheel is always a problem, with no good solution other than with a seat that slides fore and aft, so check to see that it does. Adequate clearance is important during docking operations, for example, when it may become necessary to get in and out from behind the wheel quickly. We don't want a fit so tight that we get hemmed in.

Wheels are routinely found mounted anywhere from vertical to horizontal and all angles in between. A horizontal mount means anywhere from horizontal to about 15 degrees. The sport fisherman will do more maneuvering than any other type of boat owner, so it is important to note that the wheels of nearly all fishermen are to be found in the horizontal position by reason of the fact that the wheel can be turned easier and faster from this position. Conversely, vertically mounted wheels tend to be better for straight-line steering - as in a sea way – when constant course adjustments are needed. Hence, we always find vertical wheels on ships and larger motor yachts.

Fig.13-2. The Edson mock Rybovich wheel in forged aluminum is one of the best horizontal wheels available. Note the configuration and the finger grips on under side. The original design was by John Rybovich back in the late 1940's.

However, wheels mounted on angles do not offer the best of both worlds. Adjustable tilt wheels, in my view are more style than substance because they don't tilt sufficiently to make much difference. Stylish express cruisers are likely to have smallish wheels who's position on the helm is determined by considerations of style, and therefore without regard to comfort. Far too many have unusually small, sports car type wheels that are ill-suited for use on a boat. Some are so small as to become fatiguing after more than 30 minutes of operation. When it comes to steering, it's a very bad idea to sacrifice control for style.

Check the clearance between the wheel and the engine controls. I've seen numerous boats where my hands on the wheel collided with the controls during close maneuvering, which can be both aggravating and painful. Needless to say, when such situations are encountered, there is almost no chance of correcting the problem.

Engine controls are often badly placed, either being too close to the wheel, or set at a bad angle. The most common fault are controls set on an angle that first requires the operator to lift them. As the arc of the lever reaches a certain point, this causes the operator to have to turn his hand around in order to continue pushing them through the arc of motion. This is a very aggravating set up that you probably don't want to get stuck with.

There are many good reasons to be wary of boats where chic styling appears to be the main attraction, and helm seating arrangements are one of them. I've run across a lot of express type cruisers and even some "motor yacht" types wherein the designer tried to put as much seating next to the helmsman as possible. One of these arrangements is the long bench seat that seats three or more people. Let me just mention the reason why most people prefer to sit on the end of rows in a movie theater or airliner: no one likes to be boxed in, and boxing in is exactly what such seating arrangements do to the helmsman.

My complaint with such designs is that the operator cannot get out from behind the wheel fast in an emergency, such as a docking operation that isn't going right. Yet another bad design is the one that isolates the operator in sort of a separate cockpit or island, isolated from the remainder of the cockpit. Sea Ray is the builder who I most often encounter such ill-considered designs. Whether it's a cockpit or flying bridge layout, experienced boaters will tell you that it is critical for the operator to be able to move in and away from the helm without undue restrictions.

Engine Control Systems

The question of whether single or dual lever control systems are best is mainly a matter of personal opinion. Single level controls can get a little dicey when docking because of the tendency to push too hard on them, thereby accelerating more than anticipated. For this, among other reasons, I remain preferential to dual lever controls.

Costly electronic controls have been on the market for about a decade now, my conclusion is that electronic controls are downright dangerous. The apparent reason d'être behind

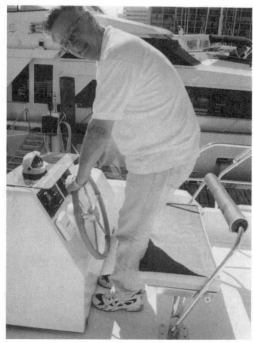

Fig.13-3. Bad helm station ergonomics are so easy to overlook that we tend not to notice until it's too late. This extreme example illustrates just how bad it can get. Ideally one wants to be able to both stand or sit comfortably behind the wheel.

Fig.13-4. The owner of this old 42 Bertram took an already good design and made it even better. Note digital tachs at center flanked by engine gauges. The emphasis is on function and yet it still looks good.

electronic controls is ease of movement, and that is precisely the problem: they move too easily, and cause too many opportunities for accidents, particularly when docking. There is no doubt about it, the number of serious accidents caused by these controls has risen in proportion to their numbers.

The levers move so easily that all it takes is an accidental bump to cause a hard acceleration. This can be an accidental bump by the operator, or even anyone standing nearby. In one case that I know of, a child inadvertently grabbed the lever as a handhold, throwing the boat into reverse and causing a collision. In another case, an engine was thrown into reverse at high speed with disastrous results.

Yet another complaint is that these computerized controls can be knocked out by lightning, not merely direct strikes, but merely nearby strikes, thereby leaving the vessel powerless. Combined with electronic fuel injection systems and other engine controls, bizarre incidents have occurred whereby engines have started up by themselves, or failed to shut down or respond to control inputs in any way. I would suggest that you think very carefully about whether it is wise to submit critical engine and vessel controls to such fragile computerized systems. This is one area where the KISS rule should reign supreme.

The other two control types are hydraulic and mechanical cable. Hydraulic systems are more or less perfected, and only occasionally cause trouble when hydraulic leaks or system damage occurs. Mechanical cable systems are the most reliable, yet their weakness has always been friction that causes the controls to be stiff. Another historical weakness is that controls constantly exposed to weather have been prone to seizing up, but this is a problem that is in decline. The reason is that manufacturers make a wide variety of controls of differing quality and price. The cheapest are steel cables in plastic coated steel jackets. They will, of course, rust up and seize if water gets into the cable sleeves.

Of late, most builders have changed over to higher quality cables so that I find frozen controls on towers and bridges far less frequently than in previous years. My view is that good quality mechanical controls are the best and most reliable option for mid size boats. Even if one should freeze up, the cost of replacement is nothing compared to problems with $10,000 electronic control systems.

On the sea trial, be alert to throttle controls that will not hold a position, but constantly fall back from the position in which they are placed. There are a variety of causes for this, some of which may not be corrected inexpensively. Controls like this are more than extremely annoying, for you cannot be expected to stand there and hold them in position. Consider the operation ability of the boat to be severely compromised, the cause found, corrected and paid for by the seller.

Steering Systems

The quality of steering systems is as variable as engine control systems. Virtually all such systems found in mid size boats will be hydraulic, and for the most part are trouble-free, though the cheaper systems found in entry-level boats are likely to simply wear out in around ten years owing to inferior quality. Replacement costs are not high. The most common wear point is at the wheel shaft seal that, when worn will develop oil leaks. Check the under side of the helm unit for fluid leaks. Aluminum hydraulic cylinders in wet locations may corrode so severely that they require replacement.

One of the more important aspects to check on with steering systems is the number of full turns the wheel will take from side to side. This should be neither too much nor too little. A system that has too many turns overworks the helmsman; a system with too few does the same thing, causing an excessive number of very small adjustments. Three full turns, or 1/1/2 turns to each side, is considered to be optimum, and tha is most commonly found.

Also check the steering tension. Unless there is a large, vertical wheel, we don't want it to be too easy nor too stiff. The wheel should turn smoothly with no noise or chatter, both of which will signal some sort of internal problem. With the higher quality systems like Hynautic, the steering wheel pressure is adjustable. During a sea trial, the vessel should track straight with the wheel in the centered position. If the boat veers when the wheel is let go, there is a problem that should be investigated, one that may be costly or even impossible to correct, so beware of this condition.

Helm Panel Layouts

Helm layouts often suffer the same design foolishness as seating arrangements, by virtue of attempts to design panels like those of cars. Boats are not cars, and they have a whole lot more instrumentation, gadgets, switches and controls than cars do. Very often, there is no rhyme or reason for the layouts of panels other than mere stylistic appearance. Over time, ill-conceived layouts are likely to become very aggravating to owners as they constantly have to search the label of each and every switch to find what they're looking for because there was no logic to the layout. Or they put switches in clumsy locations because the designer wanted a clean, uncluttered appearance to the panel, with the result that there are a bunch of switches under the wheel or below the wheel, or between the seat and the aft face of the helm panel where one cannot see the switch label.

Tiara, Hatteras and Bertram historically have had the best helm layouts probably by virtue of the fact that the owners of such boats have more experience, and that these builders tend to be less dependent on style to sell their products. If such things are of importance to you, it would be worthwhile to take a good look at how these builders create an ergonomically functional panel. Going aboard one of their boats, even a stranger rarely has trouble locating a particular switch.

Another consideration for helm panels is how to protect them from weather and spray. Despite what manufacturers say, or what you may believe about any instruments being water proof, few truly are. I constantly find gauges and instruments full of water with condensation showing on dial faces, which means that if it hasn't already failed, it soon will. Whether it's up under a windshield or not, a good-fitting, waterproof and UV resistant cover is essential.

Tops & Covers

Now that melanoma has caught a lot of people's attention, the importance of well-designed and good fitting tops is more important than ever. It is hard to overemphasize the need for good-fitting tops and covers of the highest quality material. In the boating biz, we call this stuff "soft goods".

By the time we've owned a couple of boats, we eventually come around to understand the importance of well made protective covers. By that time, we can't help but to have noticed the tens of thousands of dollars worth of deterioration that has occurred that could have been prevented. It never ceases to amaze me that in walking down a pier, there is at least one brand new boat sitting there with no covers on it whatsoever, not even the helm. Apparently some people believe that boats are made to withstand that kind of abuse. Unfortunately, they aren't.

Sure, putting covers on, taking them off, and then finding a place to stow them is inconvenient. But so is taking a 50% depreciation hit at resale time. This doesn't have to happen if you get in the habit putting covers on things that need them. The two issues to consider when thinking about covers is material quality and fit. Getting this stuff to fit right, especially when a lot of zippers are involved, is a laborious process, so there is no reason to expect a good fit at a bargain price.

It can't be said that all soft goods provided by builders are low quality; however, most that I've seen are and believe me, low quality stuff is not worth paying for because it will deteriorate so rapidly. And if poor quality material isn't involved, badly fitted enclosures are. Yes, tops and enclosures are expensive, but that's part of the cost of boating. My view is that only top quality material is worth paying for. The way to get it is to go to a custom *marine* canvass shop. Simply tell them that you want the very best quality material available.

Most people get competitive estimates when having covers and enclosures made. This is a mistake for the inevitable reason that we never get the best quality at the lowest price. Then consider that the bigger the boat, the more important good fit becomes. This stuff is hard enough to deal with without having to put up with poorly fitted enclosures and covers. Therefore, I recommend the best canvas shop you can find and pay the price for a job well done. Forego that other $1000 piece of toy electronics that you don't really need; you really do need good covers and enclosures.

For both expresses, motor yachts and fishermen, I recommend full cockpit covers. If you don't want that, then at least get drop curtains coming down from the arch or Bimini. These things can be used even while underway and keep out wind driven water and dirt in any case. When it comes to enclosures, you have two choices: you can get the ones without smilies (a smilie is a U-shaped zipper in a clear plastic enclosure used to facilitate easy opening, without having to remove the entire enclosure) and simply remove them, or pay the extra money and get the ones with zippered smilies and not have to remove them. This is where good quality comes in, with having all those zippers work properly because the fabric didn't shrink and the fit was right.

Fig.13-5. Mildew loves certain kinds of plastic. This is into the plastic and can't be scrubbed off.

Fig.13-6. Search lights would be useful if the dang things ever worked. 90% of the ones I test don't. This one is one year old and full of water. A waste of money. Buy a portable instead.

Cockpit Appliances

Primarily a new boat consideration, wet bars in the cockpit most frequently contain ice makers, refrigerators, sink, faucets, cabinets and drawers, and perhaps more. That's all very nice – until the sun and salt water gets to it. Ice makers do not belong outside, exposed to the sun. These things are barely insulated well enough to keep ice frozen inside the cabin. Outside, the ice will usually fuse into a solid block of ice in a few days, plus sun and salt plays havoc with these interior grade appliances. Don't be fooled by the nice stainless steel sheathing on the door face; inside it's all painted steel and aluminum. Otherwise, these ice makers will do fine inside the boat.

If pneumatic cylinders are used on lift up bar tops, make sure they are stainless steel and not painted steel.

Refrigerators suffer the same problems, but in reality can withstand the marine environment even less well than ice makers.

Freezers on sport fishermen have improved substantially in the last decade now that better insulating foams are available. Most of these work out reasonably well, though one should not expect them to remain frozen for months at a time. Cockpit freezers are basically for short term use only, and when not in use should be emptied and defrosted. These freezers have to have both an internal box drain and a provision for dealing with the condensation the units inevitably produce. On boats that have them, be sure that condensation is not leaking into the engine room and causing damage as occasionally happens.

On going through the boat shows in recent years I find that many builders have wisely ceased placing refrigeration equipment (other than bait freezers) in open cockpits. However, that was not the case throughout the eighties and nineties.

Hardware

The two biggest problems with hardware are plastic and steel. Plastic hardware like door pulls, latches and so on simply will not hold up to UV. The steel pneumatic cylinders we see on so many hatch and other covers these days will rust, and rust badly. Unless they are the much more costly stainless steel versions, you can expect to have to replace a rusty mess in a very short time. Plain steel hardware does not belong on boats.

The only material that has proved to be deterioration resistant is stainless steel so that hardware made of any other material must by nature be considered inferior. Plastic proves to be a bane rather than a blessing. If it doesn't break because it is naturally weak, it gets wasted by the sun or becomes unsightly after fungi begins to feed on it.

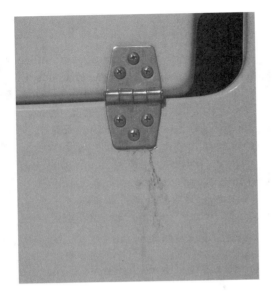

Fig.13-7 & 13-8. LEFT: This hinge is on a boat that is so new it doesn't have its first owner, yet it is starting to rust already. That's because it hasn't been bedded and crevice corrosion is attacking the under side that traps water. ABOVE: Plastic hardware doesn't belong on a boat since it usually ends up like this.

Aluminum was once widely used for exterior boat hardware, but one look at a twenty year old boat reveals why aluminum has fallen into disfavor. The majority of boats that I saw at recent boat shows had little or no aluminum on them. Anodized aluminum holds up to sea water well, but it does not hold up to numerous types of cleaning products and so often becomes badly and permanently stained. It is also highly vulnerable to crevice corrosion that takes place on the blind side. In some local areas, industrial air pollution such as sulfur dioxide also stains or even corrodes anodized aluminum.

The more plastic and aluminum hardware a boat has on it, the sooner the appearance will deteriorate and value depreciate. Items such as plastic pie ports, antenna bases, hinges, latches, lights and search lights perform very poorly. So do cast aluminum hardware such as anchor winches, searchlights and flood lights. Anything that is painted metal is likely to be cast aluminum or possibly even zinc. Expect the finish to deteriorate very rapidly.

Navigation Instruments

More electronics are purchased for show and tell and bragging rights than any real or perceived need. I find that radars, large video sounders, fancy GPS plotters and so on tend to get very little use. Dealers, of course, will do their best to convince you that you should buy these gadgets. I suggest careful consideration based on the following points. Most likely you can put the money to better use elsewhere.

Radars

There are some areas where these devices are necessary, perhaps not all year, but during certain seasons when fog is common. The Gulf coast in winter, fall and spring is one and I'm sure that you can think of a few other areas like San Francisco Bay.

The better quality and larger display radars can also be very good navigation aids. There are many instances where I've used a 72 mile Furuno as the sole device because the signal and display are so good. I wouldn't try this with one of the economy LED display radars that often leave a lot to be desired. Personally, I don't think the LED radars worth the money. The worst CRT unit is better than the best LED. Further, the signal strength of small, bargain radars is far too weak to be of real value. If you need radar, by all means spend the money to get a good CRT unit.

GPS/Plotters

The only problem with GPS is that they are too accurate and far too many boaters are coming to rely upon them exclusively. There is a very good reason why the opening screen on virtually all GPS units warns against this. Low cost GPS displays do not contain the necessary data that a navigation chart does. This is causing huge numbers of boaters to run aground and have other accidents because they relied upon the GPS only. They think GPS takes the place of learning how to read charts and navigate manually. I know this for a fact, for the large majority of mid size boats that I now survey don't even have any charts aboard, a notable change from ten years ago.

There is no point in knowing where you are unless you know something about the nature of those waters. You are not running a sea worthy vessel if you don't know how to navigate. And rest assured that the law will back me up on that statement, though laws don't seem to command much respect these days.

The most widely used GPS/Plotter in larger boats is the Northstar 951X. Its main strengths are a large display and a very intuitive operating system. This is a unit that one can actually figure out how to use without a manual. While on the expensive side, if I had the need for a really good system, this is the one I'd buy and foregoing other niceties to get it.

Depth Meters

These days we see a lot of multi function electronics. That may or may not be a good thing, but when it comes to knowing the depth of the water you are in, I'd say these are not good things. My recommendation is that you purchase a dedicated digital readout meter, one that has a LARGE display. The depth meter is one of the most used and relied-upon instruments, one that needs to be located front and center to capture your attention. With a multi function instrument, one either has to cycle through the functions, or the depth is displayed simultaneously with much other data in tiny numerals and therefore it is more difficult to locate and certainly does not capture your attention as it should.

Autopilots

Autopilots aren't optional equipment anymore and a boat in our size range that doesn't have one is usually considered as deficient. You've probably noticed that boat helms aren't set up like cars, you can't sit comfortably behind the wheel for hours on end. That's because on a boat we can get up and move around, whereas in a road vehicle we can't.

Even if we're not traveling long distances, an autopilot is a useful thing to have. They're meant for use offshore, out of the way of heavy traffic. There was a time when inexpensive autopilots weren't worth the price you paid for them, but that has changed. My experience over the last ten years is that even the cheap ones are reliable and function reasonably well. They will not, however, hold a course as well as the better units in more difficult conditions.

What about integrated systems where the autopilot is linked to the GPS? The average boater is unlikely to find it worth the additional cost and time it takes to learn and utilize these complicated systems. They are best for very long range cruising and repetitive voyages. For most boaters, manual use of autopilot and GPS are more than adequate and probably a time-saver, too.

Other Systems

Air Conditioning

Air conditioning in boats today is pretty much considered standard equipment, though it's priced optionally. When boats in this size range don't have AC, it is considered lacking and will be valued considerably lower because of the much higher cost of installing add-on AC. My advice is to get it with a new boat whether you really want it or not, just as with a car. Otherwise, you'll pay a significant penalty at resale time because it is much more costly to retrofit a boat with AC later than the original factory installed cost. Marinair and Cruisair are the two most widely sold systems.

One of the few things to consider about AC is whether the capacity is adequate, a more important consideration in the south than other environments. I bring up the point because I find too many boats whereon the AC capacity is inadequate. Either the number of units or the capacity of the units is incapable of keeping interior temperature comfortable. This becomes especially important as more and more builders think having

Fig.13-9

no opening windows in a boat to be a good idea.

If a boat is lacking in opening windows, pay close attention to whether the AC cools the boat adequately. How much window glass a boat has is a major determining factor as to AC adequacy. What we often find is that a builder in the northern US failed to consider AC requirements in states like Florida and Gulf coast states. Unfortunately, we have no nifty formulas to tell us how much cooling capacity a boat should have because there are too many variables such as insulation, expanses of window glass, routing of ducting and so on.

Motor yachts and fly bridge sedans require greater capacities because the engines are located beneath the cabin areas where engine heat radiates upward. Conversely, express boats with engines aft of the living spaces require considerably less capacity, often only one or two units.

The following example will give you an idea of how a boat can have adequate capacity in terms of raw BTU's but not cool a boat adequately. This fifty footer had full window glass all the way around the house perimeter amounting to 164 square feet of glass. In addition, the forward windshields were very shallow sloping 3' x 4' panels of glass amounting to 36 square feet of nearly horizontal glass. The sunlight radiating through this glass produced temperatures of 150 degrees on the inside directly under the glass. That alone, was enough to ensure that the AC couldn't overcome radiation from the sun, but the system had other problems.

Next, the salon unit had ducts that were run through the engine room, ducts that only had minimal insulation plus leaks so that the outflow temperature into the salon was a mere 68 degrees. I found that the bilges in the boat were getting quite cool while the salon wasn't, indicating that there were a lot of leaks in the ducting. Additionally, several of the self-contained units split off too many ducts to other areas so that none of them were capable of cooling the space intended because the air flow was so weak.

In all cases where we complained to the builder that the AC was not cooling the boat adequately, they fought us tooth and nail because to correct such deficiencies is very costly.

A general rule for flybridge sedans which typically have a lot of window glass can be figured thusly: A forty-two foot boat has a salon 10' x 12' x 6.8' for a total of 816 cubic feet. Normally, a single 16,000 BTU unit will handle this adequately in Florida so it will do fine everywhere else, too. The forward quarters we'll figure to be about the same area volume for a total of 1600 cubic feet. But the forward quarters don't have any windows, so we'll reduce the need here by 25%, which translates to 12,000 BTU. Thus an adequate system configured for high temperatures would be 28,000 BTU total or 20 BTU/ft^3 for salons and 17 BTU/ft^3 for under deck quarters.

The only way to be sure is to check out the system on a hot, sunny day allowing sufficient time for the system to cool the boat down. Keep in mind that with a hot engine room and blazing sun, this can take quite a while. Plus, on boats people go in and out rather frequently. Here are some additional tips:

- Express cruisers are easier to air condition than most other types because of the lack of window glass. A typical forty foot express can get by with as little as 24,000 BTU.

- While draperies on windows help some, don't expect them to be a big help in keeping temps down.

- For boats with large sloping windshields, sun screens are usually necessary. However, it is better not to have to rely on sun screens due to increased maintenance they cause. They collect dirt on windows and are time consuming to put on and take off.

- When getting a survey, make sure your surveyor checks out the AC system. He should have an infrared thermometer and test the output air which should be between 50 and 60 degrees.

- Make sure there is a return air vent from the space being cooled to the AC unit and that *the unit is not pulling air from the bilge.*

- If the bilges are getting cold, there are serious leaks in the ducting.

All marine air conditioners are reverse cycle, which means they are capable of heating also. However, heating capacity diminishes in inverse proportion to outside water temperatures. With water temperatures below 45 degrees, heating ability is rather poor.

Water Makers

Desalinators or reverse osmosis technology is highly developed so that small, relatively affordable systems are available from numerous manufacturers. The most important thing to be aware of about these systems is that they are rather maintenance intensive. If operated in very dirty water such as rivers, the expensive membranes foul up very quickly, so they are best for use in clean water. Secondly, the systems go sour when not used regularly and therefore need to be laid up when not in use, a time-consuming proposition at best.

R/O systems are most suited for long range cruising where availability of good water is limited, such as when island hopping. These systems are not suitable "water cleaners" because you're fearful of contamination in local water supplies. Though they do remove most impurities, the cost of doing so is rather high. It is best to use faucet type filters for this purpose.

Because of the highly corrosive environments in which they function, don't expect the lesser expensive units to perform as well or last as long.

Water Fixtures

Wash downs, salt and fresh, as well as showers have almost become standard items. Saltwater wash downs are useful for fishermen who will use a lot of water, but don't want to use limited fresh water. Shower heads on flexible hoses are useful for washing the salt off after swimming and diving. Unfortunately, the large majority of these fixtures are cheap indoor quality fixtures that deteriorate rapidly, even when set inside a little locker. If you really need such fixtures, it would be beneficial to have the cheap fixture changed out for a good quality all stainless fixtures that are available in abundance.

Fresh water wash downs, like those nifty coil hoses, are particularly nice for the cruising yachtsman who doesn't like fighting with heavy hoses or living on a salt-encrusted boat day after day since you'll constantly have salt on your hands and clothes, which then gets smeared all over the interior of the boat as well. Even if dockside water isn't available, I like to wash down the cockpit area immediately after running to get the salt off hand rails and all other areas where we have frequent body contact, like seats and so on.

Here's where I get frustrated with those cheap $60 water pumps that we find on so many boats that will only bring pressure up to about 10 psi, suitable only for a sink spigot. I want water pressure at about 25-30 psi and only a more expensive pump will provide that. If you're buying new, you may want to check this out if you, too, want a little more pressure than is normally provided. If you're big on showering aboard, you'll be glad you made the change.

My preference is not to have a dedicated exterior shower fixture, but instead prefer the set up found on sport fishing boats which consists of only two quick-connect water connections in the cockpit, fresh and salt, to be used with just one coil hose and nozzle, or shower attachment, which is then stowed away when not in use. In most cases one can forgo the shower attachment and just adjust the hose nozzle to a fine spray instead of having all that extra rigmarole to pay for, clean and maintain. No faucets, no indoor shower head and hose to tangle with and no special cabinet to have to keep clean.

Chromed bronze quick-connect fittings are readily available and in most cases dedicated shower faucets can be pulled and junked, replaced in the same location as the original fixture to fill the existing holes.

Navigation Lights

Can you imagine an auto maker installing something on car that blocks the headlights or tail lights? That's almost unthinkable. But it happens that boat builders, dealers and other equipment installers will install equipment on a boat that blocks the running lights, so it's no surprise that incidents of night collisions are increasing dramatically.

This is a quick and easy check to make. Once you know the running trim of the boat, simply make sure that all four running lights are visible from either ahead, abeam and astern in accordance with their required angles of display: Side lights, 90 degrees, forward white, 180 degrees, stern light, 180 degrees, anchor light, 360 degrees.

Navigation lights should be good quality but very often builders resort to installing only the very cheapest kind that have problems such as not being water tight, or made of plastic that deteriorates rapidly.

Ground Tackle

This term means everything that is associated with anchoring, including the anchor itself. In order to avoid making mistakes and incurring unneeded expense, the novice boater needs to give some serious thought as to how much anchoring he expects to do. If you don't have the right set up, anchoring not only becomes a hassle, but can be dangerous as well.

For serious anchoring, one type of anchor is never enough since one type does not work equally well in all types of bottoms. It will help to know generally what kind of bottom is most common in your area and purchase the type of anchor recommended for that.

Whether you plan to do a lot of anchoring, or you'll simply regard the anchor as emergency equipment, I strongly recommend that you do not skimp on anchor size, since an undersize anchor is little better than no anchor at all. Don't forget that an anchor is every bit as important a safety device as a fire extinguisher. The main emergency is following engine failures.

Because ground tackle is also emergency equipment, it should be ready to go at all times. Never detach anchors from their rodes and be sure to keep rodes free of tangles. If the engines fail while heading out an inlet, you want that anchor ready to let go in 60 seconds or less.

Fig.13-10, 3-11 & 3-12. For those who are serious about anchoring, a top quality dual gypsy vertical capstan windlass as this Galley Maid unit is ideal. BELOW RIGHT: Low priced windlasses are usually equally low-powered as exemplified by this small drive motor. BELOW LEFT: The least expensive are usually little more than rope retractors that are often function poorly, resulting in severe tangling.

Anchor Windlasses

Combination chain and rope gypsy windlasses have become very popular because they are substantially cheaper than standard windlasses. They are also supposed to be self-tailing, to be operated from the helm with but a push of a button. The only problem with this is that the so-called combination gypsy is not a combination gypsy at all but a chain gypsy used to pull rope that will chew up anchor rodes over time.

Other windlass styles include aluminum bodied winches made from cast aluminum and are painted. These tend to corrode at a very rapid rate and become unsightly. I recommend against all aluminum windlasses. The most common problem with winches is that they end up mounted in a chain locker immediately under a hatch which may leak water onto the motor and associated electrical apparatus and destroys it.

Bow Thrusters

These things suddenly became the rage with new boat sales, thanks, apparently to good salesmen. My view of bow thrusters is that they are a costly and unnecessary toy. Twin engine boats really have no need for a thruster. Single engine boats, boats with deep keels and boats with deep propeller pockets are those that will benefit from a thruster. Otherwise, to avoid this unnecessary expense, all you have to do is to learn how to operate your boat properly. There is also a huge stray current risk in placing a DC motor attached to a propeller below the water line and outside the hull.

As I pointed out in earlier chapters, some boats are so poorly designed and handle so poorly that these devices are actually needed to overcome design defects. *Caveat emptor.*

Hydraulic Transom Platforms

These devices have been around for nearly a decade but have not generally caught on perhaps due to the multitude of problems that have been associated with them. Their purpose is to store and launch a tender, or most often a jet ski, from a hydraulically operated platform attached to the transom of a vessel. While obstensibly a good idea, all of the ones I've seen have had big problems. Initially, they were sold as after market items to be added to large Sea Ray expresses.

The first problem was that neither Sea Ray nor any other builder had designed their transoms to support the tremendous leverage these devices impose and ultimately a lot

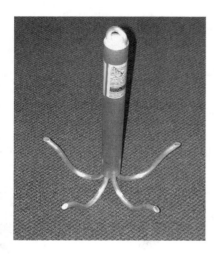
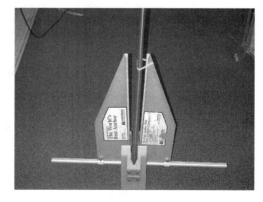

Fig.13-13 & 13-14. The grapnel, left, AKA grappling hook is handly for short term anchoring on hard bottoms such as rock, coral and oyster beds. RIGHT, the Danforth type is the standard multipurpose anchor.

of transom damage ensued. Faced with a lot of complaints, Sea Ray ended up creating their own product, offering it as optional equipment.

This did not solve the second problem, which was that the lifts are made of aluminum, along with other metals such as stainless steel. As can be seen in the photo below, the entire lift mechanism remains submerged all the time. The transom damage complaints were followed by complaints of severe corrosion. In more than a few cases, the corrosion was so severe that the submerged mechanism failed within a year or two.

The problem is one that both Sea Ray and the other manufacturer should have known: You cannot use aluminum underwater in conjunction with bronze and stainless steel propellers and shafts because the aluminum will become anodic to those more noble metals and will disintegrate, which, of course, it did. In other words, the whole aluminum mechanism becomes sacrificial to the other metals. Again, one has to wonder if the engineers aren't sitting at home, collecting unemployment.

Safety Gear

Boaters will often spend $10,000 or more for electronics but not as little as $1,000 for a life raft. Of course, a boat sinking is something that only happens to other people. Unfortunately, sinkings occur more frequently than most people are aware of because most incidents never make the evening news, or even the local papers. If you're heading offshore, I strongly recommend the purchase of at least a soft pack emergency life raft which are available for under $1,000. This is particularly important for those who are boating in cooler waters since survival times in cooler water is much less than in warmer water.

 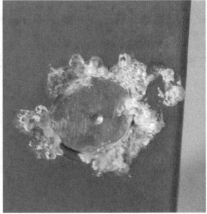

Fig.13-15 & 13-16. This is a never titled 2003 model Cruisers boat that had only been afloat for a few days. At right is a close up of a stainless steel hinge pin in the lift mechanism that aready shows advanced corrosion.Imagine what will happen to it in a year!

A number of people perish every year, not because they don't have life jackets, but because they weren't wearing them or couldn't get at them as the boat was sinking. Here's why: Most sinkings occur very rapidly, at least from the perspective of the passengers on board. Because the minimum required Type II PFD's are bulky, they usually get stored away in some difficult to reach location.

Actually, sinkings don't happen rapidly, but are the result of the boat hull filling up with water without anyone being aware of that. The water ingress often reaches a terminal level by the time the problem is noticed and then the boat goes down very fast, taking the life jackets with it before anyone can get to them because of all the mayhem and confusion going on.

This situation can be avoided by purchasing the zippered, vest type jacket preferred by sailors. These are very easy to put on, comfortable to wear and will stow away in half the space of other types. These are especially good for children that should be wearing a jacket at all times.

E.P. I.R.B.'s (pronunced epurbs) or Emergency Position Indicator Radio Beacons should be considered mandatory for anyone heading offshore in large bodies of water such as the ocean or great lakes. Life jackets are of little help if no one can find you. More importantly, your communications equipment may fail when needed. Epurbs transmit a constant signal that is picked up by a satellite and can be monitored by the Coast Guard are preferable to the older FM frequency type.

Boaters can spend a life- time boating and never have to use a fire extinguisher, so these things get very little consideration. The proper attitude to take is to expect that someday you will have a fire, and it may be at sea where your very life depends upon your ability

Fig.13-17. The vest type PFD is more comfortable to wear and takes up less space for stowage. This is the best type for children whom you want to be wearing continuously while on board.

to put it out. I can tell you truly that of 100 boats I survey every year, more than ten years old, if I'm lucky maybe I'll find one in that hundred which had their ten year old automatic fire extinguishing system inspected and tested. Due to corrosion and other factors, these devices and fire extinguishers tend to fail to function after only a few years, so if you have these devices but they've not been serviced in years, you might as well assume that you don't have them, because they'll not likely work when needed.

As for fire extinguishers, I recommend that you have at least double the required minimum, and that you have a variety of different types, including CO2 and Halon. The reason is simply that one type doesn't work for all fire types or circumstances. The bicarbonate of soda or powder type is the most common, but you don't want to ever use one in the engine room. That's because the material is abrasive and will damage machinery.

The CO2 is best for confined spaces where the fire source can't be seen or reached. Since it puts out the fire by starving it of oxygen it will put out any kind of fire except electrical arcing. I should note here that fires tend to occur at locations that one cannot see or reach, so the CO2 extinguisher is doubly important. CO^2 can also cause engine damage though it is preferable to bicarbonate. Halon can also cause engine damage, though this is much more rare and remote possibility. Most allegations of Halon causing engine damage prove to be false.

Dry chemical extinguishers are best for open fires that are not common occurrences on boats, yet these are the most common types found on boats, probably because they are so cheap. A galley stove fire is a good example where a dry chemical extinguisher works well, but so do the other types.

For a typical 36 footer, I recommend the following:

    2 - 5 lb. CO2
    2 - 2.5 lb. Dry Chemical
    1 - 2.5 lb. Halon

This recommendation takes into account that at least one of those units will fail to operate. Lean toward larger rather than smaller capacities where possible. Minimum size should be 2.5 lb. capacity.

For boats over 40 feet, fire extinguisher placement is critical and you need to think about placement. What so often happens is that a fire occurs in a location that cuts off access to the fire extinguishers because of heavy smoke. The question arises as to where people will be and can they get to an extinguisher. For example, I often see very large extinguishers located in the engine rooms of sport fishermen, but in the event of an engine room fire who could possibly get to them? Thus, the best placement is probably not in individual cabins but the approaches to those spaces.

Also consider that it may be a stranger that needs to put out a fire on your boat. Should your wife consider fire extinguishers unsightly and wants you to hide them away, now you know how to answer her objection.

The Coast Guard has reduced its annual fire extinguisher inspection requirement for any unit with a pressure gauge. Let me assure you that just because an extinguisher has a pressure gauge that shows in the green, that does not mean that the pressure hasn't escaped. Gauges can and do freeze up or stick. I recommend that fire extinguishers be tested every two years, automatic systems every three years.

Chapter 14

The Art of the Deal

Ships are but boards, sailors but men:
There be land- rats and water- rats,
Land- theives and water- thieves.
  - The Merchant of Venice

Considering the high value of boats, buying one is a lot easier than buying real estate and normally with far fewer pitfalls. While many buyers of mid size boats are moving up from smaller boats, many will be encountering the world of yacht brokers and federally documented vessels for the first time, so I'll discuss these issues too.

Hull Identification Numbers (HIN)

One of the first things you should know about used boats concerns the model year and date of manufacture. Most people just look at the last two digits and assume that that is the boat's year. Not so. The last two digits are the *Model year* which may not the same as the year it was built. The third digit from the right is the actual year of build. The letter preceding this is the month of build. Thus, a number ABC1001B889 indicates that the boat hull was molded in February, 1988 as a 1989 model year. If you were purchasing that boat in December, 1989, you could be looking at a boat that is nearly two years old. You already know that some builders are putting out new boat models a half year in advance, so that it is entirely possible to mistake the actual age of a boat by as much as 2-1/2 and it would all be legal!

When it comes to used boats, if this is of particular importance to you, try to find out when the boat was originally sold. Often times a call to the builder will net the date on which the boat was sold to the dealer, and who that dealer was. Most have the info computerized and will readily give it out over the phone. Or, you may find, as I often do, a packet of manuals that will reveal the date the boat was commissioned or similar dates on commissioning invoices.

Federal Documentation

The desirability of federal documentation ebbs and flows around federal tax laws that change almost as rapidly as the weather. The term we use to describe this is simply, "documented." At the time of this writing, there are few, if any, significant benefits to documentation. One of these applies mainly to lenders when a mortgage is involved. Many lenders will require documentation as a requirement for the mortgage and the reason why is called a First Preferred Ship's Mortgage which gives the lender first claim on the vessel as collateral over and above any and all other claims that might be levied against a vessel. So if your lender insists on documentation, now you know why.

What differentiates documentation from state registrations is that any claims against the vessel, say liens against unpaid boat yard services must be filed and recorded against the document through a federal court. A recorded claim will appear on the DOT central file until such time as it is cleared. Therefore, when purchasing a documented vessel one can be absolutely certain as to whether one is getting a clear title with no claims against it by checking the document abstract.

Under federal rules a documented vessel is treated as a person and the vessel itself can be held to certain liabilities, particularly as respects money. A down side of documentation is that the vessel itself can be arrested by federal marshals after a claimant posts a bond and goes through the federal process. Getting a boat unarrested is not easy, and cannot happen until cleared by a federal court.

In contrast, tort law of the states applies to state registered vessels wherein such claims do not have to be recorded. Nearly all states issue boat titles except Alabama and possibly a few others. Titles at least provide an owner with some kind of document and therefore official proof of ownership. Under most state laws vessels do not have liabilities, only the titled owners do. No one can arrest a vessel, size or impound it as can be done with documented vessels, however, the usual practices of mechanics liens can apply when a repair facility has custody of a vessel and can refuse to return the vessel to the owner based on an unpaid bill. Of course, laws vary from state to state.

Under federal law, states are permitted to assign their own HIN's in special cases which are complex and I won't go into here. The letter Z is reserved for this purpose so that a prefix of FLZ would indicate that a Florida state assigned number was issued. This facility has been subject to a lot abuse and fraud so that buying what we call a Z boat is very hazardous proposition. Very often Z boats are boats that were sold as salvage, or recovered as salvage under a total loss situation and rebuilt. Personally, I would not do it under any circumstances because there is really no good way to research the validity of the boat's pedigree.

There was a time when documentation had a huge tax benefit wherein one could register a vessel in another state and thereby avoid high state taxes. However, most boating states have closed this loop hole by means of various residency requirements. For example, an out-of-state owner can keep a boat in Florida for up to six months, after which it must leave or pay the Florida tax. God help you if you cheat and get caught because the penalties are very stiff. Fortunately, the federal "second home' income tax deduction pretty much relieves the strain on over-taxation until the next Democrat majority congress once again decides to soak the rich as they did back in 1990 with their 10% luxury tax. As a boat owner, "the rich" means you.

Getting Into the Right Frame of Mind

The purchase of a boat is a business deal and should be approached as such. The biggest mistake I see buyers make is to approach the purchase as a happy day. It never ceases to amaze me how unbusinessman-like someone can be while spending a half million dollars. They'll do things personally that they'd never do in a business transaction apparently because they are lulled by a recreational purchase. Salesmen, brokers and even sellers will sense and take advantage of anyone with that kind of attitude. Be calm, be polite, but also be very business-like to the point of being cool.

That is especially important with new boat salesmen. It is wise not to bring family along, for good salesmen will play them off against your better judgement. That includes wives who are regarded as being "easy." Some of these people are well trained at playing the game of wife against the husband. If you must bring your wife along, counsel her not to show emotion or make any comments within earshot of the seller or broker. Tell her to look, but behave like an ice lady.

Boat Shows

Boat shows are a good place to look but not a good place to buy. Like an auction, there are too many people bidding up the price and the whole idea of the show is to create a buying mood, not a discriminating or negotiating mood. Boat shows are too much like carnivals and are designed to foster vanity and impulsive spending. Moreover, someone has to pay the high costs of putting that show on, and hauling all that product to and fro. That someone is the people who buy boats at shows.

New Boats

How About Demos?

Sometimes good deals can be found on demos. However, you have to ask yourself why any dealer would invest that huge sum of money in a demonstrator, for it means a serious loss of revenue. Few dealers will. More often than not a demo is a boat that the dealer ended up having to take back for some reason before a title was ever issued. However, it does happen that a dealer keeps a boat around for use at boat shows as well as a floor model that after a while gets a little beat up. Imagine what can happen when a boat has been hauled around to four shows and ten thousand people have trudged through it, poking, prodding, pulling, opening and closing just about everything. Not a pleasant thing to think about, is it?

Dealers may have demos in the thirty foot range, but you can be sure that there are none in the forty foot range as this is just too costly. For larger boats, it's usually the builder who does the placement, with shares being paid by participating dealers, which is why they want you to fill out those "registration" cards before they even let you into the exhibit, yet alone on the boat.

If you do find a demo make sure that the builder will stand behind it. The biggest issue, of course is warranty, and since you have two of them, boat and engines, pay close attention. What you particularly need to know is when the warranty period starts. Does it begin the day you take delivery, or did it begin the day the dealer started using it as a demo? What relationship do engine hours have to the warranty?

Dealers do keep big boats in "stock," allowing only serious prospects on board because they are selling a new boat, not a beat up show model or a demo. A new boat should have less than ten hours on it, and certainly not more than twenty. Demos typically have a lot more and I've seen them up to around 150 hours. These are often boats used by the manufacturer for shows and then sold off to a dealer. They will usually have observable wear and tear (carpet, wood cabin soles and other high traffic areas, upholstery may show a little wear on the corners, etc.), but otherwise look new. Most reputable dealers will disclose these facts. But, you do need to consider the possibility that a one year old used boat will have fewer hours and wear and tear on it than a demo, and may also be priced lower because it has been titled.

If the warranty begins the day you take delivery, then you are essentially getting a new boat with a few hours on it, perhaps a little scuffed up. But with the great advantage of a lower price. If the deal is based on the *duration* of the warranty, then you are getting a used boat, and the price differential should be substantial. I can think of no better advice than to take the time to call the warranty department of both the boat and engine manufacturer and ask them about their policy for demos. That's the only way you can be sure.

Seasonal Leftovers

These are a possibility and offer the chance of substantial price reductions at the expense of selection, current model year, and very likely some wear and tear. Note here that a demo or a seasonal left over may be the same thing. Most new boats sit outside exposed to sun and rain and are going to be a bit worse for wear, so that price reduction may not be solely based on the passing of the model year. I have seen a lot of new boats sitting out for long periods of time that have considerable damage, including water damage to electrical stuff, the interior or upholstery. This is especially true of smaller and entry-level boats where lots may be jammed with boats.

Approach these boats as if they were used or "almost new." Often they will have substantial engine hours — say 20 to 40 — because they've been moved around a lot. With floating boats, engines have to be run just to keep them oiled up, so some hours will accumulate there. The reality is that most so-called left overs are basically undesirables that didn't sell, very often because of low horsepower and somewhat less often because of a style that isn't popular. Then there are some dealers who will take the opportunity to temporarily convert stock to personal use.

Model years of larger boats are not as important as, say, with vehicles, or at least it shouldn't be, not with products this large and expensive. That's why the federal government allows some latitude to builders. Moreover, it happens often that boats do not get sold in the year they are built. What counts most is the year a boat was launched and commissioned.

Trade-ins Doing a deal based on a trade-in is the worst possible deal you can make unless you figure your boat isn't worth much. First, you'll get nowhere near what your trade-in is worth, and you are giving the dealer the opportunity to juggle the numbers. In all likelihood he'll smell a very eager buyer and will raise the price of the new boat as well.

If there's any possibility that you can sell your current boat at a fair price, I recommend that you do so if your money means anything to you.

Buying a Trade-In

My experience with dealers reselling trade-ins over the years has not been good. All too often they failed to look the boat over carefully before accepting it, and on discovering it's a dog, are often desperate to get rid of it. That doesn't mean they let it go at fire sale prices, but more often try to cover up or misrepresent the condition. Trade-ins should be approached with great caution.

Dealerships

There has been a tremendous amount of turmoil with larger boat dealerships in recent years. Traditionally higher priced boats such as Hatteras, Tiara and Viking limited dealerships to higher-end facilities that had the expertise to properly deal with these sophisticated products. Now we find Hatteras dealerships given to marina chains whose primary business is high and dry marinas that deal mainly with smaller boats. Obviously, this does not bode well for larger boats.

The reason why this development is bad news is that there is a huge variety of small boats, engines and equipment, so much so that it's very difficult for service personnel to keep up with it all. But when you add larger boats, which are vastly different than small boats, well, I doubt the nature of the problem requires further explanation. Why this has happened is simply a matter of money: profits. The traditional large boat dealer required a significantly higher markups to cover the cost of his operation, including the kind of expertise that more monied boat owners demand. By going with small boat dealers and in many cases, yacht brokers, who may not have any service facility at all, the boat builder can force the dealers into lower margins with higher boat prices to the to the builder. When we have small boat dealers attempting to service large boats. a lack of expertise is bound to manifest into service quality complaints.

One thing you should be aware of is that even the National Marine Manufacturers Association has been so worried about the low level of customer satisfaction that it has instituted a number of technical training programs in association with the American Boat and Yacht Council, the objective being to reduce the excessive number of complaints.

Optional Equipment

For the most part, the options offered by boat builders tend to be limited toward structurally oriented items where the buyer doesn't have the opportunity to purchase ready-made, bolt-on products, such as hard tops, swim platforms, seating modules and so on. Very few offer electronics or open market add-ons. Soft goods, such as tops and enclosures, are often an option but are not always the best quality available. I recommend checking out the quality of these items before you buy as low quality soft goods are not worth paying for. As for the structural type items, these will usually be better made than after market custom stuff.

Dealer Markup

This is the question that everyone wants the answer to, and the one for which there are no good answers. Dealer markups are nowhere near what they used to be twenty years ago. Markup varies widely with the value of the boat; the lower the value, the higher the markup and conversely with higher values.

A $150,000 boat typically will have a target mark up of around 20% which equates to $30,000.00. That has to cover all their overhead plus their floor plan financing, which is likely to be around 8- 10% of that amount because it's short term financing. That leaves the dealer with 10-12% to play with, which isn't much. You'll note I said a "target" markup because that is the bottom line the dealer will be shooting for, but he's likely to start shooting much higher.

Some few builders publish a MSRP, though most don't. The MSRP locks the dealer into how much he can ask, whereas if there is no MSRP he can ask whatever he wants. The contract between dealers and builders usually varies so that the dealer who sells the most will be given the greatest leeway to set his own prices. This is one of the reasons why there is so little dealer loyalty toward builders these days. It's dog eat dog and a lot of dogs get eaten.

Another example: Sea Ray has both dedicated Sea Ray dealers as well as smaller dealers that are brokerage houses and small marinas. Do they all purchase their boats at the same price and use the same markup? Evidence suggests otherwise, though we'll never know the answer because we'll never see a dealership contract with the builder. With this builder's boats, I've seen as much as a 40% difference in the price of the boat sold to customers.

So where does that leave us with regard to the markup question? Precisely nowhere because the correct answer to the question is that there is no way of knowing short of doing a lot of leg work to find the lowest price or bribing a dealer to tell you.

Selecting a Dealer

This is the second most important decision you can make to the actual choice of boat. The dealer can be either your best friend or worst enemy since a good dealer will go to bat for you when something on the boat isn't right. Note that if you head out of town to get the best price, you're not going to have a selling dealer to go to bat for you unless you're willing to bring your boat that long distance back to him, which is unlikely. Think this over before making a decision to go for the lowest price. There are no magic formulas for selecting a good dealer. All you can do is take the time to ask around. Phone calls to a couple of marine surveyors might produce some informed answers.

Used Boats

Beginning the Search

Whether you're buying new or used, before you begin the actual task of going around to look at boats, it will save you a lot of time and money to first commit your requirements to writing. Take out the old yellow pad and make a list of your requirements; this will help clarify your thoughts. Make a list of the primary and then the secondary requirements. The primaries are the things you must have, while the secondaries are the one's you hope to get as well, but will include things of lesser importance that you may have to give up in this world of compromises.

Once you've got that done (and the chairman of the board agrees with it!), you can begin the search. There's no better place to begin than on the Internet which is revolutionizing the used boat sales world. One can either do a search based on a search engine, or go directly to advertising sites like yachtworld.com, boattrader.com or any number of others. The nice thing about the Internet is that, unlike print media the 'Net is current and normally will contain more details than paper ads. They'll also contain more pictures, but be careful about what you try to determine from photos. No seller takes pictures of things he'd rather not have you see, so like all advertising, pictures don't tell the whole story, but can be used to get a general impression. It's a mistake to try to discern condition from a photo. In that regard, photos lie.

Locating Boats

If you live in a major boating center, chances are you won't have to travel far to find the right boat. But most people don't live in major boating centers and unless they happen to get lucky, chances are they'll have to travel to find the right boat. Obviously, that poses problems of time and expenses so that you'll want to do your best to minimize them.

One of the first problems is that sellers lie a lot. The most common complaint I hear is about the seller who claims his boat is in excellent condition. When the buyer arrives from out-of-state what he finds is a clapped out dog that didn't look anything like the pictures he was given (probably taken eight years ago!)

There's a way to cut through the fog and get closer to the truth, but it will involve a bit of work on your part. What you need to do is learn a bit about the art of interrogation for it is quite possible to get the seller to reveal the true condition of the boat without his realizing he is doing so. This technique involves keeping the seller on the phone for quite a while by asking some well-considered questions. What we don't want to do is to cut to the chase by asking pointed questions like "What's her overall condition?" Clearly such a general question is going to get an equally general answer, "Oh, she's in really great shape!" whatever "great" means.

What we have to do is to get down to specifics such as,

> What does the gel coat look like?
> Upholstery?
> When was last major engine work?
> Any machinery major overhauls" Can you provide invoices?
> Last bottom paint, hauling?
> How old is the interior carpet?
> How old is the soft top and enclosures?
> Have you replaced any electronics lately?
> Are there any damages on the rub rails, hull sides"
> Are there any blisters on the bottom? Have you ever repaired blisters?

It's best to prepare your list of questions in advance and have them written down in advance before making the phone call. Keep in mind that before you go to look at the boat, you've probably got only one shot at this on the phone. In asking a lot of questions, what we're doing here is trying to keep the seller off guard and say more than he intends to say. The objective in asking so many pointed questions is to let the seller know that you're going to be extremely upset if you travel a long distance to look at the boat and it is not what he represented it to be.

This tactic works especially well with brokers who will have the hope of selling you some other boat if you don't buy that particular one. That's one reason why they tend to misrepresent. It wouldn't hurt to tell a broker flat out that you're likely to fly off into a violent rage if he's fibbing to you.

Brokerage Boats

As we move up in size of used boats, increasingly they are represented by brokers. I know a lot of people do not have high regard for brokers when they are buying, but somehow their opinions suddenly seem to change when they're selling. Fact of the matter is that selling is usually more difficult than buying. It's time consuming and the seller has to put up with a lot of 'tire kickers" who may just want to go for a ride as an afternoon's entertainment.

Like used car salesmen, generally yacht brokers have a bad name. However, not all deserve to be painted with the same brush: there are the good as well as the bad. A good broker, even though he represents the seller, will do everything he can to make your purchase as pleasant as possible.

The most important thing to realize with selling brokers – that is the brokerage house who has the listing – is that they have more of an economic interest to sell that particular boat than, say a broker who is not selling his own listing, for in that case, the commission is being split whereas in the former it is not. Brokers will do their best to try to steer you toward their own listings.

You have the option of buying direct from the listing broker which, of course, is the seller's agent. However, you have the option of using any broker to buy any boat who will then end up splitting the commission with the listing broker. In most cases the non listing broker will represent your interest better as far as negotiating because he has no interest in keeping the sale price as high as possible. He'll work harder to negotiate it down to what you're willing to pay, and possibly do a better job of that than you can because he knows the ropes.

Transacting the Sale - Used Boats

Considering the high value of boats, transacting the sale is much easier than for real estate. The process begins with making an offer, which is either accepted, rejected or countered. Once an offer is accepted, a broker will request a deposit, and so will most individual sellers. The amount of deposit varies, but can be up to 10% with 5% probably being closer to the usual. The broker is supposed to place that deposit into a dedicated escrow account. The purchase agreement you sign should indicate the amount of deposit and the terms under which it is refundable.

Purchase agreements are normally made "subject to survey." You'll note that this is a very vague term that basically allows the seller to reject the boat after survey for just about any reason. Its intent is to cancel the deal if, on survey, the vessel shows up unanticipated problems. Note here that if you are not getting the vessel surveyed, the subject to survey clause does not apply and you are then locked in.

Almost all boats going through survey will have unexpected problems. Typically, this results in a revised offer based upon the estimated cost to correct the deficiencies. It is often the case that the seller offers to correct the deficiencies. If these deficiencies are significant, I strongly recommend that you do not accept that offer, the reason being the seller's motivation to take shortcuts to whatever work is needed. Yes, there is an element of risk in making settlement based on an estimate, but it's certainly not as great as letting the seller make any repairs.

For documented vessels, the vast majority of buyers elect to use a professional documentation service. Because of the complexity of dealing with federal forms, and the length of time it takes, most people find it well worth the several hundred dollar fee. A service will also get the job substantially faster because they get preferential service from DOT.

Transacting sales of state registered boats is the same process as auto titles with one caveat, especially for smaller boats. It is wise to check the title with the state agency to make sure that everything is in order before you complete the transaction. In some states you can do this with a simple phone call; you'll need the registration number and vessel HIN. California is one exception where the state will not give out this information. Pay close attention to who is the registered owner and whether there are joint owners.

When faced with joint owners the deal goes forward based on the assumption that both owners are agreeable to both the sale and acceptance of your offer. That could easily be a false assumption when things like divorces are involved, so be sure to confirm with the seller that both registered owners are not only willing to sell, but are in agreement with the signed and accepted offer.

When purchasing a used boat, be sure to get a bill of sale stating who is selling the boat, for how much and what date the transaction is completed.

For Sale, OBO

By-owner sales can be a little more difficult, especially if the seller doesn't understand and accept the standard routines, especially regarding surveys. Before agreeing to the purchase, it's best to question the seller as to his availability to complete the survey, which is the most common sticking point. Typically, a survey is going to take close to all day. The seller needs to be available to operate the boat, but if he says he can't get away from work, that the survey has to be done at night or on a week end, you're probably going to run into difficulty. On a brokerage deal normally the broker will provide a paid captain to operate the vessel, as well as being present himself, but with a OBO deal you're missing these vital ingredients.

Surveyors will not perform surveys in the evening, and since almost everyone ends up asking for surveys on the weekend, most surveyors will not be available on weekends. Before handing over any money, be sure to ask the seller about availability for survey. I've run into some real cranky sellers on OBO deals who wanted surveys done at their convenience.

Sellers's Expense, Buyer's Expense

Completing the transaction involves certain costs, some of which are born by the seller, others the buyer. The seller's expenses are limited to the brokerage fee plus the cost to hire a captain to operate the boat on survey and sea trial. The buyer pays the surveyor and the haul out cost. Sometimes a boat with an extremely dirty bottom is encountered, which has to be cleaned before it can be surveyed or sea trialed. Note here that a proper sea trial cannot be conducted with a dirty bottom as this will prevent a proper evaluation of the engines performance. The cost of a quick cleaning may run up to $100 or so. This gets handled in one of two ways; either the cost is split between buyer and seller, or the seller bears the whole cost if the vessel fails to pass survey. Be sure to discuss these costs with the seller or broker before going to survey. *All yard charges will have to be paid at the time of the survey.*

OBO Contracts

In the majority of purchases, financing will be involved on both sides of the transaction. In this case, you will need to have an advance discussion with your lender before you proceed. He will then work out the details of the closing with the seller's lender. It is important to work this out before you give a deposit to avoid causing problems with the final settlement.

The lender won't much care how you write your contract but I recommend that you should make a written contract between yourself and the seller. The purpose of the Purchase Agreement is to spell out what is expected of each party in concluding the transaction and need not be full of complicated legalese; it can be written by anyone in plain language. The points to be addressed as follows:

- Parties to the contract
- Names, addresses, phone numbers
- Date
- Description of vessel (builder, model, year, HIN
- Total purchase price
- Amount of deposit, date deposit received
- Terms of sale (subject to survey) and any special considerations
- Final date for closing (2 to 4 weeks is typical)
- Signatures and dates

While I haven't heard of many instances with problems of deposit refunds on brokerage deals, OBO deals may be a different matter. Sellers often don't know what the proper protocols are. That's why I recommend that it's best to spell out in the contract the terms for deposit refunds, such as:

Seller warrants that all equipment and machinery is in good working order with exceptions, if any. The buyer has the right to cancel this contract and demand a full deposit refund in the event that, upon survey, any equipment and machinery fails to perform in a satisfactory manner, or that survey reveals that there is damage, deterioration or degradation of any structure equipment or component that would affect the safety, sea worthiness and value of the vessel.

Co-ownership

Husband and wife owners do not often pose a problem, but one does need to take extra precautions with other forms of joint ownership, particularly partnerships that have a too high frequency of breaking down into warring factions, not unlike marriages. I would strongly recommend that you consult an attorney before closing a deal involving partnerships, or let your lender deal with it. It would be wise to have a signed document from all owners certifying that there are no claims against the vessel and holding you harmless from such claims. Note that in any case, it is reasonable to ask for a signed hold harmless agreement from the seller.

Boat Fraud

The worst cases of boat fraud I've ever seen involves brokers or dealers running off with escrowed deposit funds and, in one case, the entire payment for a boat. Boat sales fraud is not commonplace, but it occurs with sufficient frequency that it bears being discrete. The best way to avoid boat fraud is to use common sense and follow good business procedures; "Trust but verify," as Ronald Reagan put it. Verify numbers and dates. Read all documents. Deposits should only be made into verified escrow accounts, and never in the name of a broker or salesman.

Whenever financing is involved, whether on behalf of buyer or seller, the lended will aways insist on the use of a trusted closing agent. If there is no financing, I recommend the use of documentation agents who are usually licensed and can offer sound advice. I do not recommend that payment checks, other than deposits, be made out directly to the brokerage.

Chapter 15

Boat Shopping

There's no doubt about it, going boat shopping is an arduous task, particularly for used boats. Fortunately, the Internet has made that a lot easier for used boats. Even so, it is still a very time consuming process. So in this chapter I'll give you some tips on how to avoid wasting time and money.

New Boats

Shopping for new boats is fairly straightforward, since nearly all mid size boats are sold through dealerships. Unfortunately, collecting boat brochures is of little value because, whereas years ago brochures were chock full of useful information, today they are nothing more that assemblages of slick pictures. In recent years, it has become very difficult to obtain even the most rudimentary technical information. Web sites are usually just mirror images of the brochures.

Boat shows may or may not be the best way to see the largest variety of boats and really get a close look at them, depending on the number of dealerships in your area. Personally, I find boat shows to a rather poor venue for looking at boats closely, and much prefer going to a dealer showroom on Monday morning when no one is there and I have the boat all to myself instead of trying to look through a crowd. If you can get to a major boating center where there are numerous dealers, this is by far the better way to view boats up close and personal. True, you'll have a salesman hanging on your back like a second shirt, but maybe you'll become adept at shaking them off. I do all my previewing of new boats at dealerships.

Test Runs

These are tougher for new boats than used because you'll have to demonstrate a very serious interest before the salesman will go to all that trouble, but you may be able to finagle one without a deposit if you can convince the man you are really serious. For used boats, all you have to do is make an offer and give a deposit which will be refunded if you don't like what you see.

Used Boats

The used boat market is unique in that it is now essentially a nationwide, rather than a local market as it once was. Boat buyers seek and travel far and wide to find not only the right boat, but also the best price. It is also a fact of life that the greatest numbers of boats are to be found in a relatively small number of major boating centers, the largest, of course, being Fort Lauderdale long known as the boating capital of the world for the simple reason that there are more boats in that city than any other by far.

The major boating centers also tend to garner more boats for sale by virtue of gravity; it's much harder to sell boats that are located off the beaten path, or in areas that are more difficult to travel to. A lot of boats are moved to Florida for the sole purpose of resale. Thus, it makes sense to begin one's search in the places where one is most likely to meet with success.

The Internet is the place to begin, for the vast majority of boats over $100,000 will be listed there. It has a great advantage over brokerage ads in magazines because it eliminates the "teaser" ads which are ads for boats that probably don't exist and are just designed to get you to call them. Yachtworld.com is one of my favorites because of the way it is set up. It is much too costly for brokers to insert teasers on this site, so the boats listed there are real, often with a large number of photos and reasonably good info.

You can find listings of smaller, less expensive boats on proprietary or dealer web sites, though most of these seem to have very limited information. Keep in mind that the Internet is constantly changing so that what I write this week could well be wrong by next week.

In a very short time sitting at the computer, one can gain the listings of nearly every one of a particular model boat for sale. It's also a fair statement that, if it's not on Yachtworld, it's not seriously for sale. Yes, there are boats that are only advertised in local papers or magazines, but they will get nowhere near the exposure that one gets from the Internet.

Of course, the problem with ads is that the advertiser can say whatever he wants and there is no guarantee of accuracy of anything contained therein, which is how we can end up spinning our wheels.

It is also true that because of the worldwide exposure that the Internet provides, the idea that you're going to search far and wide for the best deal becomes futile. Why? Because the Internet levels out the playing field and anyone with an ounce of sense can very quickly find out what a given boat is worth since the asking prices of so many are readily available. Therefore, Internet listings make boat asking prices more reflective of true worth than ever before. In other words, there are far fewer sellers that are asking prices that are out of line simply because excessive pricing stands out like a strobe light on a moonless night. If an asking price is well above all others of its class, the seller had better be able to explain why or he isn't going to be getting many calls.

I trust that for all those of you who ask "What is a boat really worth?", my point here is clear. A boat is only worth what more than one knowledgeable buyer is willing to pay for it, regardless of what any price book says. While the Internet has become a great leveling influence, it still does not make your job all that much easier for there are still the issues of condition to deal with, travel, surveys and getting a boat back home.

It may be surprising to newcomers that boat buyers will travel a thousand miles or more to buy a boat, but they do so routinely. Most often this is because finding a boat in the condition or with the engines they want, but also at times due to the equipage, entails a lot of looking and phone calls. Price and age are other reasons. Is this worth the cost of travel and returning the boat to home? Apparently many think so, though for reasons that might be surprising.

The Florida Market

By far, South Florida has the largest boat market anywhere in the world due to both the 12 month season and nearly unlimited and cheap dockage, plus the fact that so many snowbirds head south in the winter.

The beauty of the Florida market is that one can combine winter vacationing with boat shopping. In a weeks time, one can see more boats, both used and new, than one could anywhere else. On top of that, airfares tend to be quite low, though one is likely to run into problems with both airline and hotel bookings during peak travel times.

One of the reasons so many boats are sold in Florida is that the buyers often plan winter vacations in conjunction with their purchases; they plan to use the boat in Florida, the Keys or Bahamas, as well as turning the return trip home into a cruise. Florida is an easy cruise to anywhere in the Atlantic and Gulf states, as well as many of the Mid-South via the Tenn-Tom waterways.

Others, particularly those from the Great Lakes and West Coast areas put the boat on a truck and ship it home, which brings up the cost of shipping. The boat transport business has become refined enough that many buyers find the shipping costs to be reasonable. I can't quote prices because they are highly variable by region and overhead clearances.

Fresh Water Boats

I am often asked about fresh water boats, why they command higher prices and whether the condition tends to be worth higher prices. My answer is yes, they generally are. The reasons go beyond just being in fresh water and also extend to conditions of use. The majority of fresh water boats are located in the Great Lakes where boating seasons are notoriously short. Not only are engines run a lot less, but the boats are hauled out for winter and the engines winterized. To make a long story short, this greatly cuts down on internal engine corrosion that occurs in salt water as a result of the exhaust pipes being half submerged. That very wet, salty environment causes rust on valves and cylinders, resulting in premature engine wear. This sort of deterioration is reduced by at least 75% in the fresh water environment.

The down side of many fresh water environments has to do with the use of wood in boat construction because wooden structurals will rot much faster in fresh water, whereas salt is something of a preservative. Also, the air pollution produced in industrial regions also takes its toll on the exterior of northern boats, particularly upholstery, canvass and aluminum, often offsetting the strong UV damage that occurs in the south.

Generally speaking, I find the average fresh water boat to be in better condition as respects environmental deterioration than, say the Florida or Gulf Coast boat.

Other Regional Considerations

Absentee ownership of boats is a situation in which an owner keeps his boat at a location far from home, usually because there is no boating where he lives, or because another area is preferable to his own. All throughout the US there are popular areas where there are large numbers of boats with absentee owners.

I doubt you need me to explain why boats with absentee owners tend to be rather poorly maintained. I confess I was not aware of how serious a problem this could be until I moved to an area that has a large number of such boats. You can probably save yourself a lot of wasted time and money by finding out where the boat is kept versus where the owner lives. The odds are very high that if he's far away, the boat won't be in great condition.

How can I make such a sweeping, politically incorrect allegation? Easy: people who don't live near their boats don't have the time to perform the necessary maintenance, and as I explained in the first chapter, paying someone else to do it is beyond the budget of most boat owners. Not always, but most of the time.

This doesn't mean that you should automatically exclude such boats, but be prepared to try to cut through the fog to get the truth of the matter before you buy plane tickets or drive a long distance. Many such absentee owner regions are easily identifiable, such as the Florida Gulf Coast, Florida West Coast (snowbirds) and the Carolinas are but a few. The Florida peninsula has a large number of snowbird boats, but as the population of the state has grown at incredible rates, the percentage of the these versus locally owned is actually small.

Making Your Own Appraisal

What is the value of a boat, and how is it determined? It is often said that the value of anything is whatever someone is willing to pay for it. That is not entirely accurate since there are times when unknowledgeable buyers will pay more than a knowledgeable buyer would. Therefore, anything that is for sale may be worth more to some people than others. This is really no help to us, so what we are really asking is what the "fair market value" of the boat is.

The fair market value of a boat can be defined as the price that more than one knowledgeable buyer would be willing to pay. If there are two knowledgeable buyers who agree that a price is reasonable, is this not more convincing than one? The way to determine that would be to research recent sales records for what others have paid for a particular boat. Unfortunately, there is no agency that collects and makes such information available, so we have to resort to another method. That method is to look at current *asking prices* of either identical or comparable boats, or both, since such information can be collected and studied.

This is fairly easily done by collecting all available advertising media, including the Internet. For many years my own method of making appraisals was to sit down with publications such as *Boat Trader* and the various yachting magazines, scanning these for ads. Using an Exacto knife and a glue stick, I cut out the ads and glued them onto a piece of paper. Or, if you're using the Internet, write all pertinent info down. Once I had a sufficient number of boats – hopefully at least ten — I make a list of all boats that have similar engines and equipment, as well as making a guess about condition. With the advent of Internet listings this has become a lot easier because all you have to do is print out the listings and then collate them.

Let's say I find ten ads, each of which lists an asking price. Of these ten, the majority will fall within a certain price range grouping, while several others will fall into an extreme of highs and lows. These get tossed out as being unrepresentative and the remainder of the pricing is totaled and averaged out. We know, of course, that sellers ask more than they expect to get, but the question becomes one of how much more. There are no hard and fast rules except that we know if one asks too much, their phone is unlikely to ring. We've already thrown out the high extremes, which are likely to represent those who are asking too much, and in taking our average, it's a pretty good bet that it will be fairly representative of the usual mark up of around 10%, perhaps up to 15%, over what a seller really expects to net.

Another thing to do is to evaluate each of the ads closely in order to determine how each boat relates to the others. This, in terms of extra equipment, and whatever the seller has to say about the condition, which may or may not be true, but there's nothing we can do about that. Having done that, we make additional adjustments based on whatever differences we can glean from the ads.

It should go without saying that when an asking price is unusually low, there is a good reason for that. The reason will nearly always be that this particular boat is in lesser condition than others. Many buyers are immediately attracted to the one with the lowest price. My experience is that this is almost always a mistake. If you're going to travel far to follow up on the lowest priced ad, expect to be disappointed over the condition when searching out the lowest or lower priced boats.

Using this method will yield an appraisal that is as close as anyone can get. Naturally, the more boats one has in the sample, the more accurate it will be. Also, that this method works best for the more popular makes and models where obtaining a representative sample is most possible. But what do we do about makes and models that are more rare, such as custom boats, or limited production boats, and for which we may not be able to find any similar boats for sale?

In this case we have to turn the method of using comparables. Comparables are boats of similar type, size, quality and with the same engines, but not the same builder or model. Even if you're not very experienced in boating, if you assemble a grouping of comparably sized boats and simply average out the prices, even that will help to evaluate pricing better.

If, for example, you are looking at very popular boats, say Sea Ray, where there are dozens of listings for just one model, it then becomes possible to extrapolate a lot from all those ads. For example, one could enter them all into a spread sheet and perform all sorts of analysis on them. You can even calculate the average annual difference in price from year to year, or find out how much more valuable one type of engine is over another.

Appraisal Books

The question to ask about books is whether you think appraisal books reflect prices, or do books set the prices? This question is particularly valid in light of the fact that there are no central clearing houses for used boat sales. So, how do the book makers arrive at the pricing contained therein? In the used car market, there are large regional auctions where trade-ins taken by dealers are sent to be sold. That is how so-called "wholesale" prices are derived.

There are no such wholesale auctions for used boats yet there are books that list "wholesale" prices. Where do they get those prices? The answer is that they invent them. In nearly all cases, appraisal books derive their pricing from a declining balance depreciation method that is applied to tens of thousands of boats via mindless computers, and so the answer to our first question is that books set prices, prices do not make the book.

There are also some books that give a "trade-in" price. Boat dealers do not like to take trade-ins and they generally avoid doing so. So, again, where do these "trade-in" prices come from? Probably from somebody's opinion of what trade-in prices should be.

The simple truth is that books are created for the benefit of brokers and dealers, not the boating public. As one who has been studying these books for years, I do not recommend that you use them, but apply the method I described above. Moreover, books cannot reflect current market conditions, but only past economic conditions, which may have changed.

For example, at the time this book was written, the economy was in recession and prices were falling. Books could not, and did not reflect that fact. In that case, would you really want to refer to a book and pay the indicated price?

Regional Variations

For larger, higher priced used boats, regional variations are likely to occur. This can result from factors ranging from popularity, to supply and demand. A lack of general suitability to a particular region can also play a part: inland type boats in coastal regions, sport fishing boats in inland regions and so on. If a boat is not well-suited to a particular region, it's not likely to command a top dollar price.

Yet another important factor that influences pricing is how well a brand has been established. Used boats with names that no one has ever heard of are a hard sell simply because such a boat is largely unknown, and smart people tend not to invest large sums of money in the unknown. Reputation is important, and lacking a strong reputation, a particular boat will not command as high a price as better known brands do. If you're going to be buying a relatively unknown brand, you'd best be paying less than the more popular comparable boats.

Fickleness of Pricing

I'm often amused by clients who are trying to get a deal, a real steal on a used boat. That's because the used boat market is so closely watched by so many, that I only see someone buy a good boat at significantly below market maybe once in ten years. By and large, the vast majority of buyers paid a fair price for their boats, which is as it should be.

It happens from time to time that certain boats, due to increasing popularity or economic circumstances, may actually rise in value or not decline in price due to scarce availability. Such phenomenon tend to occur mainly with sport fishing and multi purpose boats. Then there are times when fuel prices rise dramatically with the predictable result on prices of fuel efficient boats. Such happenings are not normal, are usually short-lived, and can result in someone theoretically paying too much, and then losing out when conditions cause the value to suddenly drop more than expected. Such events are usually unpredictable and not much different than playing the stock market, though potential losses are not as great.

When these events do occur, they are not reflected by "book" prices and can cause trouble with lenders who do use books for evaluating financing. Such problems can usually be overcome by getting a second appraisal, since book values can only reflect the past, not the present.

How much of a variation am I talking about? Consider the older model 45-46 foot Hatteras that several years ago became extremely popular. In part because there was a dearth of high quality boats that size on the market, combined with the fact that there was a huge spread in prices between late model and older boats that size. A gap as high as a half-million dollars. So, if you wanted a high quality 45 foot sport fish convertible at a price under $500k, the older 45 Hats were the only way to go. Thus, we saw prices on these boats rising from the upper $100's to the upper $200's and into the lower three hundreds in a very short period of time, price increases approaching 50%. Those prices have since retreated somewhat, but not nearly as much as they rose.

Sea Ray is another example of how the market can react to supply and demand. Throughout the 1990's Sea Ray sold a lot of boats, and at prices many experts felt were not justified, but those were the high-flying years of the technology bubble. How they did that is another story, but suffice to say, the day came several years ago that the market was suddenly flooded with late model Sea Rays of all sizes, resulting in many sellers taking a bath to get rid of them. Here's a case where we often saw a lot of boat owners who were upside down on their loans, thanks to clever financing. Many, if not most, of those buyers got into those boats by the allure of very low interest loans, zero percent down, and long financing periods.

When the Internet bubble burst, followed by the tech bubble, suddenly the market was flooded with those boats. That slick method of selling boats came back to haunt Sea Ray, just as it has with the automakers who invented it. Now Sea Ray is closing down production to stem the bleeding. There are many other builders who have since followed suit and will no doubt meet with the same bad end.

Zero down, zero percent, zero payments. Heavenly, right? Wrong, it turns out to be pure hell for the boat buyer and builder for it creates the illusion of getting something for nothing, when the fact is that the costs are increased for both, since all such deals do is mortgage the future to pay for the present.

Repossessions & Salvage

There isn't a week that goes by that I don't get at least one call from someone asking where they can buy a boat real cheap, as in salvage or reposessions. I'm going to be real blunt about this because it's something I've observed for nearly four decades: the holy grail of the free lunch.

There are no free lunchs, folks. None. At least not for honest people. Reposessed boats are usually floating disasters. Salvage boats are called such because someone -- usually the owner or insurance company -- has deemed it beyond reasonably worth repairing. Otherwise, it would have been.

In the majority of instances, salvage and repos are sold for more than they are worth. Moreover, the kind of people who think they can repair salvage boats and fix up abused reposessions usually have no concept of the extent of what they are getting into, nor do they have the facilities or the resources to engage in extensive repairs. But worst of all, they don't have the money, a fact that almost guarantees that they will fail to achieve what they set out to do. As I pointed out in Chapter Three, these people grossly underestimate costs because they are not sufficiently expert to be able to make good estimates.

That they don't have the money to see such projects through to a successful end is apparent by the very fact that they are messing around with such a foolish idea. If they did have the money, they wouldn't bother but instead just go out and buy a good boat and avoid all the work and heartache.

Chapter 16

The Survey & Post Survey

In the opening chapters of this book, we went into considerable detail about the nature of the boat building industry. I didn't do that just to be controversial, but to point out that buying a boat may entail considerable risk, and to explain how that risk comes about.

Most marine surveyors recommend having a new boat surveyed because a survey can go a long way toward eliminating much of that risk. People may say, "Oh, those surveyors are just trying to get more business for themselves." Certainly, that is true, but the reasons why they recommend new boat surveys are also true.

During the course of writing this book, I've kept track of the people who've contacted our company for help with new boat purchase problems. Just to give you a general idea that there is no exaggeration of the above statements, the following is a short sampling of the tribulations that a few new boat buyers have been subjected to.

- Two months after the purchase of a new boat, the owner hears a rumor that his boat may have been involved in a highway transportation crash. On further checking, he found out that this was true. He was sold a new boat that had been damaged, repaired and sold as new.

- One year after purchase of a new 35 footer, the owner is still fighting with the dealer and builder about an extreme vibration problem. He's told by the dealer, after numerous attempts to solve the problem, that they have done all they can do, and that the owner will just have to live with it because, in their view, the vibration is "normal." Our survey of the problem revealed that the engines were improperly mounted and the problem was corrected within a week though the owner had been struggling with the problem for months.

- Engines won't push the boat at the advertised speed and engines smoke excessively. Neither dealer nor builder nor engine reps are able to solve the problem. Again, the boat owner is told after nearly a year of futile efforts to correct the problem, that he just has to live with it. A check of the boat's exhaust system shows that the pipes and mufflers are undersize and do not meet the engine manufacturer specs. That was something the engine manufacturer should have picked up on, but didn't. After the owner hires a surveyor and a lawyer, builder is forced to change the exhaust system at a cost of nearly $20,000.

- A new 35' boat purchase ends up with the starboard engine seizing up. Engine is replaced under warranty. Fifty-five days later, the same engine throws a rod. Engine is again replaced. Six months later, the same engine freezes up again. This time the engine manufacturer refuses to warrant the problem, blaming the owner for negligent operation. A survey determines that an underwater exhaust system is improperly designed that causes water to enter the engine. We had four clients with this same problem on the same model boat.

- A new 39 footer goes back to the dealer nine times to correct the owner's list of 42 defects, some minor, some serious. Eight months later, only 22 of the items have been corrected and the dealer refuses to do any more. Owner is forced to hire an attorney and file suit. Oddly, most of the problems are fairly easy to correct.

- The owner of a new boat becomes suspicious when he discovers that it looks like a lot of rework has been done to his new boat. There are lots of filled screw holes and obviously moved or removed equipment and wiring. Plus the engines had nearly 50 hours on the meter. Several weeks of investigation turns up proof that the boat had been sold once before and was taken back by the dealer on a failed financing arrangement, or so they claimed. Continued investigation revealed that the original buyer had refused to pay for the boat because it was developing cracks in the bottom.

This is but a very small sampling of the kind of problems that surveyors routinely help new boat buyers with. The reason why such things happen is because dealers and builders operate on very thin margins and because correcting defects can be very costly, so there is an incentive there, if not to resist correcting them, then to do a less than acceptable job of correcting them properly.

A new boat check-out survey can go a long way toward avoiding such problems by discovering many of the problems before you fully pay for the boat. Keep in mind that once you pay for the boat, you lose most of your leverage; also, the law allows the manufacturer to attempt to repair any and all defects. In my entire career, I have only once seen a builder take back a boat and return the buyer's money. No builder is going to do that unless forced by a court to do so, and that only after every effort to repair it has failed. Thus, from the legal standpoint, the deck is heavily stacked against you.

Used Boat Surveys

Getting a survey is a relatively straight-forward process, but finding a good surveyor is not. Surveyors tend to concentrate where the boats are, meaning the major boating centers. It can be a lot more difficult to find qualified surveyors in other areas. There are a lot of unqualified surveyors out there, as well as surveyors who get all their business as referrals from yacht brokers. I trust that you can see why that might be a problem.

Yacht surveyors aren't turned out by universities or colleges. Most enter the business after gaining experience in allied trades. Four surveyors whom I personally know are ex brokers. Many others come from the boat repair business; some spend years as captains, while yet others were marine insurance adjusters – all people who have a strong background of first hand experience with boats. As for licensing, only one or two states require surveyors to be licensed. While I see numerous surveyor ads that claim they are licensed, that license is probably a local occupational license.

What about the surveyor societies? Well, almost all surveyors are a member of one of them and that is no guarantee of competence or integrity.

Probably the best way to go about finding a good surveyor is by getting referrals from people without competing interests. These could be anyone from boat yard managers to marine insurance agents, or even other surveyors. It couldn't hurt to call up a few surveyors and ask them who, other than themselves, they would recommend. Any name that keeps on coming up is likely to be a good one.

What Surveyors Do

Knowing something about the marine surveyor and his work will help you understand what he can and cannot do for you. A pre purchase survey is a process of trying to find out if a boat has any faults. *It is not a process of proving that a boat is fault-free,* for the cost of doing that is economically prohibitive.

By necessity, a survey is a process of discovery by means of inspection. As with getting a physical exam of your body, the basic exam is only cursory; it is not invasive. Of course, it is possible to obtain more complete physical exams depending on how much one wishes to spend, which could be in the tens of thousands. The same applies to boat surveys; the surveyor could probably be a lot more thorough, though a basic standard has evolved based generally on how much buyers wish to pay, just the same as with medical exams.

However, the typical boat survey tends to be much more comprehensive than the typical medical exam in terms of complexity. The basic structures, the hull, deck, etc., are visually inspected where the trained eye of the surveyor is likely to pick up on any faults, for his eye is the very best tool he possesses. It may also involve things like hammer sounding and the use of moisture meters, though the later has proved to be rather problematical in terms of interpreting meter readings.

Hull inspections involve inside and out, which is one reason that surveyors complain about boats that are built without any, or very limited, access to the hull. If he can't see it, of course he can't inspect it.

Plumbing and systems are subjected to visual inspection and test operation, and the larger the boat, the more extensive these systems become. Sea water plumbing systems are extremely important from the standpoint that sea worthiness is totally dependent on the integrity of the plumbing.

Other critical areas for inspection include the fuel systems and tankage and the engine exhaust systems, owing to the extreme amount of damage, injury and even fatalities that faulty systems can cause. Equipment is tested to the extent that that is possible. Don't expect suvreyors to launch tenders and test tender engines and other equipment such as jet skis, dive compressors and other unusual equipment.

Most surveyors will also not test computer systems, complex entertainment systems and prove the function of integrated navigation equipment because to do so requires expertise that he doesn't have.

Survey Logistics

To conduct a good survey, the surveyor needs to do things in a proper order, as well as having adequate time to do his job. Note that the surveyor is in a position where he does not have complete control over the boat, for it does not belong to him. All too often events cause him to become rushed or otherwise prevent him from doing as good a job as he would like. In addition to having the weather to contend with, he is often faced with interferences such as brokers or owners who want to rush things along, or too many people being on board the boat for him to work effectively. The surveyor will greatly appreciate his client stepping in when these things happen, as he has no authority to direct anyone to do anything; he can only request.

It is very important to limit the number of people on board the boat during the survey. The survey and sea trial should not be used as an opportunity to bring friends and family along for a joy ride, for they will only distract the surveyor. It's rather difficult for a surveyor to ask the members of the owner's family to please get off their own boat. Bear in mind that you probably couldn't get any work done with five or six people running around your office, so don't expect the surveyor to be able to do a good job under similar circumstances.

Which leads me to scheduling and the timing of the three main parts of the survey. Most surveyors prefer to have at least several hours with the boat at the dock, before heading out for sea trial and hauling. He needs first to familiarize himself with the vessel and its systems, as well as ensuring that it is ready for the sea trial. All too frequently, some problem crops up that, if not discovered earlier, would lead to an aborted or failed sea trail and possibly even a breakdown that causes serious delay. If breakdown does occur, don't expect the surveyor to hang around while the problem is being fixed.

All too often brokers try to rush the surveyor because that means he's not going to do as good a job. They'll come up with myriads of excuses why the haul out and sea trial must be done first. Since this is a process that you are paying for, the surveyor is going to need your help in making sure that the salesman doesn't manipulate the survey. Some brokers will go to extraordinary lengths to do just that.

Sea trials are best scheduled after the haul out, primarily to ensure that the bottom and propellers are clean. If not, the performance test of the boat and engines may be seriously impaired. This will lead to a delay and the need to do another sea trail after the bottom is cleaned, and the surveyor will probably charge extra for that.

Since no surveyor wants to try to work in an engine room where the temperature is 130 degrees and risk burning himself on hot engine parts, most surveyors will start with the engine room first. That's yet another reason why the sea trial shouldn't be attempted early in the day. It's imperative that the engines not be run before the surveyor arrives.

The haul out is normally the least time consuming part of the survey, often taking no more than a half-hour. The buyer pays the cost of the haul out and should be prepared to pay that fee to the yard unless he has made other arrangements with the broker.

Engine Surveys

Many surveyors will do surveys on gas engines, but never on diesels. With larger boats, there is simply too much else to do for the surveyor to do engine surveys as well. Surveys are almost always done in one day because of the problems and costs involved with extending it for more than one day. Completing a survey involves the cooperation of a lot of people, thus the need to get the job done as expeditiously as possible.

Because a diesel engine costs at least three times as much as similar powered gas engine, it doesn't make a lot of sense to forgo a complete engine survey, so you do so at considerable risk. Just because engines are fairly new doesn't mean that there can't be anything wrong with them. Even new engines occasionally have problems with them.

Most hull surveyors will conduct their work concurrent with the engine surveyor, allowing the whole job to be completed in a day.

Compression tests on diesels are not conducted as part of the "normal" survey. The reason is that this is very messy, time consuming and difficult, as well as costly. There are other things the surveyor can do instead, such as obtaining crankcase pressures. The engine surveyor will recommend a compression test if there are symptoms that point to possibly low compression.

The following are the checks usually performed by a professional engine surveyor:

- Thorough visual inspection, both static and full speed.
- Turbo boost pressure
- Exhaust back pressure
- Cooling system pressure test
- Cooling system zincs
- Crankcase pressures
- Oil Pressure, temperature, drive oil pressure, alternator function
- Strategic Infrared pyrometer checks
- Digital RPM readings and determination of transmission slip
- Engine room temperature and barometric pressure
- Engine mount test
- Transmission magnetic particle test
- Transmission slip test
- Oil analysis

While this is not a compete description of all that a good diesel man will do, it will give you an idea of what constitutes a thorough survey.

Oil Analysis

Many people over estimate the usefulness of oil analysis. It is essentially a technique for evaluating engine wear *over periods of time*. The way that works is to compare differences in wear metal readings from one analysis to the next. It is much less useful at attempting to take a one-time "snapshot" of engine wear conditions. For example, it is necessary to know how much operating time engine oil has been subjected to in order to evaluate wear metals. It is common place today that sellers change their engine oil when putting the boat up for sale to subvert this process.

One thing oil analysis can do very well is to detect engine coolant and salt in the oil (which is always indicative of a serious problem), as well as anything else in the oil that shouldn't be there. An engine has only to be run for a short period for this to show up. So that being foxy and changing the oil isn't likely to hide leaking coolers, cracked castings and so on. And since no one ever changes transmission oil, running an analysis on transmission oil can definitely prove useful.

An EDAX or spectral analysis can identify wear metals and other chemicals in oil and will yield a table of particles in parts per million. The problem comes about how to interpret the results, for it presumes a known normal wear rate, plus the amount of operating time on the oil. If these factors are unknown, then wear metals analysis is useless unless the results indicate extraordinarily high PPM's.

Borescoping

A borescope is a fiber optic device that allows one to look into closed or small places, like inside of engine cylinders. Back in the hayday of the the two cycle Detroit Diesel, those engines were such that there were inspection ports that allowed one to see the inside of cylinders and piston rings. That's about the best possible form of inspection one can get. Unfortunately, four cycle diesels have no such facility but the borescope is a device that facilitates some degree of visual inspection.

Borescopes would be very widely used for engine inspections but for the fact that the field of view is extremely limited, roughly about 1/4" diameter. Because of that it would take days to attempt to inspect all the cylinders on an engine. However, the borescope can give a more limited view of internal cylinder condition, thereby making it a good and valuable evaluation tool.

Electronic Diesels

Electronic Diesels operate off a CPU and virtually all of them have facilities for recording some types of engine data such as overheat events, low oil pressure and so on. Most of these will even record the date of such events. With the manufacturer's software, it is possible to download and read this data. However, you should also know that it is also possible for a dealer or anyone with the software to erase recorded data, as when a major repair occurs. Caterpillar engines are an exception to this where only those posessing a passcode can erase data. For Volvo, only dealers can read or erase data.

Just because the CPU does not contain negative data, it doesn't mean that a negative event hasn't occurred. Erased data will be retained by the manufacturer, however, and is usually accessible to engine surveyors who have the software. This is very expensive, so only a few of them do. If you can find an engine surveyor with this facility, so much the better.

Gas Engines

Gas engine surveys are simpler to perform, and almost always include a compression test. As noted previously, some surveyors will do the engines while others won't. Unfortunately, I've never heard of anyone specializing in gas engine surveys as there apparently isn't enough of that kind of work anywhere to support such a specialist. However, many boat yards – particularly the full service type – will provide a mechanic that is capable of doing a check out. Rarely, however, are these people so into it that they write reports like professional engine surveyors do.

Concerning compression tests, inboard boats can be just as hard to compression test as stern drive boats. Often times, the engines are hard against fuel tanks, making it nearly impossible for the surveyor to get his compression tester threaded into the spark plug hole. There are times when he gets the spark plugs out, but cannot get them back in, or runs the risk of cross threading them. This accounts for why so many surveyors simply refuse to do it. What starts out as an apparently simple job ends up being difficult and time-consuming.

However, it far better to test at least a few cylinders than none at all. If they can get at only the inboard or outboard cylinders, then at least that much should be done, for even just a few cylinders will yield a good general idea of internal condition.

The gas engine survey should consist of the following:

- Cooling system pressure test
- Examine cooling system, checking coolant condition
- Check front and rear crankshaft seals for leaks
- Check all belts and hoses plus water pumps
- Alternator output
- Check distributor cap condition
- Fuel system for leaks
- Crankcase pressure
- Examine valve train for rust and condensation
- Oil condition, though usually it has been recently changed (don't bother with an oil analysis if engine oil is new)
- Dip transmissions with magnets
- Check output shaft seal for leaks
- Test engine mounts (back down test)

Generators are subjected to the same basic inspections plus a full load voltage and frequency test.

After the Survey

Many buyers don't know what to expect from a survey report. The written report should be a statement of fact and is not the place for speculation, opinion or advice. Most reports are essentially a negative document, meaning that it deals with what is wrong with the boat as opposed to what is right. What is right is assumed based on what is not wrong.

In recent years a lot of new people have entered the field of surveying and the reports of some of these people can be pretty amazing. Some read like sales brochures or a bill of materials while others are epic tomes running dozens of pages long. Apparently, the more pages, the more impressive the report is supposed to be.

It's my experience that the reports of the best surveyors tend to be the shortest reports, mine included. That's because they don't see any point to supplying the client with a pile of paper that he has to wade through just to find some pertinent information. A good report is one that gets to the heart of the matter quickly. The subject is condition and performance and the surveyor should stick to that.

Dealing With Issues

You've spent months, possibly even years researching the ideal boat you want to buy. The big day finally comes when you have found it, have made an offer, and it has been accepted. The boat has gone to survey, which is now complete, and the survey report is now in hand. Just one problem: Despite the fact that the boat looked great before you made the offer, the survey didn't quite confirm your expectations.

Your dream boat has some problems. Not the usual run-of-the-mill nigling list of minor faults like burned out light bulbs or loose door hinges, but a serious problem or two that's tending to turn your head in other directions. Perhaps it's an engine problem. Or maybe it's a combination of things that, each taken by themselves is not enough to turn you away, yet taken together are more than you want to deal with.

This is a fairly common dilemma that you should have some answers for before you make that offer. For no matter how good a used boat may look on the surface, the potential for the discovery of some hidden faults runs high. We've seen it happen again and again. The discriminating buyer has made the decision that he wants to buy a used boat that is in first class condition, deciding that he's not going to accept anything less. Moreover, he's willing to travel far and wide to find exactly the right boat.

The problem arises that first one boat, and then another, have gone to survey and have turned out less than anticipated. There are problems, but he doesn't want any problems. Yet he's already got another problem in that he's now spent a good deal of time and money seeking out his perfect boat, but is yet to find it. His costs are piling up and he's getting frustrated. So what's a buyer to do?

There are several important realities that used boat buyers need to keep in mind in order to keep the problems you may face in their proper perspective. These are as follows:

1. Boat owners sell their boats for a lot of reasons. Foremost of these is that for one reason or another, they can no longer afford the boat, or to maintain it in the condition in which it should be maintained. Most often, that means that they've simply run out of money. It's now time to sell. This translates to the fact that a very large percentage of used boats for sale are going to have deferred maintenance. That means that no matter how good the boat looks, the buyer should expect that the survey is going to generate a list of problems. If the buyer is not prepared to deal with this reality, then maybe he should be looking at new, rather than used boats.

2. With a large percentage of boats for sale, routine maintenance comes to a standstill as the owner anticipates it being sold soon. Selling takes a lot longer than expected, so the lack of maintenance starts to pile up. Expect that a significant number of things have stopped working, foremost among these are air conditioning and various pumps.

3. Be aware that if you were subjecting a new boat to the same sort of survey, you'd probably come up with a similar list of problems or potential problems, so the notion that buying a new boat eliminates the hassles found in used boats usually isn't true. In many cases, as exemplified at the begining of this chapter, new boats may be found to have *more* problems, by virtue of the fact that they are not tried, tested and can have existing bugaboos to be discovered and corrected.

4. Keeping a cost perspective. That used boat is selling for only a fraction of what the new boat costs. The difference is called depreciation. If the original price was $100,000, but the used price is now $65,000, that's $35,000 worth of depreciation that the buyer is not paying for.

5. As with a road vehicle or house, one can't keep taking out without putting back in. Things that wear out have to be repaired or replaced. This is what depreciation is all about, and why you're not paying a new boat price. Sure that includes things like not getting a warranty, and having a lot of the shine worn off. But it also means things like deferred maintenance that the owner hasn't taken care of.

6. By now you know that if you purchase a new boat, the price you negotiate for it is not the price you pay. Nor will you be able to just write the check, hop aboard and go. There is that costly and time consuming factor called "fitting out," which includes getting it ready and working out the inevitable bugs that come

with most used boats. Even impulse buyers usually end up discovering that there is a big time lag between completing the purchase and having cocktails on the aft deck. Both new and used boats are much the same in this respect.

Before you get going, there's a lot of work to be done and money to be spent. Cutting to the chase here, considering and preparing for certain inevitabilities will ease the way for you.

Over 90% of all boats sold every year are used boats. There is an extraordinarily good reason for that. The fact is, used boats represent exceptionally good value.

First, no matter how good it looks, expect problems, expect some disappointment. In return for that good value, there will be these realities you have to deal with.

The most important thing you can do is to realize that an attempt to find a perfect boat, one with no problems, is not likely to be the best avenue of approach. This is the old story of the devil you know versus the one you don't. It is very possible that you could take three very good possibilities to survey and have all three turn out the same. Then where are you? Frustrated and disappointed, right? Never mind a bit poorer for all the money you just spent on your search.

So let's take a particular example here. Let's say that you've found what looks to be the ideal boat, but the survey turns up a couple of things that you'd really rather not contend with. Say the generator took a dump for some quirky reason, and has to be replaced. And let's say it's got a window leakage problem that is going to cost a substantial amount to resolve. The owner didn't resolve this because he wasn't willing to spend the bucks. He tried to dodge the issue but now it's come back to haunt him. And you.

Assuming that you've already decided that this is the type and model boat for you, the greater problem is the question of whether the next boat you look at isn't going to be much the same. Consider:

All boats of the same age, make or model are likely to have similar problems.

Similar types of machinery, equipment and other problems tend to occur at similar times in any boat's life span. Similar to the way mufflers, shocks, brakes, etc., on road vehicles tend to wear out at similar intervals.

The question boils down to whether to reject the first boat and move onto the next? Or should you attempt to resolve the issues by negotiating price and getting them repaired? Consider too, that for the typical diesel cruiser that you've traveled a long distance to purchase, you'll probably end up spending at least $2,000 on survey fees and travel, maybe more. Do this a couple times and the cost gets serious.

The time to consider this is before you make the offer. Think about it and get yourself a general idea of what you're willing to accept. How much more in time, travel, surveys and other expense are you willing to spend looking for a boat with fewer problems? How far would those additional expenses go toward fixing the problems found on the first boat?

In most cases, dealing with the problems found in the first boat is the right course of action. The exception is when a boat turns out to be a real dog. Unless you are looking at very late model boats, the odds are high that you'll encounter the same thing in the next one you look at. Yes, it's going to take a bit more time and effort. But the inherent advantage in this situation is that you now know what you've got. The repaired things get repaired and you are unlikely to have to face those issues again.

This is particularly true when it comes to major machinery problems such as engines and generators. Let's say we've got a 10 year old boat and the survey determines the engines are clapped out. They need overhauls. Is the next 10 year old boat likely to be any different? Okay, let's say the next boat has engines that aren't blowing clouds of smoke, but they've got a lot of time on them. Which deal ultimately offers the better security? Buying a boat for which you *know* the engines have a limited remaining life span, or one in which the engines are already clapped out, but you are able to negotiate the price and get them overhauled?

With the former boat, in return for the hassle of getting engines rebuilt, you end up with the confidence that fresh engines give you. With the later, you avoid the immediate inconvenience, but have to live with the knowledge that your engines can crap out at any time. Sure, it can be hard to see it this way because of the added hassle you have to face up front. The question is, do you want to face that issue now, or put it off into the future? No one wants to buy a boat that needs fixing and then have to face a repair project. The fact is, with a used boat, there is a lot you're not paying for. Something has been taken out that needs to be put back in.

The issue is inevitable. The question is: when do you want to face it and get it out of the way?
The smart way is to deal with it NOW.

Negotiating Deficiencies

The surveyor's report will contain a list of deficiencies that will likely range from very minor to quite serious. Within the brokerage business, there is a generally accepted standard as to what constitutes a negotiable item. Not all of the items on that list can be used to negotiate a price reduction, or mandate a repair. There is no hard and fast rule about this since much depends on how the boat was represented by the seller.

This is an issue that you should discuss with the broker or seller *before* you sign a purchase agreement. Precisely what category of defect or fault is negotiable? Typically terms such as "major faults" are used. A better definition would be "any fault that affects the safety, seaworthiness, performance or *value* of the vessel," or any significant fault that is contrary to how the boat was represented.

> Example: The boat cruises at three knots slower than represented.
> Example: The engine mounts allow too much engine movement.
> Example: Circuit breakers keep tripping while on generator power.
> Example: Bottom is blistered.
> Example: Alternator isn't charging and a sea water pump is leaking.

Examples of faults that are not subject to negotiation consist of normal maintenance, such as the bottom needs painting, boat needs painting or compounding, enclosures are deteriorating, seat cushions worn out, anchor is rusty, hinges are broken, lights not working and so on.

Generally speaking, accumulations of deferred maintenance aren't negotiable; that's something you should have sized up on your preliminary inspection and should be reflected in the price. If it turns out that the boat overall is in worse condition than you anticipated, all you can do is revise your offer based on this, but to try to do it based on estimating costs is likely to prove futile.

Sometimes sellers will do silly things like advertise their boats as "turnkey" or use other buzz words like "mint". Such terms imply that there is nothing wrong with the boat. In that case, the buyer is justified in hitting the seller with every fault listed in the survey report.

Who Makes Repairs?

I've seen a lot of deals written wherein the owner agrees to repair any faults. This is a bad idea, for reasons that ought to be obvious: there is no assurance that repairs will be done properly and the buyer has no control over this situation. The proper way to word the contract is with words to the effect that seller will cover the cost of repairs, through repair cost reduction of price. Then the buyer has the repairs done in his own way.

I've had a lot of customers who told me that they don't want to do it this way because they don't want the hassle of getting the repairs done. You are setting yourself up for a fall if you let the seller make repairs. The exception to the rule would be when the seller turns repairs over to a qualified facility and you have assurance of that fact in advance. In that case, be sure to review the work order before signing the acceptance.

Estimating Repair Costs

No doubt about it, this can be a problem. You already have plenty of experience with repair people who tell you that they can't give an estimate until, (a) they've torn the item down, or, (b) they've had time to thoroughly analyze the situation. Making a good estimate is very time consuming and costs the yard money to do so. Since they already know that they are unlikely to get a job out of it, they'll likely give you the brush off, especially a busy yard when faced with small jobs.

This situation finally got so bad in my insurance claims work that I began as a matter of course offering to pay for estimates. In most cases I more than got my money's worth since the yard was no longer facing a losing proposition and the estimates I got tend to be a lot more thoroughly thought out and detailed. Paying a qualified person several hundred dollars can end up saving you thousands on larger repairs when that quickie estimate turns out to be way too low.

Usually the buyer just asks the surveyor to estimate the costs, without realizing that the surveyor is unlikely to be able to give a good estimate. Unless he does insurance work, how would he know what costs are? Therefore, I don't recommend that you rely on surveyor's "rough, don't hold me to it" type estimates. When substantial dollars are involved, you've got to go to the people who do this sort of thing every day. At the very least, try to get the yard man to sit down with you and go over your list; he can "ball park" it better than anyone else. An exception to the rules are engine surveyors, who are often also in the repair business (by necessity); these guys know repair costs.

A Few Other Tips

It's okay to hang close to the surveyor and observe what he's doing. This shouldn't bother him and it will give him the opportunity to point things out to you when necessary. However, avoid bombarding him with questions as this will distract him.

If you do observe a situation developing where the surveyor is being distracted by too many people around him, try to intervene diplomatically and "clear the decks." The surveyor may be reluctant to address the situation himself. After all, he's not in a good position to ask people to leave a boat that doesn't belong to him.

I've seen quite a few otherwise good deals go down the drain because the buyer kept badgering the seller with problems found during the survey. You should not discuss any survey findings during the course of the survey with either the seller or any broker. There are good tactical reasons for not doing so. Survey deficiencies should be dealt with at a predetermined time.

Selling brokers are notorious for badgering surveyors for survey findings while the survey is underway. As your representative, your surveyor should not tell a broker or seller anything unless you approve that. After all, you are paying for this information and it belongs to you; the surveyor has no right to divulge it without your approval. It should be made clear to broker and/or seller that a specific time will be set to discuss the survey findings. Instruct your surveyor to not divulge information until you are ready.

Discuss the surveyor's findings with him first, in private, before discussing with the seller or broker. It is very bad form for buyer, selling agent and surveyor to sit down and discuss survey findings together for the first time. You need time to digest this info and make your decisions without being rushed or feeling pressured by an experienced salesman and given the "golden tongue" treatment.

About the closing: it is unwise to plan a closing for the same day the survey is completed, though far too many people do so. First, the surveyor needs time to write his report; over-night he's going to "sleep on it." The way he feels about something today may not be the way he feels about it tomorrow; he may even need to do a bit of research. You're asking for trouble if you close before you've read his written report, and if it contains information that he did not give you on a verbal summary, remember that you're asking him to be alert and thorough *after* a hard day's labor. He's tired and therefore prone to forgetting things at that point.

Chapter 17

Boat Builders by Company

In the Final analysis,
The thing that separates,
The good, from the bad and the ugly,
Is that the management are boat builders first
And corporate executives second.

The following commentaries are my observations of a boat builder's products based on their historical performance and therefore does not necessarily reflect on that builder's current product line. I can't possibly be familiar with the boat lines every boat builder world wide, yet alone the tens of thousands of models produced over the years. But I am familiar with the older and most well known names and their history, a history that is important from the stand point that this book deals with used boats as well as new. Larger boats can have very long life spans indeed, sometimes up to thirty years, making the historical record of individual boat builders doubly important.

When it comes to quality, there have been numerous boat builders over the years that have tried to produce more than one line of boats of varying quality, and just as General Motors produces Chevy and Cadillac, the idea doesn't work very well. A Cadillac, as we all know, is just a fancy Chevy; the overall quality isn't any better. That is precisely the problem that boat builders, who try to market a range of boats of varying quality, have; even if they do produce a higher quality line, it gets tainted by association with the lower quality line, especially if the later develops big problems. This can make the attempt to size up some builder's products on a generalized basis very difficult.

Companies

Albemarle

Although this North Carolina company has been around since the 1970's, it's only recently made a splash on the national scene, particularly in the all-important Florida market where, if you can't make it here, you're not likely to make it anywhere. Albemarle builds both outboards, stern drive and inboard drive boats of moderate quality to 35 feet, but fairly heavy duty, deep vee hull construction. Most of those I have seen are not cored hulls. They've gained a following for what they lack in fanciness, they more than make up for in ruggedness.

Albin

Albin has been a major importer of Taiwan-built boats since 1967, both sailboats and trawlers, the later of which we have some examples of truly awful quality as evidenced by how poorly they have held up. Rotting decks, leaking windows, rusted steel fuel tanks and massive blistering are among the common complaints.

Beginning in the mid 1990's Albin started their own production facility in Connecticut and began producing higher quality boats, such as the 28, 31 and 35 Express that have proved popular. Blistering hasn't shown up on these later models and the construction and engineering appears solid. Many are designed for combined fishing and cruising, depending on outfitting. Sedan models often available with or without bridge and dual controls, a rare option these days. Dual controls are highly desirable for anyone living in short-season climates.

As usual, price is typically an indicator of quality, for these boats are not price-leaders. Noted for more traditional styling, there is more emphasis on durability and practicality. Hull shapes range from single engine deep keels, to peculiar fin keels to convention shallow vees with stub keels. Some models have cored bottoms.

Azimut

This Italian builder is known for (what else?) what some would call extreme Mediterranean styling and a marked emphasis on luxury appointments in the Italian style. Once associated with Benetti, Azimut was known primarily for large yachts that competed with other builders based primarily on style and price. The liberal use of stainless steel, burled walnut, bird's eye ample and the like, often gave the illusion of overall high quality. In reality, these boats often had serious quality problems, including severe structural problems resulting from a lack of expertise in the use of foam cores in the hulls.

The boats were often long on looks but short on engineering. Examples include creating hull- integral fuel tanks with a foam cored hull, something that is prohibited by American standards ABS and ABYC because the fuel weeped through the glass into the cores, saturating it with fuel oil. Another well-known faux pas was the incorporation of hull integral exhaust piping that didn't get adequate water cooling and thereby burned the cored hull in way of the exhausts. Huge mistakes like these basically destroyed those boats, and Azimut's reputation along with them.

In more recent years Azimut has entered the mid size boat market with models starting at 36 feet and marketed by Sea Ray, but I've yet to see one.

Bertram Yacht

Only a novice entering the market for the first time needs any introduction to this famous builder, founded by Richard Bertram in Miami in the late 1950's. Bertram became the benchmark against which most other boats were measured. Noted for superior styling of boats that still look stylish today after twenty years or more, very deep vee hulls, its engineering expertise and high quality, Bertram became famous for their sport fishermen. Today, when the word Bertram is spoken, what comes to mind of many people is only sport fishing boats. However, Bertram built more than fishing boats, including motor yachts up to 58 feet and large numbers of smaller sport boats and runabouts, the later of which are highly prized collectors items today.

Unlike many other builders, this was a company with management dedicated to research and development and solid engineering. Seat of the pants boat building was something that was just not done at Bertram. Among all builders Bertram, along with Hatteras, has the overall best track record of product reliability and overall the fewest structural problems across a huge line of different boats over decades. That's an accomplishment no other large builder can even come close to bragging about.

Yet another factor that made Bertram such a success was its employees that stayed with the company for decades. Richard Bertram began hiring Cuban exiles shortly after Castro's coup d'etat and built up a very loyal and well-trained labor force.

Like all builders of high quality boats, Bertram hit on troubled times with the recession of 1989 and the 10% luxury tax and was unable to recover. The company all but closed down and was purchased by the Italian Ferretti Group. Still located in its original plant in Miami, the company produces only a handful of 30, 39, 50 and 60 footers, all convertible style boats.

There are numerous Bertram models today that are still hot items in the used boat market, so if you're in the market for used boats, don't overlook Bertram just because you've heard that they're fishing boats. Look for yourself and be your own judge.

Bayliner

This Bellingham, Washington based company might be called the Chevy of the boating industry. Changing hands several times in its 35 year history, since 1986 it is a Brunswick company along with Sea Ray, et. al. Bayliner had long been owned by conglomerate U.S. Marine which was bought out by Brunswick a few years ago. Among the mid size class, you'll find more different Bayliner models out there than any other builder. And that, perhaps, is the problem. Too many fast model changes for the sake of marketing strategy and not enough time to perfect them.

Experts in the business generally rate Bayliner quality at the lower end of the scale. Along with their pricing, that should be no surprise to anyone. The company definitely targets the entry level market. Nor should it be any surprise that their boats have had more than their fair share of structural and other problems.

The company seems to mimick the marketing of Chris Craft of old, turning out everything from 16 foot runabouts to (lately) a 57 foot motor yacht. Naturally, a company that tries to be all things to all boat buyers is not going produce superior products across the board. Their boats compete with others based primarily on price.

One of the positive aspects of Bayliner boats is that they seem to be one of the last to start messing around with cores in their hulls. In the older models, you won't even find cores in the hull sides. Like most others, they did use balsa in the decks, so one has to be careful about that, but hull failures were rare.

Bayliner is not without its success stories and a couple notables are the 4550 Pilothouse Motor Yacht, produced for nine years, the 3870/3888 Motor yacht, also produced for nine years and the 3270 Motor Yacht produced for 13 years. All are superior products (for Bayliner) due to the number of years these boats had time to be perfected.

Back in 1987, U.S. Marine created a new line of boats named Maxum. This was believed to be an attempt to separate larger boats from the Bayliner name by virtue of the fact that the company was derogatorily called Bumliner by its detractors. The quality of Maxum boats might have been a tad better than the usual Bayliner, but the new brand simply failed to take hold.

Now that Brunswick is in charge, they've decided to launch yet another new line named Meridian Yachts, which I would judge an equally bad idea for one very simple reason: Creating a new brand is an extraordinarily difficult thing to do. This is particularly true when the brand is not created out of a whole cloth, but is merely a transparent effort to fix corporate mistakes as Meridian clearly is as much as Maxum was.

None of this would be of any account to us whatsoever but for the effect that failed brands have on the resale value of those products.

Blackfin

Here's a company that I know a lot about because I briefly worked for them as quality control manager. This company specialized in the smaller sizes of sport fishing boats with a number of superb deep vee hulls by designer Charley Jannice. Contrary to what some say, no Blackfin hull is a copy of a Bertram. They produced a limited number of different models with long production runs, allowing for plenty of time for them to be perfected. From the 25 and 27 foot combi, which were available in either outboard or inboard versions to a diesel powered 38 Convertible, superb sea keeping abilities are the hallmark of Blackfin. Except in most recent years, the hulls were all solid fiberglass and heavily built. Hull failures were unheard of, but fuel tank corrosion has been a problem in some models.

Two of their boats, the 29 Flybridge, and the 32 Flybridge (sometimes called the 33 sport fish) are true classics, two of the finest performing boats ever built. A couple of later models, the 29 and 31 Combi are also superb designs and excellent performers. Credit for these superb designs also goes to naval architect Charles Jannice. In the late 1980's Blackfin attempted to break into the larger boat market with thirty six and thirty eight foot models, neither of which did well because the company lacked the capital to refine these boats to the level of their smaller boats. Blackfin succumbed to the 1989 recession like many other builders and never fully recovered. Though new ownership, Saltshaker Marine, is turning out a few boats, Blackfin hasn't been able to return to its previous market force. What I have seen of the new boats is that they are considerably more refined than the older Blackfins, which were a bit behind the times in terms of mold making.

Boston Whaler

Originator of the famous foam filled cathedral hulled whaler, a boat that was used as a tender on just about every large yacht in America and elsewhere, the company entered the mid size boat market in the mid to late 1990's, continuing to advertise unsinkable boats. Their boats are still built using a similar method of using foam between the hull and inner hull liner. This allows them to eliminate most of the structural members that most other boats contain.

The early Whalers were not without problems with this construction method as the foams occasionally continued to expand over time, or becomes compressed due to impacts. I've seen a number of instances in the Conquest models where the inner cabin liners showed heavy cracking. In my view, the jury is still in deliberation regarding this construction method's ability to hold up long term.

Buddy Davis

A North Carolina builder since the early 1970's, Buddy Davis sport fishermen became famous for their extreme bow flare and beautiful classic styling which is still the hallmark of this semi-custom builder. The typical Carolina hulls have deep entries and flatten out toward the stern giving them very good rough water performance with no sacrifice in speed. Most of the boats tend to be quite fast. Their smallest boat is 47 feet. Many of their cold molded wood hulls are still in service.

Cabo

This west coast builder got its start in 1991 and came out of the starting gate touting extremely high quality, attempting to compete with a sport fishing market centered on the East Coast. Not an easy feat to pull off by some California boys. My take on their earlier models is that they failed to live up to their advertising. That, combined with rather high prices, made them a tough sell in Florida, but with time they managed to gain a foot-hold.

Cabo produced some nice boats, to be sure, but the performance and engineering didn't quite measure up. They were too new in the business to avoid the kind of mistakes that more experienced builders didn't make like undersized exhaust systems and poorly installed aluminum water tanks glassed into the hull. Add to that a hull that was far too shallow to go messing around the Gulf Stream with. Another example was the Cabo 35 which had the engines half under the salon and cockpit decks with no aft engine room bulkhead. No experienced fisherman wants to head out to sea in a boat like that.

But time heals all wounds and Cabo continues to improve their product, deepening up their hulls and improving the engineering. Now producing boats up to 47' with the Cabo 47 Convertible. The larger models are too new for me to have had any experience with to comment on.

Californian

Another West Coast builder that tried to compete on the East Coast, this company began life as the Marshall Boat Co.in 1972, ended up being bought by Wellcraft, repurchased by Marshall, resold to Carver, thence to Genmar and thence not to be heard of again. That's probably best for everyone.

Carver

A Wisconsin based company that, in my view, concentrates on the inexperienced boater, the inland water boater, and the price conscious markets, or those who aren't terribly discriminating except for styling, the company currently builds numerous models from

25 to 60'. In business since the early 1960s, Carver has always been an entry-level price boat, styling themselves as builders of "affordable" boats. They were one of the builders of the original floating campers, boats of exceedingly low quality. Like Bayliner, the company has produced more models than anyone can count. It began selling boats in the Great Lakes region, and like Sea Ray in the early days, seemed to lack salt water experience. Early on, their boats gained the reputation of being floating campers, which is fine as long as you know that's what it is and do not mistake it for a sea going boat.

In 1991 Carver was purchased by Genmar, the holding company that strives to dominate the marine industry. The company then began expanding into the larger boat sizes and motor yachts. With price and trendy style as the predominant marketing focus, sound engineering has taken a back seat in my experience. While Carver occasionally does things worthy of praise, all to often, there is much to criticise. Extremely thin laminates, weak framing systems and balsa cores are among the complaints. Carver has always been a price-driven builder, which is responsible for most of their problems.

Today Carver produces motor yachts up to 57 feet which have extraordinarily high centers of gravity and are regarded by experts as being more suitable as river boats than sea going yachts.

Cheoy Lee

This famed Hong Kong builder after teaming up with a number of famed western yacht designers like Olin Stevens and Jack Hargrave to produce a very popular line of sail boats, then branching out into power boats, particularly trawlers and larger yachts, the later with U.S. designer Tom Fexas. The company achieved its peak of U.S. boat sales in the late 80's and early 90's after Cheoy Lee moved into the large yacht business. Then the company made some seriously bad management decisions when it was hit a substantial amount of bad publicity over issues of poor quality and construction, including angry owners putting their defective boats on display in boat shows. Cheoy Lee seems yet to recover from this fiasco. There haven't been any mid size offerings since 1994. The quality level of their older boats is such that they haven't held up well over the years, but they're not much different than most other Taiwan build boats of the genre.

Chris-Craft

Once a venerable name in boat building, formerly the largest and probably most skilled in the world, Chris-Craft made a successful transition from wood to fiberglass boats, and was one of the pioneers in production fiberglass boats with incredibly few mistakes. Yet it did not continue to do well financially with the advent of the Viet Nam war, high taxation and a faltering economy, so that repeated successions of new management and ownership, as well as mismanagement, left it a shell of its former glory by the early

1980's.

The company was resold so many times that by the time the wheeler dealers were done with it, not much was left and even less of the proverbial Chris-Craft quality. The bones were eventually picked up by OMC (another badly managed company), focused on small boats for a while, but couldn't resist the allure of larger boats and finally went bust along with OMC in 2001. Since 1974, the company has had such a checkered history that it would take a separate volume to describe what they've done in the way of boat building in the last quarter century, but there have been almost no examples of their production worthy of much discussion.

The Commander series of boats built in the 1970's were heavily constructed and many people find the restoration of the sport fish and a few other early models to be worthwhile. The Catalina series are basically light weight budget boats many of which now grace the back lots or have already gone to the grinder.

Crownline

Another midwest boat builder (Illinois) who's geographical heritage is telling. Hasn't made much of an impact on the saltwater scene with shallow vee hulls, stern drive power and low pricing, a decidedly fresh water pedigree. Inland builders traditionally have had trouble moving to the salt water markets due to a lack of understanding of issues of the "salty big blue."

Cruisers, Inc.

Here's a mid west builder that's hard to pigeon hole. In the 70's and 80's, most of their production was decidedly entry-level and often of the "floating camper" genre with goofy names like Villa Vee, producing some truly awful boats, most of which have long gone to the grinder, or currently grace the back lots. By the late 80's some interesting examples pop up. Not particularly good quality, but good enough for the money, the peculiarly styled 4280 Express Bridge is a good design that performs well. One only wishes it were a bit better quality.

By the early 90's, Cruisers had revamped most of its production to mostly express models followed by a styling and marketing trend that closely resembles Sea Ray with a very similar product line up, including a few tear drop-windowed motor yachts. Latest production quality is also similar to Sea Ray. My experience with Cruisers is that good quality and engineering has been very inconsistent so far, wherein I find some good boats and some not so good.

DeFever

Arthur DeFever is a West Coast naval architect known for his trawler designs that bore his name and were built in Taiwan. Most of these boats ranged from 42 to 72 feet and demonstrated fairly good quality with his supervision of construction. Construction years go back to the mid 1970's. Hull shapes are usually modified hard chine designs with deep keels and are basically planing hulls. There were, however, a few round bilge exceptions like the Alaskan 49 which also had a hard chine version, the 49 Pilothouse.

East Bay

Another trade name of American Marine, it is not widely known but offers a couple of interesting Express and Sedan models of decidedly Down East styling from 38 to 49 feet. The deep, fine entry hulls handle steep chops extremely well. Quality and pricing is similar to Grand Banks.

Egg Harbor

This company began life in 1946, founded by John Leek and Russel Post, names associated with Pacemaker and Post Marine, the later of which is still in business. Egg Harbor was most renouned for its mahogany, carvel planked 36' sedans but later branched out into a large number of Pacemaker copy cat sport fishermen and motor yachts. Or is it vice versa? Hard to say. In any case, Egg fell on hard times and was taken on by Fuqua industries and merged with Pacemaker in 1966. The 1973-74 Arab oil embargo brought that venture to a close and the company languished throughout the 1980's though a few boats were turned out by Egg while Pacemaker, burdened by a mountain of warranty claims, quietly sailed into the sunset.

Through the 1980's to date, the company struggled on under a variety of ownerships, going through a few bankruptcies, federal indictments for misuse of government loans and other unpleasantness, Egg Harbor has remained a marginal company and market player. A few of the older sedans still offer good value such as the 33 and 36 models, though many others are fraught with problems.

Formula

Often highly regarded by sport boat owners, Formula entered the mid size, entry level boat market in the early 1980's without making much of an impression though gaining considerable market share. The boats were low to mid level quality(despite contrary advertising) and often incorporated serious engineering problems such a improper engine placement with water backing up into the engines, as well as rotting balsa cores and upholstery. Using a lot of not very durable materials, these boats deteriorated at an astonishing rate, so much so that most today have either gone to the grinder or are quietly gracing the back lots until the storage claims are settled.

A family owned company operating under the name of Thunderbird Industries, Formula has made forays into the 40 foot diesel express market without making a big splash or gaining much market share in salt water markets. From what I've seen, I'd say that a lack of salt water experience is the reason why this Indiana based company hasn't gained the respect it desires.

Fairline

This English import has one of the most nicely detailed hull framing systems I've seen in a long time. My two surveys of the Fairline Squadron 46 and 50 were pleasant surprises. They are big on foam coring, including cored bulkheading and some interesting framing systems. I do not know of, and have not heard of any problems with their construction methodology.

Unfortunately, there is the usual English lack of consideration for machinery maintenance with one of the worst engine room layouts I've ever seen. In the Squadron 50 with Caterpillar diesels, I was unable to move from front to back of the engine room because there is so little room. Otherwise, solid engineering and mid level quality. Very racy European styling from 40 to 65 feet. May look impractical but designs are usually intelligently done. Moderately priced.

Feretti

This Italian builder of high quality boats, also the current owner of Bertram, seems to be dedicated to quality and limited production by turning out a mere 60 boats a year at last count. Definitely priced to their quality, the smallest is a 46 footer starting at close to a million bucks.

Grand Banks

Parent company American Marine was founded in 1964 and the boats built in Hong Kong with U.S management since their relocation to Singapore in 1998, a literally famous builder of trawler style boats which are hard chined planing hulls with big keels. The hulls have been progressively modified to achieve ever faster speeds of just over 20 knots and still have good fuel efficiency.

As Asian built boats go, these are standouts for higher quality and better overall engineering. Usually loaded with teak they tend to be maintenance hogs particularly when the ½" thick teak decks start to wear out. Substantially higher priced than all other Asian imports, The Grand Banks reputation causes them to hold value very well, whatever else one might think of them. If you're thinking of an Asian trawler, you should definitely consider Grand Banks with nearly a dozen different sizes and styles over the years. Later models have substantial improvements over earlier models.

Gulfstar

This long defunct company started up in St. Petersberg, Florida in 1971 and produced a very large number of sailboats and low price round bilge trawlers from 36 to 53 feet. Unfortunately, their hulls were fraught with problems, often of a serious nature. Since I know these boats well, I can say that I know of no rhyme or reason why some go bad and others don't. Large numbers of them have deteriorated to the point of no return. At this point in time, I wouldn't suggest these boats as a viable option to all but the most desperate to own a larger boat. Caveat emptor.

Hatteras

Here's one builder that needs little introduction, but I will give it one because the reasons for its success are so exemplary. Founded by North Carolina textile manufacturer Willard Slane in 1960 reportedly for no other reason than that he wanted a fiberglass fishing boat. Up to that time, of course, all such boats – or at least 99.9% of them – were wood. Slane created a company that pioneered production fiberglass boat building, which along with Bertram and Henry Hinckley, are the oldest fiberglass boat builders still in continuous business. Chris Craft, of course, was another pioneer that did not remain continuously in business.

Hatteras, along with Bertram blazed the trail of boat building R&D that most others only followed or copied. Note here that so many others did not survive because what they were doing was copying the methods of others without having the full understanding of what they were doing. Hatteras and Bertram put serious money into permanent engineering departments so that they wouldn't be experimenting new materials directly in their product line, putting both themselves and their customers at risk. In other words, this was a company that not only knew what it was doing, but also why.

Those early philosophies stayed with the company through a succession of corporate take overs that more or less allowed Hatteras management to operate independently. The lone exception was the four years in which North American Rockwell, a defense contractor, owned the company. Rockwell brought in their bean counters and aerospace engineers and screwed things up royal. They even managed to screw up a basic DC wiring system. Fortunately, the NAR reign was short lived and the company was then sold to AMF, the dedicated maker of quality sports equipment. AMF wisely let Hatteras management do what they did best, building boats.

Probably the thing that helped Hatteras along the most was their dedication to standardization. Not only did this allow them to utilize the right materials, process and good equipment throughout their entire line of boats, but also proved a great benefit for boat owners. Hatteras wasn't a Rolls Royce of quality; instead, it became a pillar of good, solid, consistent and reliable quality that was basically the same throughout the entire line of boats. If I could sum it up in a phrase, it was consistent quality. That did wonders for their reputation. Other builders would cheapen up their smaller boats unmercifully, gaining a bad reputation that would carry over to their larger boats – how dumb can management get? Hatteras wisely stayed away from the cheap boat market.

By the mid 1990's when the company was bought by Irwin Jacobs Genmar, it not only stayed away from cheap boats, but Hatteras moved completely out of the mid size boat market. The smallest 2001 model is 50 footer tipping the scales at well over a million dollars. Under Jacobs leadership, Hatteras had also attempted to enter the mega yacht business and failed miserably. By 2002, Hatteras was but a shell of its former glory, producing only a handful of large sport fishing models and one motor yacht with a total annual sales of a mere 80 boats. Fortunately for us, the company has left behind a huge array of, by today's standards, very high quality used boats. Later models predominate in sport fisherman, but earlier models will be found in small motor yachts, opens, convertibles, a few express styles and a number of "back porch" boats, all of which offer superb value when decently maintained. Although not very fuel efficient, nearly all are superb sea keepers.

Now that Genmar is done gutting this once-great yacht builder, Jacobs has sold the remnants to Hatteras to Brunswick Corporation, an ill-advised union if ever there was one. Hatteras appears to be doomed to go the way of Chris-Craft.

Intrepid

A notable builder of very high quality and superbly designed outboard boats, the company has made an occasional foray into the inboard market including the 395 Walkaround and the 38 Evolution. At the present time no new inboard boats are in production.

Island Gypsy

Asian Built trawler style boats since 1975, formerly Kong and Halvorsen.

Jefferson

Indiana based importer of a variety of Asian built power boat styles from a variety of yards since 1982.

Kady-Krogen

Two US designers teamed up to design this line of Taiwan built , mostly round bilge, trawler style and character yachts 36 to 54 feet. Many are real trawler hulls, achieving only displacement speeds. There are numerous reliable reports of cored hull problems with later models, though I have no personal experience with them.

Luhrs

Another poor man's sport fisherman, this company once known for its "floating campers," made a remarkable change beginning around 1992 with its focus on the sport fishing market. The price leader in its class, the company has done a remarkably good job turning out low priced boats with very few major problems. Hulls tend to be on the fast but shallow side although not excessively so but similar to earlier Viking and Pursuit. Good value for the money but lacks the refinement and overall quality of higher priced competitors.

Having hit the high production, low price market big time, its later models are beginning to reveal some problems and mistakes.

Magnum Marine

Although it's been around a long time, this Miami builder of late has largely confined itself to a high end line of Mediterranean style go fast boats, marketed almost exclusively in Europe, and has always been involved in building heavy duty "cigarette" style muscle boats that give the term "power" boat another meaning.

Mainship

This US builder has produced a few boats worthy of note, though strongly tending toward entry-level price boats that are not highly regarded among experts. A few later models such as the Pilot 34, a distinctively Down East style express and sedan versions, though the express is particularly nice looking. Another is the 350 and 390 trawler style which are the same boat, albeit with the transom extension length added into LOA. This is an interesting design with a very large bridge deck and moderate size cockpit.

Maxum

Started in 1987 as a division of U.S. Marine, a la Bayliner, the company was reporting that it would market boats that were "upscale' to the Bayliner brand. Maxum has a large market in smaller boats in the western US, which is no surprise in that they are headquartered in Washington State. However, the Maxum line of purportedly higher quality mid size boats hasn't seemed to make much of an impression in the major markets. I have not been able to distinguish any difference in quality between Bayliner and Maxum other than more extensive use of polished stainless steel.

The SCB4600, the largest Maxum model is a decent enough boat, though when looking through the glitz and glitter didn't seem to be much better quality than cousin Bayliner. Very light and fast with small engines, it's a fair weather flyer only due to a shallow bottom. Most of the beauty is skin deep, but that's all you're paying for anyway.

Navigator

This west coast company was started by the above mentioned Marshall in the late 1980's after the Californian brand was sold to Wellcraft. The company builds boats up to 63 feet with emphasis on the larger sizes as well as competing strongly on price.

I shudder when I come across builders of large boats that compete almost solely on price but Navigator has been a pleasant surprise to me. My take is that these are lightweight boats designed for good speed at low power (760 HP in a 53' boat is pretty miserly). Not exactly sea going yachts, they have rather flat bottoms, which accounts for the speed and will do best at protected coastal cruising. Layouts are very spacious and conducive to vacation homing or live aboard.

Overall, I find the quality to be where it is most needed and not invested in a lot of fru-frus and gimcracks for the sort of people who are attracted lots of bright, shiny objects. But not exactly spartan, either. Engine room layouts were intelligently done. I didn't find any major engineering faults with the half-dozen or so that I have surveyed. I call it a cut above Carver, good value for the money, just don't expect it to be more than it is.

Ocean Yachts

Referred to by some as the poor man's sport fish, others will find the term pejorative. Their line of boats over the years have had a long history of problems that has tarnished its reputation from which it has yet to recover. Definitely a price leader, I haven't been on any of their boats in the last few years.

Pacemaker

At one time, one of the better known names in boating, it was a rival of Chris Craft particularly with regard to price. The company went out of business in 1981 and the quality of its boats is such that they are now of an age where the purchase of one would not be economically viable. The style and tradition was carried on by Egg Harbor into the 1980's with its flying bridge sedans (aka sport fish), many of which are still going strong and worthy of consideration.

Phoenix

This Miami builder has lived up to its name on more than one occasion, but it's just one of many builders that have had trouble staying in business long-term. Frank Piedra, the company's founder, was also that of SeaBird fame. In the 1980's Phoenix was very popular in the Florida market with their Jim Wynn designed 29-38 footers, more than one of which were Bertram look-alikes. Generally soundly built, they lacked the production expertise and refinement of Bertram. Though many of these boats have gone into disrepair, their designs are good enough, and construction of sufficient quality to make for good handy man's specials. Go faster and have shallower bottoms than comparable Bertrams. The late model 34 Express and 35 Convertibles, though only a few were produced, are pretty nice boats.

Post Marine

A limited production, privately owned builder of sport fishermen and convertibles ranging from 42 to 50 feet since the early 1970's. Leaning toward shallow bottoms and high speed, these boats tend to be favored by Mid Atlantic sport fishermen. Moderate quality and leanining toward the lower end of price range for class. Generally regarded as good value and well-designed.

ProLine

American Marine Holdings, the parent of ProLine, is also the owner of the remnants of Phoenix. Back in the 1980's ProLine was building decidedly "price" fishing boats that did not do much to earn the company much respect. The company was subsequently sold somewhere around 1990 after which the product line underwent profound changes, mainly for the better. Known mostly for outboard boats, the company has recently offered several inboard powered models, and express cruiser in 1997 and an open sport fish in 1999. I've yet to see one up close.

Pursuit

A brand of S2 yachts and cousin of Tiara, the Pursuit line was once the small boat brand of that company, these boats have grown in both size and quality over the years to the point where they are almost indistinguishable, except for the fact that Pursuit is now the dedicated line of sport fishing boats. They are among the higher priced boats of their class with a quality level to match. Whereas earlier models were known to suffer occasional hull and trim problems, later models do not.

Earlier complaints of too shallow hulls were remedied sometime in the mid 1990's (I don't know the exact year but believe it was around 1995) producing hulls that handle seas the way any sport fisher should. Today, Pursuit is highly regarded in all quarters producing multi purpose and sport fishing boats from 25' outboards to 34' diesel inboards. So far they are unique in using NidaCore plastic honeycomb cored cockpit decks since about 1992 that don't rot.

It is interesting to note that S2 did not make the same mistakes as Chris Craft and others by tainting its high quality Tiara line by making the Pursuit models too cheap, and although earlier models were of demonstrably lower quality, the Pursuit line has steadily increased in quality to the point where there are few noticeable differences.

The company has made few big mistakes and has a very good record of handling complaints.

Riviera

This Australian builder has been struggling to make an impression in the U.S. market with a number of Bertram look-alike convertibles. They also make some not too flashy express and/or open style boats. The hulls aren't as deep nor is the product as well refined as a Bertram. Later model boats are considerably better than earlier offerings. Though they're price competitors, the few I've surveyed I would classify as good value for the money. Resale value of newer boats hasn't held up well, largely due to lack of brand recognition, making for some very good used boat buys. This is very typical of foreign imports that haven't established brand recognition. The designs of their larger convertibles seems to waver between Viking and Bertram look-alikes, so much so that it's hard not to notice.

Sea Ray

We now come to the one name that often leaves me at a loss for words. I suppose that if anything is responsible for this Brunswick company's enormous success, it is style and slick marketing tactics. The company has the most elegant dealership showrooms and the slickest salesmen in the industry. It's the first boat builder to reach the billion dollar sales mark. Sea Ray thrives on first time buyers and bends over backwards trying to keep their customers as second time buyers with an agressive sales and trade in program. It's one of the few boat builders with dealers actively involved with taking trade-ins, something that is very, very risky in the boat sales business, but definitely creates repeat buyers.

Sea Ray makes more annual model changes than any other boat builder I've ever seen. The company also has a history of making mistakes, often big ones, such as the coring of their large boat bottoms with balsa, no doubt due to being so market driven that they often seem to loose sight of the fact that it is boats they are building, not designer fashions. This company is the epitome of corporate boat building and shameless pandering to vanity buyers.

Although it sells more boats than anyone else, the company has more than its fair share of complaints, disgruntled customers and lawsuits. Of late, Sea Ray has built and sold so many boats that used ones have become something of a glut on the market as of this writing, no doubt its record of screw ups has not helped used boat owners any to liquidate their holdings.

Tiara

Another S2 Yachts product, Tiara has gained a well deserved reputation for moderately high quality boats and a track record of very few mistakes and very good customer service. In recent years the designs have tended to stray from its earlier focus on solid design and practicality without excessive frills, to swallowing the shiny lure of a bit too much glitz. This has pushed prices up and sales down. Though they've done some goofy designs lately – like tables that pop up out of the deck – to going overboard in making things round, thereby moving from classic styling to trendy. In my opinion the quality is starting to slip as perhaps the management is spending too much time examining what Sea Ray is doing in the design-marketing department. Perhaps the current crop of woes at Sea Ray will straighten out their thinking.

Tolly Craft

A west coast builder who's boats aren't seen much on the east coast, "Tolly" has been around a long time, gaining a well deserved reputation for good quality, well-designed boats, the larger examples of which are exemplary. Most of the designs are by naval architect Ed Monk. Styling is often simple without being simplistic. If Tolly Craft owners seem sort of cultish, it's not hard to understand why. Most of their older boats from the 1970's are still going strong.

Trojan

One of the early builders of economy plywood boats, Trojan also built some pretty good mahogany boats, too. The F series of fly bridge sedan cruisers had a long run of popularity in the 70's and early 80's. Not exactly built to last for 30 years, there are still some around. As they moved into larger fiberglass boats, they produced some truly awful motor yachts and double cabins.

The 1980's saw the introduction of the International series. At one time, Trojan was owned by the same parent as Bertram, the Whitticar Corporation and for a while there was a company named Bertram-Trojan, Inc. which is the name you'll find on some of the Internationals. Most of the earlier Trojan models have gone to the grinder already and are now doing service as picnic table planks.

The Internationals were all designed by Harry Schoell with his patented "Deltaconic" hull. I never understood why the patent since I didn't think that this design produced a particularly good ride, plus they were not the least bit efficient. They were flawed by hollows in the hull shape that created resistance. However, these boats were notable for having rather heavy solid fiberglass hulls, intelligent design and sold at a moderate price. Spacious but have very cramped engine rooms. Nice styling that holds its appeal, the main models were Convertibles and Expresses, the later of which are probably the better all around boats. Like a lot of older boats, they're rather fuel hungry. They're still attractive buys to people who want newer boats but can't afford them.

While Trojan is still in business, today, the company is only a shadow of its former self. The only two examples of its recent production offerings left me more critical than impressed.

Viking

This company, once a builder of wooden boats, is best known for its high end sport fisherman, yet it has always produced motor yachts in various numbers. Following the 1989-91 recession, the company went bust, reorganized and changed its tune, upping the design and quality of its sport fishing fleet and then launching on a joint venture with British builder Princess Yachts to produce Viking Sport Cruisers.

Their sport fishing yachts are among the finest production boats of their type. From the 1970's through the 1980's. Vikings are distinctive for their straight lines and, some think, their boxy-looking styling. The most common complaint – common to many Mid Atlantic builders – is that their bottom configurations are too shallow. On the other hand, they are more efficient and go faster with less power. Hull shapes were deepened up somewhat in the early 1990's.

Wellcraft

Here's another company with a past clouded with serious product defects and numerous lawsuits, followed by bankruptcies and changes in ownership. Recent examples of product under the latest ownership seems to be continuing the historical pattern. Today, mainly a builder of outboard boats, Wellcraft once built inboards up to 46 feet. Beginning in 1999, Wellcraft teamed up with Riviera of Australia and jumped into the sport fishing market with a 39 foot sport fisher billed as "affordably priced."

In older boats, look out for rotted balsa cores in decks, rotting stringers, extensive disbonding, hull cracking and fatigue, rotted transoms of stern drive and outboard boats, and in latest models problems with grid liners.

Companies by Quality Category

Entry Level Builders

There are a fairly large number of builders of what are known as entry-level boats that compete in the market based primarily on low prices. For the most part, I find their quality levels nearly indistinguishable from builder to builder, model to model that assessing these differences isn't always possible.

So what do I mean by "entry-level"? If you don't already grasp the meaning, it refers to boats wherein the primary appeal is to first-time buyers or people with limited knowledge about performance, quality and sea keeping abilities of vessels. Obviously, if someone doesn't know much about boats, that person can't make sound judgements. Most builders of entry-level boats seem to prey on the ignorance of the buyer. The much lower prices often don't represent good value for the money, much as a cheap watch that doesn't keep accurate time isn't worth anything, no matter how little you pay.

Such boats typically mimic the auto industry with an over-emphasis on styling where form is more important than substance. Styling is often trendy with an emphasis on imitation luxury. Overall quality levels, and often engineering, are below what I consider to be a reasonable minimum that would ensure a reasonably long service life. Certainly there will be owners of these boats who will not agree with my assessment, but that is my take on these builders. These include:

Azimut	Larson
Bayliner	Mainship
Californian	Maxum
Carver	Monterey
Century	Ocean Yachts
Chapparal	Regal
Chris Craft*	Rinker
Crownline	Silverton
Doral	Sunseeker
Formula	Trojan*
Four Winns	Wellcraft

In addition to the above builders, there are literally hundreds more whose impact on the market is so small as to be relatively unknown outside their own locales.

Mid Level Builders

The following is my list of what I would call mid level quality builders, which are fewer in number than entry-level boats. They are most distinguishable by their higher prices because the higher quality is usually not visible to the untrained eye. Designs are usually more practical, and the boats sometimes less dependent on glitz. There is a large preponderance of sport fishing types in this category. Foreign builders are included as well.

Note that for any given builder, the quality of his boats may not be consistent over the years so that the products may change categories over time. Moreover, even experts can have reasonable differences of opinion. My criteria is how I perceive their historical offerings.

Chris Craft (Pre 1980)	Post Marine
Egg Harbor	Pursuit
Fairline	Riviera
Luhrs (Post 1992)	Sea Ray
Navigator	Squadron
Phoenix	Viking Sport Yachts/Princess

High Quality Production Builders

This category includes both production and semi-custom boats because it is often difficult to differentiate the latter. The following are the most widely known, though there are many others.

Albin*	Little Harbor
Bertram	Offshore Marine
Blackfin	Post Marine
Buddy Davis	Sabreline*
Grand Banks - American Marine	Tiara
Hatteras	Viking Yachts
Hinckley	
Magnum	

* Quality is likely to vary between models and years

Builders not included in this chapter have probably produced such low volumes that I do not have sufficient knowledge to rate them.

List of Taiwan Boats

The list of Taiwan built boats sold in the US is extensive, owing to some 60 builders on the island, many of which turn out generic brands that any importer can add his own name to. The following are some of the better known names.

Albin	Nordhaven (PAE)
Heritage East	Nova Marine
High Tech	Ocean Alexander
HiStar	Offshore Yachts
Island Gypsy	Pace
Jefferson	PAE
Kady-Krogen	Present
Kha Shing	President
Lien Hwa	PT Yachts
Marine Trader	Symbol
Mikelson	Ta Chiao

Glossary

ABYC The American Boat and Yacht Council, the primary US boating standards society. Publishes a voluntary set of engineering standards to which most of the industry adheres.

Abaft A reference to anything aft of the mid point of the vessel; *abaft the beams.*

Abeam Directly off the beam or along side.

Aft The rear portion of the vessel, or referring to that direction; stern.

Amidships Referring to the middle section of the boat, or that general direction.

anodic A metal in a galvanic cell that emits a positive electrical charge, and will therefore corrode. Zinc is anodic to aluminum, aluminum is anodic to copper.

Anode The opposite electrical pole of a cathode. On a boat, refers to the sacrificial zinc *anodes* attached to the motor lower unit, the purpose of which is to prevent corrosion damage to the motor.

Bilge The area of the hull below interior decks; the inside bottom of the hull.

Bimini Top Originally a free-standing soft top, now corrupted to mean just about any kind of soft top.

Blister A separation between the gel coat surface and the structural laminates beneath, usually filled with a fluid comprised of water and solvents in the plastic such as styrene.

Bond The *grounding* as opposed to the ground wire in an alternating current system. A normally non current carrying conductor. Also: any wire or other metal conductor joining two pieces of metal together for the purpose of minimizing galvanic corrosion between the connected parts. This is normally a green wire or copper strap.

Bonding System The process of wiring all underwater metals together so as to equalize the electrical potential between different metals for the purpose of preventing galvanic corrosion.

Boot That part of the bottom antifouling paint that is carried above the normal water line.

Boot Stripe or Boot Top Incorrectly referred to as the waterline, a boot stripe is added above the waterline, usually as a means of distinguishing the scum line that accumulates, but also as a cosmetic adornment. The waterline defines the intersect between the top of the water and the hull.

Bow That part of the hull that meets the water, usually considered from the point where the hull begins to curve from the flat sections amid ships; the forward part of a boat. The *stem* is the leading edge of the bow.

Broaching The reaction that occurs from operating in high, following seas when the bow noses into the backside of a wave sufficiently to cause the vessel to change the direction and veer off course, usually resulting in a loss of control.

Bulkhead These can be likened to a load bearing wall in a house. Perpendicular to the centerline of the hull, a full bulkhead attaches to the sides and bottom and serve the purpose preventing the hull from twisting.

Bulwarks A ship oriented term that refers to any part of the hull side that extends up above the main deck.

Bracket A term describing any external structure used for mounting motors on the transom.

Cavitation The result of air being introduced into the propeller. In addition to causing engine overspeeding, cavitation is damaging to metals such as propellers and should be avoided at all costs.

CFR Code of Federal Regulation. CFR 33 is the applicable section relating to boating standards administered by the Coast Guard.

Cavitation A condition in which air is introduced into the path of the propeller. Since air is compressible, while water is not, this causes the engine to overspeed by reducing the load on the engine, with a resulting loss in boat speed. Cavitation is damaging to propellers and engines and must be avoided.

Cavitation Plate The horizontal plate above the propeller on an outboard motor. The cavitation plate prevents air from being pulled down from above, into the propeller slip stream. Damaged cavitation plates must be repaired.

Chine   The angle formed by the hull side and bottom of the hull.

Closed Cell Corrosion   See crevice corrosion.

Chine Flat   A horizontal surface on the bottom between the hull side and the sloping bottom sections. Normally added to provide extra lift to very deep vee hulls.

Chock   A piece of metal hardware attached to a boat that is designed to hold a dock or anchor line in a certain place, or create a fairlead at a particular angle.

Cleat   A metal device designed to attach lines to.

Coaming   Usually a raised, curved surface such as found around the perimeter of an open decked boat. A flying bridge structure is called the flying bridge *coaming*. A horizontal surface around the perimeter of a cockpit is called a cockpit *coaming*. The same for a horizontal framework around a hatch opening.

Composite   A term meaning the combination of two or more materials. Fiberglass reinforced plastic is a composite, but in marine terminology usually means a core material such as balsa or foam.

Core   Any type of dissimilar material sandwiched between two layers of fiberglass, whether solid wood, foam, balsa, plywood or even aluminum.

Coremat   Trade name for a thin fibrous material used as a core in boat hulls, usually hull sides but not bottoms.

Corrosion   Any of numerous causes of a metal being destroyed or damaged by an electro-chemical process. A process by which any material combines with oxygen in a normally occurring process of oxidation such as the rusting of steel. In marine parlance, refers to the natural degradation of metals. Electrolysis is also a form of corrosion.

Crevice Corrosion   A form of corrosion caused by water in contact with a metal where the oxygen supply is cut off, in which the water forms an acid. The acid then attacks the metal. Commonly a serious problem with aluminum hardware and fuel tanks at the mounting surface where water gets trapped in an area that gets little or no airflow; also called closed cell corrosion.

CSM   Acronym for Chopped Strand Mat, a fiberglass matting in which fiber direction is completely random and fibers are less than four inches long. May come in the form of a manufactured fabric or blown out of a chopper gun mixed with resin.

Deadrise — The angle of the hull bottom to the horizontal measured at the transom. While deadrise can be measured anywhere, the general use of the term means the angle at the transom.

Deck — Any horizontal surface of significant size that attaches to the hull, in small boats usually an exterior deck. Soles are distinguished from decks as being decks within the cabin area as in *cabin sole*.

Deep Vee — Generally considered as any hull in which the angle of the aft section is more than 20 degrees to the horizontal. A *modified vee* is one that is very deep forward but tapirs to a shallower angle at the stern.

Delamination — Since molded fiberglass is a laminated material, when the laminations separate for any reason the term *delaminated* is used to describe this condition. Also referred to as ply separation.

Displacement — The weight of a boat or ship determined by means of calculation of the amount of water the hull will displace. This is done by measuring the volume of the hull below the water line.

Dog — A heavy duty latch, usually on hatches.

Doubler — In boat construction, refers to any construction intended to make a structure stronger, such as a *doubler plate* under a mooring cleat or a sea cock in a hull; a reinforcement.

Dry Weight — The weight of a boat as measured on a scale, with all tanks empty. Usually will differ slightly from displacement.

Electrolysis — The process in which an electrical current applied to a metal immersed in water causes the metal to self destruct. The end result is the same as corrosion, but the root cause on a boat is a stray current acting to cause the destruction of the metal. The distinguishing feature of electrolysis results from an outside electrical source. See also *galvanism*.

Epoxy — A high quality plastic resin or paste that is highly water resistant. Only marine grades of epoxy resins and glues should be used on boats.

Ergonomics — The study of how manufactured products relate to the scale of the human body with a view toward improving ease of use or operation.

FRP — Acronym for Fiberglass Reinforced Plastic.

Freeboard	The height of the hull side above the floating water line at any point it is measured. *Effective freeboard* is the height above the water to any opening in the hull that would allow water to enter the vessel, such as a transom cut out or a deck scupper.
Forefoot	The curved section between the generally straight line of the bow and the line of the keel. Also refers to this general space on the interior.
Galvanism	An electrical current generated when any two materials are joined which have a different electrical potential. The common flashlight battery generates electricity by means of galvanic reaction between two metals. Carbon is a metal, which is the reason why carbon rubber hoses cause corrosion problems. Joining copper and aluminum, for example, will result in a galvanic reaction that will destroy the aluminum. The most common cause of corrosion damage to metals on a boat.
Gel Coat	A pigmented plastic resin that is first sprayed into the mold, having the dual purpose of creating a molded-in finish, as well as providing a means of releasing the part from the mold. Gel coats tend to be very porous and not very durable. The highest quality gel coats can be buffed back to a good shine, whereas poorer quality gel coats are likely to suffer permanent degradation.
Grid Liner	A fiberglass liner in which the full framing system is included; can be partial or full boat size.
GRP	Acronym for glass reinforced plastic, commonly used in Great Britain.
Gunwale	The side deck that attaches to the hull side in an open cockpit boat. The gunwale is a major structural component that provides the strength to the hull.
Half Tower	Not really a tower at all but a pipe frame top, sometimes called a Bimini.
Hatch	Any opening on a deck or horizontal surface; the nautical term for a door.
Hawse hole	A hole in hull or deck, normally surrounded with a metal flange, through which dock or anchor line passes.
Helm	Literally any device used to steer the boat such as the steering wheel. The helm station or general area is also simply referred to as *the helm*. It is not proper to call it the dashboard.

Hose Nipple   A special male nipple with ribbed or barbed construction designed to grip hoses tightly when clamped and prevent them from slipping off. Same as hose barb.

Isopthalic resin   A specific type of polyesther plastic that is blister resistant.

Keel   Typically the vertical strength member on the bottom of the hull, sometimes called the *backbone* in wood construction. Most small fiberglass boats don't have proper keels, but the angle formed by the two sides of the bottom are still properly referred to as the keel.

Laminate   In reference to fiberglass boats, a laminate is any part made of layers of fiberglass reinforced plastic, with any number of layers. A laminate that includes a core material, is often called a composite or sandwich construction.

Laid Line   The term for rope in which the fiber bundles are twisted together, as opposed to samson braid, in which the fibers are woven together. Conventional nylon rope is laid line. Samson braid is both more flexible and stinger.

Liner   Any of several types of molded fiberglass components such as a cockpit *liner* or full hull *liner*. Outboard boats typically have a full deck/cockpit liner. In the cabin it may be a molded head compartment or a complete cabin liner including the seating, galley, etc. Generally the same meaning as *shell*.

List   A boat that is not floating level on the transverse plane is said to be *listing*.

Lower Unit   The lower drive portion of an outboard motor which contains the drive gears, and which is removable and replaceable.

Marlin Tower   As distinguished from a tuna tower, a marlin tower is shorter than a tuna tower, usually about 2/3rds height.

Nobility   A term that indicates a metal's resistance to galvanic corrosion. More noble metals, gold, bronze, nickel have lower electrical potential are cathodic, while the least noble have high electrical potential are anodic such as zinc and, aluminum. If you put the two together, such as nickel and cadmium, you have a galvanic battery.

Non skid   A pattern or texture on a deck intended to make the surface less slippery.

Orthopthalic resin   A name that refers to the specific type of polyester resin, as opposed to isopthalic resin. Orthopthalic plastics are prone to blistering.

Pie Port
Any of numerous types of small, round plastic ports usually for the purpose of providing access. Name was derived from the manufacturer name *PiHi*.

Polyester
A plastic resin that is known for its least resistance to water absorption or hydrolysis, the dissolution of the plastic by water.

Porpoising
A condition in which the bow of the boat is constantly rising and falling in an perpetual and uncontrollable cycle.

Port
Any opening in a deck, hull or other structure for seeing through or to provide access.

Powerhead
The engine portion of the outboard motor as opposed to the chassis and lower drive unit.

Quarters
For purposes of location and direction, it is common to divide the boat into quadrants and refer to it such as *the aft port quarter*. Also refers to the interior spaces such as *crew quarters* or *captain's quarters*.

Roving
A woven fabric of glass fibers in which the weave is at 90^0 angles and the bundles of fibers are flat. Its appearance is that of a tightly woven plaid pattern.

Sandwich Construction
Same as composite or cored laminate. A material placed between two skins of reinforced plastic to add strength or reduce weight.

Scupper
A hole in the hull, usually the transom, for the purpose of draining water off the deck. Can also be a gap in the toe rail to let water drain off the deck; also called *freeing port*.

Sea Cock
A marine valve in the bottom of a hull used to close off the water supply to any component that uses sea water. All through the bottom openings are required to have such valves. The common gate valve is not a sea cock and should not be used in boats. Only bronze valves are recommended.

Sea Hose
Those hoses which are recommended for marine use and which have the qualities of petrochemical and biological resistance, as well as strength to resist suction collapse, pressure and kinking. Typically rayon reinforced butyl rubber. Polyvinyl and wire reinforced rubber are not recommended.

Sea Keeping	The ability of a vessel to handle open seas with a reasonable degree of comfort to the vessel's passengers; a function of the vessel's design.
Sea Strainer	A special marine filter used to remove debris from water taken into the vessel from without, particularly for pumps.
Sheer Line	The line formed by the joint of the hull and deck, usually delineated by the rub rail. The *shear* refers to this general area.
Shearing Force	The force applied perpendicular to the length of an object, as in shears cutting paper. Interlaminar shear is a shearing force along the long axis, as in the force that can cause delamination of fiberglass.
Skeg	A fin-like protuberance, usually intended to protect a propeller.
Sole	An interior deck.
Steering Ram	The hydraulic cylinder that turns an outboard motor as a means of steering.
Stern	This term is often used interchangeably with the word transom, though stern more appropriately refers to the after area of the vessel. A canoe, for example, does not have a transom, though it does have a stern.
Stiffener	A small frame used to strengthen a fiberglass panel, whether on a bottom, hull side or other surface.
Strake	Formerly referred to boats with overlapping planking, now refers to the ribs that are often found on the bottom of a hull thought to create lift. Their purpose is often the subject of debate.
Stringer	The structural frames of the hull which run fore and aft, normally the entire length of the hull. In small boats usually consists of fiberglass laminated over plywood.
Tabbing	Strips of resin saturated fiberglass fabric, typically used to join bulkheads and frames to a hull. Also referred to as bonding.
Taping	Same as tabbing. Strips of resin soaked fiberglass used to join parts together are referred to as taping.
Toe Rail	A raised portion of the fore deck around the perimeter, usually an inch or so high. It serves the purpose of adding strength and to keep things from falling overboard.
Top Hat	Hollow stringers or frames formed in the shape of a top hat. May be

foam filled but the foam is used as a laminating form and is of no structural importance.

Transducer	The device attached to the bottom of the hull that sends and receives the electrical signal from the depth sounder.
Trim	The manner or angle in which a hull rests in the water, either while at rest or underway.
Vinylester	A high quality plastic resin know for its water resistance and resistance to blistering.
Warped Plane	A hull form that is essentially a distorted vee.
Weather Deck	Any exterior deck that is exposed to weather.
Zincs	The metal anodes attached to outboard motor lower units to help retard galvanic corrosion.

INDEX

A

Abrasive boat cleaners   239
ABS   142, 435
Absentee owners 410
Abusive operation   96
ABYC standards 79, 324, 326
Acceleration performance 188
Ace mounts   298, 301
Adhesive pastes 108
Adjustable tilt wheels   373
Adjustment of bow-up/bow-down   186
After-markets   259
Aftercooled   263
Air conditioning 6, 59-60, 211, 290, 317-
    321, 326, 328-329, 332, 336, 348-
    349, 351, 382, 426
    Cruisair   349, 382
    power   318, 320
    systems 348
    units   348-349
Air
    filters   251, 289-290, 306, 349
    intakes 287
    pollution 4, 380, 410
    pressurization   17
    space   23
Airex   114
Alaskan 441
Albemarle   49, 52, 434
Albin   43-44, 52, 434, 452-453
Alloys   211, 274
Alternative Drive Systems 275
Alternating current 350
    Dock power   211, 315-316
    System failure   59
Alternator   422, 424, 429
    function 422
    output   424
Aluminum
    boats   98
    castings 190
    channel 200
    chlorhydrate   157
    cylinder heads   268
    engine   268
    fatigue   98

fuel tanks   152, 312
heads   268
honeycomb   114
housings   272-273
hydraulic cylinders   376
oxide scale   157
pistons   252
tank   152-153, 157
Water Tanks   157, 346, 438
window 211
Amateur hull design   119
American
    boats   27
    importers   91
American Marine Hino-based engines
    264
American Marine Holdings   447
AMF   443
Anchor 2, 15, 17, 61, 70, 109, 138, 168,
    204-205, 211, 228, 380, 386-388,
    429
    rode hawse   138
    size   386
    windlasses   109, 387
    Reserve   15
Anodic   389
Anodized aluminum   240, 380
Anodizing   211
Antenna 131, 380
Anti fouling   139, 274
Antifreeze   307
Antitrust violations   25
Appraisal Books   413
Approximate Service Life of Boat Compo-
nents   79
Area Sizes   61
Arneson 275
ATC CoreCell   116
Atlantic 14, 409, 447, 450
Automatic windlass   202
Autopilots   219, 382
Auxiliary
    power generator 326
    sailboat engine market   264
Azimut   434-435, 451

B

Ballasting engines   184
Balsa   23, 97, 105-107, 111, 114-116, 129,
137, 195-196, 436, 439, 441, 448,
450
    core separations 111
    cores   105, 111, 439, 441, 450
Barrier Coating   163, 239
Battery, Batteries
    banks   333
    charger 318, 328, 333-334
    compartment   311
    installation   311
    parallel switches 334
    power   331-333
    problem 334
    selector switch   17
    switches 333-334
    systems 333
    tops   312
Bayliners   43, 89, 112-113, 333, 436,
439, 445-446, 451
Benetti   434
Bertram, Bertrams   18, 24, 37, 48-49,
52, 55, 77, 82, 86-87, 89, 119, 127,
131, 147, 157, 173, 175, 179-180,
183-184, 194, 262, 311, 320, 333,
368, 375, 377, 435, 437, 442-443,
447-449, 452
    look-alikes   447-448
    old   87
    Yachts   89, 119, 320, 435
Bertram-Trojan, Inc.   449
Bi-directional fabrics   100
Bilge(s)
    pumps   17, 19, 148, 152, 334-335,
339, 342-343, 345-346, 351
    water   163, 281, 300
Blackfin 48-49, 52, 86, 194, 284, 437, 452
Blister(s)   111, 138-139, 158-167,
197, 234, 236-239, 401
    bottom   167
    development of   166
Blistering   47, 91, 103, 139, 158-167,
210-211, 234, 236, 434
    phenomenon   163
Bloat boat   53-54, 61
Blotchiness of gel coat   139, 234, 241
Blowers 290
Boarding problems   362-363
Boat
    fires   323
    ownership of   1-3, 5, 8, 12, 19,
76

surveys 417, 419
Boattrader.com   400
Bolt-on   203, 210, 359, 398
    platform extensions   359
    products 398
    teak   210
Bolts   128, 130, 137, 204, 207, 266, 296
Bond   101, 108-111, 115, 125, 148, 161,
197, 394
    failures 125
    of glass-to-foam   111
    Secondary   111
Bonding 107-110, 115, 124, 128, 147, 196-
197, 342
    putty   108, 115
    strength 108
    surface   124
Book prices   414
Borescopes   252, 276, 423
Borg-Warner   271-273
    transmissions   272
    Velvet Drive   272
Boston Whaler   124, 437
Bottom, Bottoms
    angle   176
    failure   108, 232
    panels   106, 122, 178-180
    strakes   134, 180, 231-232
Bow
    area   214
    profiles of boats   177
    pulpit   15, 205
    seat   70
    section   176, 178, 181, 346
    sections of boats 124
Brackets , motor   201, 293, 359
Bridge(s)
    area   217
    boats   45, 65
    coaming 216
    enclosures   64
    girder   119
    sedans   63, 87, 214, 359, 383, 446
Broaching   170
Brokerage boats 401
Brokers 27, 192, 393, 395, 398, 401-402,
405, 408, 413, 419-421, 430
Bronze   88, 142, 212, 271, 296, 336-341,
386, 389
    marine strainer   339
    nipple   340
    quick-connect fittings   386
    strainer 336
Brunswick Corporation   269, 444

Buddy Davis   438
Builder, Builders of
    outboard boats   450
    sport fishermen   447
    wooden boats   450
    diesel boats   251
    economy plywood boats   449
    large boats   446
    affordable boats   439
Bulkhead,Bulkheads   96, 101, 104, 117-118, 124, 126-127, 130, 133-134, 145, 148-149, 167, 195, 205, 220, 231-232, 299, 346, 438
    attachments   130
Bushings,Inc.   297-298
Butt connectors   327, 335
Butterfly valves   290, 306

C

Cabin
    companionway   324
    layouts   51
    Leaks   150
    soles   104, 150-151, 168, 220, 396
    spaces   51, 151, 187-188, 329, 332
    structures   227
    style   33
    top/foredeck   150
Cable, Cables   99, 216, 310-311, 316-317, 321, 323-324, 372, 375-376
    receptacle   324
    retractors   323
    sleeves   375
Cablemaster   317, 323
Cabo   49, 52, 157, 333, 438
CAD   18, 355
    machines   18
    system   355
CAD-CAM   354
Californian   438, 446, 451
Capillary effect   107, 160, 234
Carbide rotary planer   159
Carbon   102, 153, 252-253, 287, 293, 302, 307, 329
    fiber   102
    monoxide   302, 329
      danger   302
      emissions   329
      poisoning   329
    rubber   153
Carburetors   267-268,290, 307

Carver   53-54, 61, 191, 193-194, 301, 333, 359, 362, 438-439, 446, 451
Cast iron riser situation   306
Cat diesels   261
Cat Harbor Boats,   [See Cabo]
Catalina series   440
Catalyzed   236
Caterpillar   260-261, 289, 298, 423, 442
    engines 260, 423, 442
    mount   298
Cathedral hulled whaler   437
CCR & CAD-CAM   354
Cell, Cells   11, 15, 103, 107-109, 114-115, 319
    corrosion   103, 108
    foams   114
    structure of balsa 107, 115
Center(s)
    boat   175
    of
      buoyancy   182, 184-186, 189
      motion   184
      gravity   54, 182-183, 185, 191, 439
Centerline of hull   136
Century   55, 104, 440, 451
CG   183
Chain   15, 204-205, 321, 387-388
    gypsy   387
    locker   204, 388
Chapparal   451
Charles Jannice   437
Charter 22
    arrangements   22
    ventures 22
Chemical bonds   101, 111
Cheoy Lee   439
Chine riding   192-193
Chines   47, 134, 192, 229
Chris Craft, Chris-Craft   18, 43, 75, 87-88, 127, 436, 439-440, 443, 444, 446, 448, 451-452
Chrome/bronze hardware   88
Chronic
    interior
      leaks   126
      mildew problems 151
    leakage 150, 304
    water contamination   310-311
    window leakage   150
Chrysler engines 265
Cigarette   177, 445

Circuit   17, 59, 200, 315-316, 318, 323-325,
          335, 429
          breaker 59, 200, 317, 320-321,
                   324-325,335
                   panel   200
                   replacement costs
                   325
          breakers 17, 59, 200, 324-325, 335,
                   429
                   protection   324
Clamping action 128
Class D casting aluminum 272
Cleat   203
Cleavage strength   106-107, 115-116
Close
          maneuvering   373
          strake   134
Closed
          cavity   143
          strake   134
Co-ownership   405
Coast Guard   390, 392
Coastal cruising 446
Cockpit
          appliances   379
          cover   207
          entry   364
          freezers 379
          heights 331
          liner   129, 331, 367-368
          margins 199
          motor yacht   53
          of the Blackfin   48
          pass-through   362
          scuppers   367
          upholstery cushions   18
          of sport fishermen   116
Cocktail cruiser   50, 326
Coffer dams   216
Cold water systems   347
Colored gel coats 224
Command bridge 33-34, 43
Commander series of boats   440
Commercial duty 244, 256-257, 332
          batteries 332
          engines 257
Common
          buss   319
          PVC foam   115
Companionway   17, 149, 324
Composite   21, 102-105, 119, 268
          powder metal   268
          structures   119
Compression   99, 252, 276-277, 286-287,
          293, 422, 424

          loads   99
pressures   243
          tester   424
          testing 276-277, 293,433-3
Compressive strength   115
Compressors [see air conditioning]
Computer-aided   354
          design   354
          manufacturing   354
Computerized engine controls   375
Concave bottom section   180
Concave-shaped bottom panels   179
Condensation   111, 219, 286-287, 348-
          349, 377, 379, 424
          of atmospheric moisture 286
          pan leaks   349
Condensers   349
Conduits   216
Contact cement   145, 313
Continuous vee hull   183
Conventional   69, 271, 273, 275
          inboard straight drive system
          271
          propeller shafting   273
Convertible, Convertibles 32, 37-39, 41-42,
          48-50, 52, 61, 63, 65-66, 87, 177,
          414, 435, 437-438, 444, 447-448,
          450
          dinettes 37, 41, 66
          sport fisherman 49
          tops   52, 61, 63, 65
Coolant 245, 251, 292-294, 304, 307, 310,
          348, 422, 424
          leaks   307
          passages   294
Core   23, 97, 104-112, 114, 116, 119, 121,
          129-131, 136-138, 146, 148, 168,
          195-196, 201-204, 207-208, 210-
          211, 227, 251
          degradation   210
          materials   104, 107, 114,
          137, 146
          plywood 116
          problems   227
          saturation of   111
Cored   24, 92, 105-109, 111-112, 114, 116,
          118-119, 129-130, 136-137, 141,
          144, 146, 148, 167, 195-196, 201-
          203, 207, 210, 313, 434-435, 442,
          445, 448
          hull side 141
          hulls   105-106, 112, 116, 118,
          130, 141, 434-435, 445
          structure 129-130, 202, 210

Corrosion   98-99, 103-104, 108-109,
              131, 137, 147, 152-153, 155-157,
              161, 168, 196, 201, 203-204, 212,
              221, 246, 252-253, 264-265, 271,
              274-275, 286-287, 290, 293-296,
              305, 307-308, 311-313, 323-324,
              337-338, 342, 346, 380, 389, 391,
              410, 437
    damage 221, 287, 296, 312, 324
    crevice *[See* crevice corrosion*]*
    galvanic 153, 264
    levels of metals   168
    of
              aluminum tanks   153
              the coupling   308
    resistance   99, 109
    resistant alloys   274
    scale   346
Corrosive oxide   152
Cost(s) of
    a
              boat   5, 60, 206
              gas engine   243
              new boat   240
    boating 8, 20, 73, 378
    bronze ball cocks 338
    diesel ownership 247
    engine   275
    finance   20
    fitting   21
    fixing   74, 76
    fuel   244
    insurance   20
    an international lawsuit   92
    maintenance   69
    ownership   5, 7-8, 19, 89
    refit   78
    resin   76
    restoration   76
    rewiring 326
    the warranty   268
    diesels 265
    ownership   6, 69
Counter weights 190
Coupling/packing gland   291
Cove moldings   131
Covington   258
CPU   423
Cracked castings   423
Cracking 134, 139-141, 150, 201-203, 208,
              211, 213, 225-233, 235-236, 238,
              367, 437, 450
Cracks   98, 118, 133-134, 139-141, 145,
              149-150, 167, 197, 201-203, 208-
              210, 212-213, 223, 225-229, 231-

              236, 238, 368, 418
Crankcase pressures   422, 424
Cranking power 334
Crankshaft seals 308, 424
Crevice corrosion 137, 153, 156-157, 161,
              196, 203, 212, 305, 338, 380
Crownline   440, 451
Cruiser types   48
Cruisers, Inc.   362, 440
Cruising 10, 31, 34-36, 40, 44-49, 51, 57,
              176, 248-249, 256, 316, 326, 345,
              358, 382, 385, 434, 446
    boats   35, 326
    distances   249
    long distance   31
    types   35
    yachtsmen   31
Crusader   267-270, 294, 305
    engines 305
    Marine   267, 269
    risers   270, 294
CSM (chopped strand mat) 98, 100-101, 103,
              112, 124, 159-163, 166
Cummins engines   247, 262
Current leakage 311
Custody of a vessel   394
Cutlass bearing 301
Cylinder 245-246, 252-253, 259-261, 263-
              264, 266-268, 270, 286, 293, 328,
              337, 339, 423
    block   261
    heads   260, 263, 266, 268
    walls   253, 261

D

Danforth
    anchor   15
    type   388
Dark colored   115, 160, 236
              boats   236
              gel coat 160
              surfaces 115
Date of manufacture   393
Davit   201, 363
DC   317-318, 332-333, 388, 443
    motor   388
    refrigeration   332
    sections   317
    system battery amperage 333
DCDP   226-227
DCFB   56
Deadrise   174, 176, 178-179, 188-
    189

Dealer(s)   18, 22, 25-26, 27, 29-30,
       92, 136, 138, 256, 258, 261, 268,
       275, 277, 333, 346, 380, 386, 394,
       396-399, 405, 407-408, 413, 417-
       418, 423, 440, 448
       markups 398
Dealership   22, 25, 29, 399, 448
       contract 399
       networks   25
       stability 25
Deck
       core   111, 137-138, 196, 204,
       210
       crowned 197, 199, 210
       fasteners   141
       join/rub rail   129
       joints   126-128, 132, 136-137,
       141-142, 150, 167-168, 205, 226
              lap   141-142
       mold   220
       molding 213
       molding 206
       shell   129
Deckhouse   38, 43
Decks
DeFever, Arthur   441
Deformation of plastic   115, 236
Delaminate, Delaminating, Delamination
       109-111, 115-116, 121, 145, 147,
       197
Deltaconic   450
Depreciation method   413
Depth   47, 96, 163, 172, 174, 178, 381-382
       meter   381
       of entry   174
Desalinators   384
Detroit Diesel   258
Dicyclopentadiene resin   226
Diesel   28, 49, 67, 79, 156, 177, 194, 243-
       255, 257-261, 263, 265, 269-270,
       275-277, 279, 289-290, 292, 295-
       296, 299, 302, 304-307, 309-310,
       328-330, 356, 360-361, 421-423,
       427, 437, 442, 448
       engine
              costs   289, 421
              issues   243
              market   269
              reliability experience
              258
              risers   304
              survey   276
       fuel systems   251, 310
       generators   328-329
       German   264

       myths of 244
       oil   361
       power ratings   255, 259
       reliability 257
       soot   67, 292
Digital   276, 334, 375, 381, 422
       tachometers   189, 194, 244-
       245, 252, 254-257, 259, 261-262,
       265, 276, 289, 329, 422
              measurement   276
              readings 422
       tachs   375
Dinette, Dinettes 37, 39, 41, 46, 48, 52, 56,
       66, 332
       seat   332
       tables   41
Disbond 111
Disbonded hull sides   113
Disbonding of   110, 113
       a hull stringer   110
Discoloration of gel coat   202, 225
Displacement   45-46, 177, 180, 182, 245-
       247, 254, 256, 259-262, 266, 288,
       445
       hull vessels   256
       hulls   46, 180, 182, 256
       ratios   245-247, 260-262
Dissimilar metals 274, 329
Distortion temperature   116
Distortions of the cabin structure   212
Dock(s) 7, 11, 26, 34, 40, 53, 56, 59, 71, 89,
       127, 132, 139, 178, 185, 188, 193,
       211, 226, 244, 284, 287, 315-317,
       319, 324, 326, 331, 358, 361-364,
       421, 133, 318-319, 323, 358, 364
       arrangements   358
       pilings   132, 226
       power   211
       system   315-316
       water systems   348
       wiring system failure   59
Docking 42, 44, 56-57, 61, 63, 188, 358-359,
       372, 374-375
       operations   56, 61, 63, 372,
       374
       single engine boats   57
Documentation   394-395, 402, 405
Documented vessel   394
Doors   35, 45-46, 50, 58, 118, 149-150,
       168, 206, 359, 367
Doral   451
DOT   394, 402
Double cabin   32-33, 56
Down east   43, 57, 441, 445
       styles   43, 441

Down Easters   32, 57
Drainage
       efficiency of   207
problems   148, 214
Dripless seals   308
Drive
       belts   290
       energy   187
       motor   204, 387
       system   188, 271, 297, 299
       train   121, 244, 299
Driven shaft   256
Dual   35, 38, 41, 56, 319-320, 330, 347,
       374, 387, 434
       control stations   35, 56
       controls   35, 434
       pump system   347
       purpose bar/counter tops   41
       voltage   330
Dynamic instability   192

E

E.P.I.R.B.'s   390
East Bay   441
Economics of   75-76, 85, 337
       boat ownership   76
       new boats   85
       older boats   75
Ed Monk   449
EDAX   423
Edge grain, plywood   105
Edson   373
Efficiency of the AC system   350
Egg Harbor   18, 43, 75, 441, 446, 452
Electric
       solenoid   369
       stove   330, 332
       windlass motor   204
Electronic
       charger   334
       Diesels   423
       fuel injection systems   375
Emergency   284, 337, 343-345, 374,
       386, 389-390
       devices   343
       equipment   386
       Position Indicator Radio Beacons
       390
Enclosures   35, 54, 59, 63-65, 74, 88,
       367, 378, 398, 401, 429
       replacements   74
       soft enclosures   63

Engine, Engines
       alignment   309
       block   245-246, 258, 266, 308
       compartment   17, 145, 210, 285,
       344
       compression   286
       control systems   374, 376
       controls   216, 373, 375
       crankshaft   300
       cylinders   423
       damage   249, 259, 270, 291, 294,
       296, 300, 304, 391
       dealer   275
       displacements   254, 262, 266
       failure   12, 47, 156, 285, 310
       filters   251
       full of water   303
       heat   251, 383
       hours   245-247, 396-397
       inspections   423
       installation   181, 188
       intake   308
       life   177, 245, 247, 285, 290,
       308
       loads   299
       longevity 177, 245-246, 249, 287,
       289
       manufacturer   255, 264-265,
       396, 418
       marinizer   268
       mechanics   25, 275, 277
       mount, mounts   119, 176, 244,
       276, 297, 299-301, 422, 424, 429
               replacements   297
               test   276, 422
       noise   299, 301, 304
       oil   20, 284, 300, 308, 310,
       327, 422, 424
       performance   259
       power   187
       power ratings   255
       problems   156, 261, 361,
       425
       reliability 57, 258
       room, rooms
               accessibility   291
               intakes   251
               layouts   282, 442, 446
               temperature   290, 422
       vents   129, 251, 290, 294-295,
       312
       RPM   194
       rust   294
       service life   245
       speed   194, 253-254, 257

surveyors   259, 275, 422-
424, 430
surveys 247, 266, 275, 277, 289,
421, 424
transmission   273, 297
tuning   255, 361
wear   177, 245-246, 266, 287,
410, 422
weights 262
of infrequent operation   253
winterized   410
EPA, Enviromental Protection Agency
245
Epoxy paste   148
Ergonomic, Ergonomics   44, 358, 371, 374
design   44, 358, 371
nightmare   44
European   263, 298, 300, 329, 442
builders 329
diesels   263, 300
engines 298
style   263
Evaluating Boat Hulls   135
Exhaust 244, 249, 252-253, 267, 270, 276,
286-288, 291, 293-294, 296, 302-
306, 308, 329-331, 359-362, 410,
418, 420, 422, 435, 438
pipe   286, 291, 304
piping outlet   331
riser   270, 291, 331
systems 249, 302-304, 306, 360,
420, 438
valves   286-287
Express, Expresses
cruiser   4, 16, 38, 43, 50-51, 177,
181, 284, 318, 447
models   201, 440
style boats   50, 144, 181, 208,
254-255
type cruisers   374
types   87, 149
Exterior 4, 38, 54, 61-62, 68, 88, 91, 139,
142, 201, 212, 219, 221, 225, 340,
356-357, 365-366, 380, 385, 410
upholstery   356, 366
windshield cover 221

F

Fairline 442, 452
Federal Documentation   394
Ferretti Group   435

Fiberglass
boats   74, 87, 95-99, 102, 104,
106, 112, 115, 118, 134, 206, 354,
439, 443, 449
covering 145
fabric   101, 124, 146, 223, 233
fatigue failures   97-98
fishing boat   443
resin ratio   100
hulls   43, 99, 101, 112, 117, 163,
450
liner   42
Reinforced Plastic   338
salon headliners 215
stringers 146
surface 107
tanks   157
tubs   365
Fillets   110, 129-131, 137, 203
Finish   74, 88-89, 160, 202, 223-224, 226,
228, 234-241, 380
gel coat 240
surface 160
Fire extinguishers   21, 386, 390-392
First Preferred Ship Mortgage   394
Fischer-Panda   329
Fish   16, 40, 46, 48-51, 365-366, 414,
437, 440, 446-447
boats   49
box   365
boxes   365-366
rods   35
Flame arresters   287, 290, 306
Florida   14, 16, 64, 166, 250, 285, 321, 383,
394-395, 408-411, 434, 438, 443,
447
Gulf Coast   411
market   409
peninsula   411
state   394
West Coast   411
Flush Deck   32-33, 38, 53, 56
motor yacht   32, 53
Fly bridge   43, 123, 214, 383, 449
sedan style   43
sport fishermen   214
Flybridge Sedans 42, 150, 383
Flying
bridge
boats   45, 65
cruiser   49
layout   374
sedan   32, 39, 42-43, 48-49, 123,
255, 434, 441, 445, 449

Foam   23, 92, 106-108, 111, 114-117, 121-122, 134, 137, 146, 148, 196, 313-314, 354-355, 434-435, 437, 442
   cores   106, 108, 114, 146, 434, 442
   insulation   313
   manufacturer   114
   panels   115
Foil   313-314
Fold-Down Cockpit Seats   367
Folding chairs   367
Foreign   90-91, 93, 275, 448, 452
   builders   91, 452
   built boats   91
   imports   448
Forespar   338
Formula   245, 344, 441-442, 451
Fountain   177
Four cycle   23, 189, 245, 258-260, 276-277, 348, 382, 384, 423
   diesels   277, 423
   engines   276
Four Winns   451
Frames   47, 96, 98, 104, 118, 122, 124, 148-150, 168, 211-212, 214, 231, 355
Framing systems of boats   355
Freezers   6, 379
Fresh water   157, 250, 274, 335, 346-347, 351, 369, 385, 410, 440
   boats   410
   pumps   157, 347, 351
   Systems   346
Fuel
   consumption   28, 45, 57, 138-139, 186, 190, 194, 201, 244, 252-253, 256, 324
      charts   194
      tables   253
   contamination   209, 251, 309, 311
   cooler   250
   cost   57, 248
   delivery system   253
   economy issues   32
   efficiency   57, 186, 188, 442
   efficient boats   180, 414
   filler pipes   138
   filters   252, 285, 292-293, 309
   hogs   175, 186
   lines   310, 312
   oil   252, 435
   pump   266
   suction problem   156
   systems   243, 251, 310, 420, 424

   tanks   87, 103-104, 119, 142, 152-153, 155-157, 209, 214, 252, 265, 310-311, 346-347, 368, 437
   aluminum   152, 312
   black iron
   corrosion issues
   replacements   156
   status   368
   vents   142, 311
Fungus   168, 208
Fuqua industries   441
Furuno   381

G

G-forces   348
Galley(s)   4, 21, 36, 38-41, 46, 52, 56, 149, 220, 326, 342, 387, 391
   dinette area   56
Galley Maid   342, 387
Galvanic corrosion   153, 264
Gas
   -vs-diesel   243, 247
   boats   249, 290, 309
   engine
      longevity   249, 287
      market   271
      power rating   265
      risers   305
      sea trials   277
      surveys   424
   explosions   249
   generator   329
   power   247, 254
   pressure   110, 162
Gasket   219, 270, 294, 306
   seals   219
   surface   306
Gate valves   337
Gauges   217-221, 375, 377, 392
Gear, Gears   52, 256, 267, 271-274, 365, 389
   boxes   272-273
   case   272, 274
   casings   272
   design   308
   housings   272
   oil   273
Gel Coat,   104, 113, 138-140, 145, 149-150, 160-161, 163, 165-167, 197, 201-203, 223-229, 232-241, 357, 401
   cracking   [See stress cracks]

crazing 235
discoloration   139,202, 225
voids   140, 201, 233-234
General Motors   22, 265, 268, 272, 433
Generators   15, 59, 283, 291-292, 296,
315-320, 326-331, 333-334, 427,
429
failure   59
output   330
power   326, 429
Genmar 103, 269, 438-439, 444
GFCI   326
GM   258-261, 265-269, 271
block Engines   265-266, 271
four cycle engine 260
marine engines   269
General purpose resin   103-104, 159
GPH   20, 57, 248, 344-345
GPS/Plotters   380-381
Grand Banks   45, 56, 441-443, 452
Great Lakes   173, 390, 410, 439
Grid liners   122, 124, 450
Ground Tackle   14, 365, 386
Gulf   16, 71, 321, 381, 383, 409-411, 438
Coast boat   410
Stream 16, 438
Gulfstar 443
Gunwale 50, 137, 226, 228-229
Gutters 199-200, 205-207, 210, 214, 365

H

Halon   391
Hardtop 64, 367
heights 64
installations   367
Hardware   61, 74, 88, 110, 116, 129-
131, 137-138, 151, 195-196, 201-
204, 207-208, 217, 228-229, 338,
340, 356-357, 359, 362, 379-380
attachments   130, 151, 202,
228-229
problems with   379
Hargrave, Jack   180, 439
Hatch(es)   17-18, 116, 129, 144, 149-
151, 168, 199-200, 202, 204-208,
214, 216-217, 229, 283-284, 294-
295, 311-313, 334, 336, 356, 365,
379, 388
gutters 199
openers 284
Hatteras 18, 33, 42, 49, 52, 55, 70, 82, 86-87,
89, 136, 157, 159, 162, 173-175,
177, 180, 223, 333, 357, 377, 398,

414, 435, 443-444, 452
dealerships   398
hulls   180
management   443
Yachts 162, 223
Hawse pipe   138
Head   2, 15, 18, 36-37, 41-42, 44, 46, 49,
52, 60, 64-65, 137, 150, 173, 205,
267, 270, 277, 326, 341-343, 345-
346, 351, 354, 364, 385, 399, 409,
425, 438
gaskets 267, 270, 277
pump   351
Header beam   134
Headliners   151, 168, 215
Heart Interface   254, 315, 332, 425
Heat   115-116, 209, 211-212, 221, 236,
243, 245-246, 250-251, 259, 261,
264-265, 290, 305-308, 313, 321,
324-325, 348, 364, 383
exchangers   250-251, 264-265,
290, 305, 307
transfer 245
transition zone   306
Heating 236, 306, 324, 365, 384
ability 384
capacity 384
Helm   38, 42, 53-54, 56, 61-63, 216-217,
219-221, 284, 368-369, 371-374,
376-377, 387
area   53-54, 63
designs 221
ergonomic design371
layout 220
panels 62, 217, 220-221, 369,
376-377
seating 39, 41, 44, 48-51, 63, 104,
151, 217, 284, 356, 358, 362, 364-
367, 373-374, 376, 398
arrangements   373,63, 217, 373
stations 217, 219, 371, 374
Heritage East   453
HIN, HIN's   393-394, 403-404
Hinckley, Henry   443
Hinckley Picnic Boat   43
Hinge point   134
HiStar 453
Holding tanks   341
Hong Kong builders   439
Horsepower   28, 47, 190, 243-247, 254-
255, 257, 262, 267, 290, 397
rating 254, 257
ratio   245
Hubble 323

Hull
  blistering   166
  bottoms 137, 178-179, 187, 231, 238, 308
  configuration   345
  construction   52, 60, 74, 77, 95-96, 98-99, 102, 104, 111, 114, 119, 124, 133, 135-136, 143, 147, 167, 195, 227, 354-355, 410, 434, 437, 439, 441-442, 447
    materials   114
    method 143
  core material   137
  depth   47, 178
  design   28, 70, 95, 119, 171, 173, 175, 185-186, 255
  efficiency   194, 254
  failures 92, 97, 106, 114, 119-120, 166, 436-437
  fittings   137, 142, 335, 337-338
  Identification Numbers   393
  inspections   111, 420
  integral platforms 359
  integrity 144
  joints   128
  lengths 47
  nipple   340
  side vents   311
  sides   51, 87, 106-107, 111-114, 116, 127-128, 132, 136-137, 139-141, 150-151, 229-230, 236-237, 241, 311, 340-341, 354, 360-361, 401, 436
  skins   108, 126, 134, 166
  slamming   108, 299
  stringers 153, 299
  structures   93, 117
  style   46
  surface 188
  systems 339
  thickness   112, 161, 164
  types   175, 178
  warranty 29, 97
  year   178
Hull-to-deck joint 55, 126, 136, 150, 205, 226
Hurth   273
Hydraulic   68, 106-109, 196, 200-201, 375-376, 388
  erosion of the core   109
  jet ski platform   201
  leaks   375
  pressure 106
  systems 375
  transom platforms   388
  table   200

  trunk   43, 45-46, 56, 200-201, 229, 365
    cylinders 201
    door   200
Hynautic steering 376

I

Icemaker(s)   6, 318, 328, 379
Infrared 276, 349-350, 384, 422
  pyrometer   349-350, 422
  temperatures   276
  thermometer   384
Injection 263, 268, 277, 305, 375
  engines 277
  systems 263, 375
Injector 252, 259
  port   252
  size   259
Inspection ports   259, 276, 423
Instrument panels   217
Insulation panels 313
Insurance   2, 4, 7, 18-20, 79, 188, 248, 257, 269, 272, 346, 415, 419, 430
  company   18, 269, 346, 415
  policies 19-20
  surveyor 79
Intake   266, 290, 307-308, 339, 351
  filter   307
  orifice   307
  strainer 351
Integral 35, 127, 195, 206, 276, 323, 359, 365, 435
  channel design   206
  Platforms   35, 359
Intercoolers   244, 250-251, 260, 292, 307
  system   260
Interior
  accommodations 26, 34, 67
  carpet   401
  grade appliances 379
  Headliners   215
  layouts 46
  leaks   126, 142, 210, 217
  maintenance   4
  paneling 168
  partitions   216
  temperature   382
  ventilation   59
Intrepid 444
Inverter, Inverters 331-332
  system 332

Iron   47, 91, 127-128, 156, 247, 262-264,
        268, 270, 272, 288, 293, 302, 305-
        306
        risers   305
        tanks   156
Irwin Jacobs   103, 444
Island Gypsy   444, 453
Iso   103
Isopthalic   103-104, 163
        polyester resins   104
        polyesters   103
Italy   92
ITT Jabsco   342

J

Jefferson   444, 453
Jet Drive
Johnson-Towers   258

K

Kady-Krogen designs   46
KaMeWa systems   275
Keel   46-47, 96, 107, 117, 136, 180, 346
Kevlar   102
Kha Shing   453
Kohler   328-329

L

Laminate, Laminates, Lamination   87, 97-
        101, 103, 105-115, 117, 124, 128,
        130-131, 134, 141-142, 149, 159-
        163, 165-167, 195-197, 203, 209,
        217, 226, 228, 230-232, 234-236,
        238, 439
        cures   110
        failure   97, 230
        strength   99-100, 166
        thickness   117
        wet   234
Laminated material   104
Lap joint   56, 125-126, 129, 141
Larson   451
Layup   100-101, 109, 111, 350
        process   101, 111
        schedule   100
Leak water   288, 368, 388
Leakage problems   150, 212, 220,
        427
Leakers   56

Leaking   56, 118, 128, 131, 144, 151, 153,
        156, 200-201, 211-212, 214, 220,
        277, 292-296, 306, 308, 312-313,
        379, 423, 429, 434
        checking for Cabin Leaks   150
        coolers   423
        propeller shaft   308, 312
        riser gaskets   306
        shaft glands   296
        stuffing boxes   156
        tanks   153
        transmission seals   308
        valve   308
        water   128, 201, 293, 313
        windlass 204
        water pumps   295
        windows 214, 434
        windshield   56
        windshields channel   220
Leaks out of an engine   308
Lexan   211
Lien Hwa   453
Limber Holes   122, 146-149
Little Harbor Boats   452
Long Range Cruiser   32
Longevity of   143, 238
        boat components 80-81
        finish   238
        the hull   143
Luhrs   52, 211, 213, 445, 452

M

Mace   329
Macerator pumps 342, 365
Magnum Marine   445
Mainship   38, 46, 61, 445, 451
MAN   10, 19, 74, 85, 87, 135, 170, 264,
        282, 298, 354, 408, 422, 430, 445-
        447
Marilon 338
Marinair 382
Marinco 321
Marine
        diesel   251, 259, 263
        gaskets 270
        growth   139, 271, 274-275, 339
        Power   269
        Trader   453
Marinize
        Marinization of an automotive
        engine   270
        Marinized   265-267, 271
                version   267

versions of automotive engines 265
Marinizer of the engines 269
Marinizers 266, 269
Marinizing Companies 269
Marshall Boat Co. 438
Maxum 436, 445-446, 451
Mediterranean 33, 434, 445
Merc riser 294
Mercedes 264
Mercruiser 266-267, 269-271, 273, 294, 305-306
engines 270
risers 270, 294, 305-306
standard 271
versions 266
Mercury Marine 269
Meridian Yachts 436
Microwave 40, 319, 328
Mikelson 453
Mildew problems 60, 151, 349
Modified vee hull 48, 180
Moisture meters 147, 420
Molds 129, 139, 237, 354
Monterey 451
Mortgage 248, 394, 415
Motor Yacht(s) 14, 32-33, 43, 53-54, 77, 172, 175, 182, 191, 255, 374, 436, 444
MPI 267-268, 277
engines 268, 277
MPN 272
MSRP 399
MTU engines 264
Muffler, Mufflers 296, 302-304, 329, 418, 427
Multi-purpose boats 48, 52

N

National Marine Manufacturers Association 27, 282, 398
Navigation 12, 19, 44, 218, 380-381, 386, 420
equipment 420
instruments 218, 380
lights 386
Navigator Yachts 53, 446, 452
Neverbonds 196
New England 57
workboat style 57
NidaCore plastic honeycomb 448
Nordhaven 453
North American Rockwell 443

Northern Lights 328-329
Northstar 381
Nova Marine 453

O

OBO By-owner sales 403
Ocean Alexander 453
Ocean Yachts 177, 446, 451
OEM installation 326
Offshore Marine 452
Offshore Yachts 453
Oil
analysis 422, 424
canning 231
filters 291
leaks 308, 376
pressure 276, 422-423
spray pattern 308
trails 292, 294
in bilge water 281
Old boats 42, 73, 75-77, 79, 82, 85-87, 89, 98, 106, 121, 136, 138, 149, 156, 162, 164, 166, 171, 201-202, 208, 212, 214, 216, 228, 233, 240, 247, 283, 285, 305, 324, 326, 334, 365, 380, 414, 428, 439, 449-450
Olin Stevens 439
OMC 23, 440
Onan 328-329
Onshore navigation 44
Optional Equipment 50, 382, 389, 398
Orthopthalic resin 103, 159, 163
Outboard 86, 109-110, 143, 148, 153, 216, 245, 274, 290, 295, 424, 437, 444, 447, 450
boats 109, 444, 447, 450
cylinders 424
engine 245
sides of the engines 290
stringers 143
Overhaul cost 248, 288
Overheat condition 250
Overloaded 253, 267, 335, 361
Oversteer 188
Oxide 152, 157, 286, 293, 307
of metals 286

P

Pace Jefferson 453
Pacemaker 18, 43, 75, 344, 441, 446
PAE 453
Panish 372

Paper honeycomb cores   106, 114
PAR   342, 346
Partnership(s)   21, 405
    arrangements   21
Pedestal   63, 204, 217, 284
    chairs   63
    seat mounts   204
    seating mounts   217
    217
Performance   28, 32, 34, 49, 54, 61, 68,
    116, 169-170, 174, 177, 183, 187-
    188, 194, 201, 244-248, 252, 257,
    259, 261, 264, 266, 268, 286, 295,
    298, 329, 403, 421, 425, 429, 433,
    438, 451
    diesels   244, 247-248, 257, 261
    minimum planing speed test
    255
    penalty   187
    test of the boat   421
Perkins   264
Perko   336
Petroleum tank industry   103
PFD   390
Phoenix   447, 452
Pigmented plastic resin   223
Pilot station   62, 217
Piston   252, 254, 263, 276, 293, 423
    failures   263
    melt-down   263
    rings   276, 423
Pitching   170, 181, 189
Planing hulls   45-46, 441-442
Plastic
    air conditioning pump housing
    336
    bags   273, 275
    bait well pump   336
    cams   342
    coolant recovery bottles   292, 307
    counter tops   355
    cover   219, 368
    enclosure   378
    hardware   338, 379-380
    honeycomb   130, 448
    housings   339
    molding 125
    nipples   340
    pie ports 380
    pumps   339
    resin   47, 99, 160, 163, 223
    seat   337
    shims   153
    swimming pool strainers   339
    through hull   137, 142, 163,

335, 337-340, 365
    fittings   142
    nipple   340
Valves Fiberglass   338
windscreens   217
Platform, Platforms   17, 35, 49, 56, 67,
71, 137, 201, 323, 358-359, 361-
364, 388, 398
    brackets 359
    sticks out   363
    Integral   35, 359
Plexiglass frameless windows   211
Plumbing Systems   9, 11, 47, 315,
    335-336, 338-339, 342, 350, 420
Plywood, Plywoods   42, 47, 91, 93,
    104-105, 110, 116, 118-119, 121-
    122, 128, 131, 144-147, 167, 205,
    217, 355, 449
    bulkhead   205
    stringers 144, 147
Pneumatic cylinders   379
Poly vinyl chloride   115
Polyester, Polyesters   103-104, 111-112,
    148, 161, 163, 229, 234
    filler   229
    putty   111-112
Pop-up cleats   202
Portable spotlight 21
Post Marine   441, 447, 452
Post-cure shrinkage   236
Potable water system   347
Power
    options   89, 177, 190, 243, 319
    ratios   246
    source   25, 161-162, 210, 233,
    251, 308, 316-318, 320, 325, 335,
    391
        selection switches
        325
        switching
        325
    voltages   316
Premature   246, 259, 270, 287, 294,
    410
    component failures   294
    engine wear   287, 410
    failures   270
    wear   246, 259
Pressure
    Infrared temperatures   276
    of the main engine   330
    reducer/regulators   348
    relief valve   347
Primary circuits   318
Princess Yachts   450

Professional
documentation service   402
engine
survey   287
surveyors   275, 422, 424
marine survey   121
ProLine 447
Propeller
load   361
pockets 187-188, 388
protection   57
shafts   186-187, 244, 256, 275, 297, 299, 308-309, 312, 344
torque   192
Propellering   253, 289, 361
PT Yachts   453
Pulpits   15, 70, 109, 205, 210-211, 229
Pump   19, 42, 59, 69, 148, 152, 244, 263, 266, 273, 293, 312, 336, 339, 341-348, 350-351, 365, 385, 429
brackets 293
failure   59
heads   341
housing 336, 339
motor   42
prices   244
systems 342, 347
Pumping problems   343
Puncturing   113
Purchase
agreements   402, 404, 429
price   10, 79, 404
Purification filter   347
Pursuits 130, 153, 221, 445, 447-448, 452
Putty   108, 111-113, 115
boats   112-113
core boat   112
cores   111-113
PVC pipe   148, 340

R

R/O systems   385
Radar arch   52, 65, 364
Radars 380-381
Railing stanchion 201
Rails   41, 127, 129, 131, 137, 140-141, 150, 356, 385, 401
Raised   42-43, 46, 53, 136-137, 178-179, 214, 216, 229, 284
carlin   216
deckhouse   43
motor boxes   284

pilothouse motor yacht 53
Raritan 342
Raw water   250
Ray Hunt   183
Rear engine   17, 181, 190, 255, 331, 344
boats   181, 190, 255, 331, 344
compartment   344
Receptacles   59, 317, 321, 323-324, 359
Reduction gears 256, 271-272
Refrigeration compressor 321
Refrigerators   40, 149, 379
Regal   333,451
Regional   29, 193, 410, 413
considerations   410
variations   413
Repairing   10, 77, 158, 161, 166-167, 214, 238, 415
blisters   166
chips   238
Repos, Repossessions   415
Resale   2, 5, 50, 54-55, 67, 75-76, 85, 89, 164, 166, 178, 196, 221, 236, 249-250, 326, 367, 377, 382, 408, 436, 448
costs   5
market   85
prices   55
times   5, 67, 75, 196, 250, 326, 377, 382
values   2, 59, 76-77, 79, 164, 166, 210, 240, 276, 365-366, 393, 398, 402, 404, 411, 429, 436, 448
Resin cures   160, 227
Richard Bertram   48, 435
Rinker   451
Riser, Risers   269-271, 288, 291, 294-296, 302-306, 308, 311-312, 330-331, 342, 345
block   312
gaskets 270, 306
leaks   291
loop   311, 345
style   305
system   295
welds   305
River boat   10
Riviera 36, 448, 450, 452
Rockwell   443
Rod holder   138
Rolling 15, 47, 49, 57, 61, 66, 170, 173, 189, 233, 286, 349
action of the boat 286
motion   170, 189

Rope   12, 99, 131, 136, 151, 204-205, 387
    locker   136, 151, 205
    retractors   387
Rotary power source selector switches
    325
Round   31, 46, 57, 107, 159, 246, 337, 441,
    443, 445, 449
    bilge trawler hulls 46
    bilges   57
Roving, woven   98, 100, 112, 122, 124,
    160, 166, 208
Rub rails 127, 129, 131, 137, 140, 150, 356,
    401
Rubber insulator   298
Ruggieri 329
Rule pumps   2-3, 5, 16, 46, 77, 85, 177,
    188, 236, 250, 254, 258, 266, 282,
    331, 344, 375, 383, 428-429
Runabouts   266-267, 435-436
Running lights   386
Rust   137, 196, 201, 203-204, 214, 241,
    253, 286-287, 290-296, 300, 305-
    307, 312, 331, 347, 359, 375, 379-
    380, 410, 424
    halo   137, 201
    scale   294
Rybovich wheel   373

S

Sabreline   452
Safety Gear   389
Sagging 129, 197, 199, 207-208, 213-214,
    301
    decks   214
    engine mounts   301
    side   199, 214
Saltshaker Marine   437
Schoell, Harry   450
Scuppers   199, 206, 367-368
Sea
    cock   130, 312, 336, 338-339,
    366
    keeping 32-34, 44, 48-52, 57, 61,
    169-171, 175, 179-180, 188, 193,
    437, 451
    rails   41
    strainers 79, 285, 336, 338, 348
    trials   173, 183, 191, 214, 252,
    276-277, 289, 293, 297, 363, 376,
    403, 420-421
    worthiness   69, 404, 420
    worthy vessel   381

Sea Ray   39, 52-53, 61, 68, 97, 105-
    106, 112-113, 126, 137, 142-144,
    147-148, 173-174, 183-184, 188,
    194, 201, 220, 261, 269, 303-304,
    331, 374, 388-389, 399, 412, 414-
    415, 435-436, 439-440, 448-449,
    452
    boats   137, 143-144, 147, 303-
    304
    dealers 399
    express boats   53
    hull   112
    owners   68
SeaBird 447
SeaLand   341
Sealant 212
Seamanship course   170
Seat
    cushions 182, 234, 429
    lockers   216
    storage lockers   206
Seating
    arrangements   39, 373-374, 376
    modules 49-50, 284, 358, 365, 398
    upholstery   366
Seaworthy   11, 13, 18, 34
    boat   34
    condition   11
    pleasure craft   18
Sedan   32, 39, 42-43, 48-49, 123, 255, 434,
    441, 445, 449
    cruiser   43, 49
    models   434, 441
Self-sinking   11
Self-tailing   387
Seller   164, 167, 268, 339, 376, 395, 400-
    405, 409, 412, 428-431
    expenses   403
    lender   404
    motivation   402
    offers   402
Sellers Expense   403
Selling
    boats   415, 439
    brokers   401, 430
    dealer   399
    stock   23
Semi   45, 87, 233
    custom 87
    displacement   45
Semi-custom builder   438
Separation of core   105
Shaft   12, 137, 186-188, 254, 256, 259,
    271, 273-275, 291-292, 295-297,
    299-301, 307-309, 312, 334, 344,

376, 424
angle 187-188
bearing 307
breakage 300
couplings 259, 291, 301
horse power 256, 259
out of alignment 300
packing 292, 295, 334
seals 308
Shallow
bottomed boats 178
bottoms 35, 446-447
hulled cruiser 173
hulls 51, 447
stringer 119
vee hulls 440
water 172-173
Shore power 59, 274, 315-319, 321,
323-324, 359, 364
circuit 323
line 315-316, 318, 330
receptacle 59, 323, 324
system 274
Shower
attachment 385
faucets 386
heads 385
pump 351
stall 42, 52
sumps 6, 335
Showrooms 55
Shrinkage of the
gel coat 226
underlying substrate 226
Shur-Flo 346
Signs of
corrosion 147
excessive oil 308
leakage 150
leaks 204
water 214, 313
Silicone sealer 214
Silverton 61, 70, 89, 125, 183-184,
191, 193, 333, 451
Single engine 46-47, 57, 118, 189, 192,
388, 434
deep keels 434
power 57
reliability issues 57
Splices 335, 355
Sport
cruiser 33
fisher 447, 450
fisherman hull 53

Sport fishing 48-52, 69, 87, 169, 193,
357, 367, 385, 413-414, 435, 437-
438, 444-445, 447-448, 450, 452
boats 52, 87, 357, 367, 385, 413,
435, 437, 447-448
category 49, 169, 193
market 52, 438, 445, 450
yachts 450
Sportfishing class of boats 175
Spray
cores 111-112
ingestion 290
intake problem 290
of water 296
Stability of a boat 182, 191
Stainless
ball 337
diesel risers 305
manifold 336
molding 131
pipes 304
risers 305
tanks 157
Starburst cracks 232
Static water line 331
Steel
butterfly valve 306
cables 375
casings 312
fuel tanks 434
hardware 379
heater 347
jackets 375
parts 293, 307
Steering 184, 188, 192, 200, 217-218, 273,
365, 371-373, 376
gear 365
input 192
stress 218
systems 200, 273, 376
tension 376
Stereo system 67
Stern
drive 147, 155, 207, 264, 269-
271, 273-274, 280, 424, 434, 440,
450
of
the boat 201
a vessel 185
platform 56
section 178-179
Stewart-Stephenson 258
Stove 318, 328, 330, 332, 391
Stowaway crane 200

Strainers   79, 285, 312, 336, 338-
339, 348, 351
    screens, external 339
Strakes 134, 180
Stress
    cracks   118, 133-134, 139-140,
    150, 201, 208, 213, 223, 225-228,
    231, 233-235, 238
    loads   130
    of slamming   124
    points   117, 133-134
    test   297
Stringer(s)   91, 96, 101, 104,110,
    111,118-120, 121-122, 130,
    133,124,143-149, 231, 153, 167,
    231, 299, 346, 450
    box beam type,   95, 143, 147
    deflection   119
    top   122
Strobe light   409
Structural
    core   114
    defect   232-233
    deficiency   96
    design fault   230
    grids   122, 124
    integrity of the hull   231
    members   111, 143, 437
    problem 125, 150, 233, 237
    substrate   224
    weakness   213, 228, 367
Structures of a fiberglass boat   74
Strut bearing   297
Stub keels   434
Stuffing box(es)   137, 300, 308,156, 310,
    331
Sulphur dioxide emissions 296
Sun Bridge   43
Sunbathing   210, 366
Sunlight 59, 142, 221, 223, 236, 340, 383
Sunseeker   451
Surface
    defects 223
    drives 275
    oxidation   240
Survey, Surveys 5-6, 27, 38, 67, 116-117,
    121, 135, 138-139, 145, 165, 195,
    211, 216, 247, 259, 261, 266, 275-
    277, 279, 282, 285, 287, 289, 301,
    333, 381, 384, 391, 402-404, 409,
    417-422, 424-431, 442
    clause 402
    deficiencies   430
    logistics 420
Surveying carbureted gas engines 277

Surveyor, Surveyors   67, 79, 93, 111,
    116-117, 125, 135, 143-144, 147,
    178, 195-196, 259, 275-277, 279,
    290, 297, 300-301, 310, 324, 326,
    335, 343, 346, 350, 384, 399, 403,
    417-425, 428, 430-431
Swim platform   17, 49, 67, 71, 361

T

Tabbing 111, 124-125
Taiwan, Taiwanese   47, 52, 91-92,
    119, 159, 161-162, 234, 237, 439,
    441, 445, 453
    boats   91-92, 119, 237, 453
    trawlers 47, 237
    boats   47, 159, 162, 234
    imports 52
Tank, Tanks   15, 47, 49, 87, 91, 103-
    104, 119, 142-143, 152-153, 155-
    157, 181, 186, 189, 191, 209, 214,
    251-252, 265, 310-312, 341, 346-
    347, 368-369, 424, 434-435, 437-
    438
    coating 103
    corrosion issues 156
Tankage status   143
Taping   124
    tape fractures   125
Thermo Electron Corporation   305
Tiara   36, 40-41, 48-49, 51-52, 64, 89,
    130, 153, 174, 200, 206, 221, 323,
    368-369, 377, 398, 447-449, 452
    hull   174
Toe rail 226, 228
Tolly Craft   449
Tom Fexas   439
Top hat style stringers   148
Topaz   257
Tortional stress   149
Towing   11, 15
    company   15
    services 11
Trace Engineering   307, 332
Trade-In   26, 397, 413
Transmission   119, 250, 256, 259, 272-
    273, 276, 291, 297, 299-301, 308,
    422-423
    coupling 291
    magnetic particle test   422,
    422
    oil   250, 300, 423
    output shaft   300
    seal leaks   308

slippage 276
Transom(s)   17, 35, 45, 50-51, 56-57,
    137, 141, 174, 178, 200, 224, 303,
    331, 342, 358-359, 361-362, 364-
    367, 388-389, 445
    corner 224
    damage complaints   389
    doors   50, 367
    extension length 445
    of a vessel   388
    platform 35, 137, 358, 362, 364
    riser   331
Travel lift116
Trawler, Trawlers 32, 35, 38, 40, 45-47, 49,
    56, 90, 92, 182, 237, 248, 256, 260,
    434, 439, 441-445
    Down Easter   32
    hulls   45-46, 445
    styles   45-46, 442, 444-445
    yacht   248
Tri cabins   32, 46, 56
Tri-directional fabrics   100
Trim   68, 143, 170, 178-179, 185-188,
    191-192, 201, 216, 236, 255, 355,
    366, 368, 386, 447
    angle   178-179, 185-188, 216
    tabs   186, 192
    of   68, 185, 216, 368, 386
        a boat   185
Trojan   18, 449-451
Trunk cabin   43, 56, 229
Turbo   243-244, 250-252, 259, 276, 307,
    422
    boost   252, 259, 422
    charger boost   276
    chargers251, 307
    rams   307
Turbocharged   259, 263, 307
Turbocharger vanes   307
Twin Disc   272-273
Two cycle, Two-cycle   245, 258, 260,
    276, 423
    Detroit Diesel   258, 423
    engines 245, 260, 276
    diesel units   328
    diesel 245
Type II PFD's   390

U

U.V. damage   224, 236
Uniflite 162
UV   131, 221, 224, 377, 379, 410
    resistance   224

resistant 97, 103-104, 107, 115,
    131, 152, 224, 238, 274, 377, 379
    cover   377
    gel   224

V

Vacuum 25, 42, 102-103, 108-110, 196, 253,
    276, 341, 343, 360
    bag process   110
    bagging process 103, 108
Valve   248, 260-261, 266, 306, 308, 337-
    338, 347, 351, 369, 424
    rocker arm studs 260
    train   261, 424
VCG   182-183
Vee
    berths 37, 66
    bottomed boat   189
    drives 17, 181, 187-188, 273,
    300, 308, 331
    engine 259
    hulls   48-49, 175, 178-180, 183-
    184, 189, 434-435, 437, 440
    sections 179
Vent   142, 156, 196, 310-312, 349, 384
    cover   196
    fittings 142, 156
    hose   311
    line   142
    opening 311
Ventilation, engine room   289
Vibration problems   299
Viking
    Sport Cruisers   450
    Yachts 452
Volvo   263-264, 267, 269, 271, 298, 300-
    301, 423
    diesels 263
    DuoProp264
    engine mounts   301
    engines 263, 271
    gas engines   271
    KAMD300   264
KAMD42   263
Vortec engines   268

W

Walker AirSep   289-290
Walther vee drive 273
Warped plane   46, 178-179
    hull   178

Warranties   20, 24, 28-29, 261, 289
Warranty   2, 5, 20-21, 24, 27-30, 91,
    97-98, 140, 248, 257, 261-262, 268,
    288, 341, 396, 418, 426, 441
    liabilities 24
    period   396
    service response 262
Waste   206, 331, 341-343, 365, 378
    hose   343
    plumbing systems   342
Water
    heater installations   312
    hose   368
    injection designs 305
    jackets   270, 305
    makers 384
    spray leak   306
    tanks   91, 157, 346-347, 438
Water-lift generator muffler   329
Waves   12, 17, 57, 95-96, 108, 126, 172-
    174, 179, 181-182, 184, 186, 189-
    190, 229
Wavy hull sides   354
Weather rail   71
Weld   157, 305
    corrosion   305
    failures   157
    lines   305
Wellcraft   438, 446, 450-451
Westerbeke   328-329
Wheel   177, 217-218, 368, 371-374, 376-
    377, 382
    height   372
Whitticar Corporation   449
Wide open throttle   256, 261
Windlass   109, 116, 131, 202-204,
    387-388
Window(s)   26, 43, 47-48, 53, 59-60,
    75, 89, 93, 99, 118, 129, 132, 134,
    150, 168, 211-212, 214, 329, 383-
    384, 427, 434
    glass   60, 212, 383-384
    frames   211
    leaks   89, 427
Windshield   17, 51-52, 56, 59, 61, 64-
    65, 218, 220-221, 368-369, 377
    leakage problems 220
    walk-through   56
    wipers   369
Winter Lay Up   9
Winterize   9, 410
Wire   147, 217, 316, 318, 323-324, 327,
    335, 344, 350, 355
    connections   217, 323, 344,
    350

docks   318
    nuts   327
Wood
    hulls   163, 438
    rot-resistant   115
    stringers 118, 121-122, 146
    woodwork   212
Wood-free   104
    boats   104
Wooden
    boat builders   97
    boats   96-98, 102, 117, 122, 197,
    450
    soles   151
    structural members   143
    structures   167, 410
    window frame   47
Wynn, Jim   447

Y

Yachtworld.com   400, 408
Yanmar 264

Z

"Z" HIN boats   394
Z-drives 275
Z-F   272
    introduction   272
    Transmissions   272
Zinc fittings   156
Zippered enclosures   64

OTHER BOOKS BY DAVID H. PASCOE

Surveying Fiberglass Power Boats 2nd Edition
Buyers' Guide to Outboard Boats
Marine Investigations